Formal Assessment

McDougal Littell

THE LANGUAGE OF
LITERATURE

GRADE SIX

McDougal Littell
A HOUGHTON MIFFLIN COMPANY
Evanston, Illinois • Boston • Dallas

Acknowledgments

Samuel W. Allen: "To Satch" by Samuel W. Allen. Copyright © by Samuel W. Allen. Reprinted by permission of the author.

Doubleday Publishing: Excerpts from *The Quality of Courage* by Mickey Mantle. Copyright © 1964 by Bedford S. Wynne, trustee of four separate trusts for the benefit of Mickey Elven Mantle, David Harold Mantle, Billy Giles Mantle, and Danny Murl Mantle. Reprinted by permission of Doubleday Publishing, a division of Random House, Inc.

Lescher & Lescher, Ltd.: "The Southpaw" by Judith Viorst, from *Free to Be . . . You and Me,* edited by Christopher Cerf et al. Copyright © 1974 by Judith Viorst. This usage granted by permission of Lescher & Lescher, Ltd.

Random House: Excerpts from "America the Not-so-Beautiful," from *Not That You Asked* by Andrew A. Rooney. Copyright © 1989 by Essay Productions. Reprinted by permission of Random House, Inc.

ISBN 0-618-14647-4

Contents

To the Teacher

This Formal Assessment booklet contains the materials described below. For more detailed information, turn to the front of each section.

Tests for *The Language of Literature*

- **Selection Tests.** A Selection Test is provided for each selection or group of selections in the Pupil's Edition. Each Selection Test may use graphics, multiple-choice items, or essay questions to test students' understanding of vocabulary words, content, major issues, and the literary concepts taught with each selection. Selection Tests should be administered after students have discussed the selection and completed the Thinking Through the Literature questions.

- **Part Tests.** Part Tests are open-book tests. Students are directed to answer multiple-choice or short essay questions and complete graphics that require them to discuss or compare a number of selections in terms of themes, characters, and literary concepts.

- **Mid-Year and End-of-Year Tests.** The Mid-Year and End-of-Year Tests are open-book tests designed to check students' understanding of the concepts and skills that were taught in the units preceding the tests. These two tests are similar in format, although the End-of-Year Test is somewhat longer than the Mid-Year Test. Each test consists of a short reading passage followed by several series of multiple-choice questions and short-answer, open-ended questions. These questions test the students' basic understanding of the passage as well as the literary elements and techniques used to write the passage. The writing portion of the tests includes a prompt, which calls for the students to write a short essay applying at least one taught concept or skill. Finally, there is a short activity testing the students' editing and revising skills.

Additional Test Generator Questions

This section contains a bank of additional questions for each selection, which you can use to create customized tests for your classes. The items in this section of the book are duplicated on the Test Generator software. You are encouraged to scan these items and select the ones that would be most useful for your classes. You can then use the Test Generator software to create tests to suit your students' needs.

Writing Assessment

This section contains several tools to help you conduct holistic evaluations of students' writing, including a general evaluation form and writing assessment prompts to help students prepare for essay tests.

Standardized Test Practice

This section provides opportunities for students to develop strategies for performing well on standardized tests. Practice items are included for areas typically found on standardized tests. Each section of practice items explains the purpose for those particular items, provides an example, and describes specific strategies students can use to be successful.

Answer Key

This section includes answer keys for Selection Tests, Part Tests, Mid-Year and End-of-Year Tests, and the Standardized Test Practice.

Tests for *The Language of Literature*

Contents

*Answer Key for Selection, Part, Mid-Year, and End-of-Year Tests begins on page 221.

	Tests*	Additional Test Generator Questions

*Answer Key for Selection, Part, Mid-Year, and End-of-Year Tests begins on page 221.

	Tests*	Additional Test Generator Questions

Unit Six: Across Cultures: The Oral Tradition

*Answer Key for Selection, Part, Mid-Year, and End-of-Year Tests begins on page 221.

To the Teacher

This section contains Selection Tests, Part Tests, the Mid-Year Test, and the End-of-Year Test. The following charts indicate the types of questions and the tested concepts for each type of test in this section. Administer Selection Tests after students have discussed the selection and completed the postreading activities. Tests for poetry should be open-book.

Selection Tests

Section	Type of Item	Tested Concepts and Skills from the Selection
A	graphic device (table, chart, diagram, etc.)	selection content or the introduced literary concept
B	multiple-choice questions	selection content or the introduced literary concept
C	multiple-choice questions	vocabulary words
D	essay questions	introduced literary concepts
E	essay question	how introduced concept relates to student's personal experience
F	optional	optional

Part Tests

Section	Type of Item	Tested Concepts and Skills from the Part
A	multiple-choice or short answer questions	content of selections in the part or the literary concepts that were introduced in those selections
B	graphic device (table, chart, diagram, etc.)	compare/contrast elements from one or more selections; analyze elements within a single selection
C*	essay questions	students' personal reactions to selections; major ideas, characters, themes, literary concepts
D	graphic device (table, chart, diagram, etc.)	compare/contrast elements from one or more selections; analyze elements within a single selection

*The student chooses two of three to four essay questions to answer.

Mid-Year and End-of-Year Tests*

Section	Type of Item	Tested Concepts and Skills
1	multiple-choice questions	basic comprehension of the reading passage
2	multiple-choice questions	how the literary concepts and skills taught in the preceding units relate to the reading passage
3	short, open-ended essay questions	how the literary concepts and skills taught in the preceding units relate to the reading passage
4	multiple-choice questions	ability to analyze and critically evaluate the reading passage in terms of literary concepts and skills
5	short, open-ended essay questions	ability to analyze and critically evaluate the reading passage in terms of literary concepts and skills
6	essay question	writing ability (organization and mechanics)
7	multiple-choice questions	revising and editing ability (organization and mechanics)

*Reading passages for these tests are included in this book.

All questions appearing in this Formal Assessment book, as well as the quizzes printed in the URB, can be found electronically on the Test Generator software.

Eleven (page 26)

Selection Test

A. Think about the characters of Rachel and Mrs. Price in this story. Write down one or two traits, or qualities, that you see in each character. Then write details or examples from the story to explain how each trait is revealed. (15 points each)

Character	Trait	Details
1. Rachel		
2. Mrs. Price		

B. Write the letter of the best answer. This exercise is continued on the next page. (5 points each)

_____ 1. Which word best describes Rachel's reaction to the red sweater?
    a. upset
    b. excited
    c. furious
    d. frightened

_____ 2. From this story, you can tell that it is hard for Rachel to
    a. keep up with her studies.
    b. let other people do things for her.
    c. express herself when she is emotional.
    d. apologize for something she has done.

_____ 3. Rachel wished that she was one hundred and two years old because then she would have
    a. liked the red sweater.
    b. known what to say to Mrs. Price.
    c. stopped caring what she looked like.
    d. remembered that the sweater belonged to Phyllis.

_____ 4. How did Rachel feel about what happened in the classroom?
    a. proud
    b. pleased
    c. sad
    d. embarrassed

C. Words to Know. Write the letter of the best answer. (4 points each)

_____ 1. A sudden storm happens
    a. without reason.   b. at night.   c. without warning.

_____ 2. When you expect to feel happy, you
    a. look forward to it.   b. refuse it.   c. change your mind.

_____ 3. Something that is invisible cannot be
    a. enjoyed.   b. understood.   c. seen.

_____ 4. The word except means
    a. other than; but.   b. always; ever.   c. to take; receive.

D. Answer **one** of the following questions based on your understanding of the story. Write your answer on a separate sheet of paper. (20 points)

1. How does Mrs. Price treat Rachel? Use details from the story to support your answer.

2. How did you feel toward Rachel at the end of the story? Note details from the story that made you feel that way.

E. Linking Literature to Life. Answer the following question based on your own experience and knowledge. Write your answer on a separate sheet of paper. (14 points)

Do you think it is okay to cry in front of other people? Tell why or why not.

Name _____ Date _____

President Cleveland, Where Are You? (page 34)

Selection Test

A. Fill in the chart below by writing an event from the story for each part of the plot.
Conflict consists of opposing people or forces, **rising action** includes the main conflict
and complications, and the **climax** is the turning point of the story. The **falling action**
consists of the events that follow the climax, and the **resolution** occurs when the
main complication is worked out. (6 points each)

1. Conflict	
2. Rising Action	
3. Climax	
4. Falling Action	
5. Resolution	

B. Write the letter of the best answer. This exercise is continued on the next page.
(5 points each)

_____ 1. Why did Jerry give his brother only ten cents toward their father's
birthday gift?
a. That was all the money he had.
b. He was saving to buy himself a baseball glove.
c. He wanted to buy cowboy cards.
d. He needed money to buy flowers.

_____ 2. Jerry promised his brother Armand not to tell anyone that
a. their father was out of work.
b. he had found a Grover Cleveland card.
c. they had bought their father a blue tie.
d. Armand was in love with Sally Knowlton.

3. Which saying best describes the lesson Jerry learned in this story?
   a. It is better to give than to receive.
   b. A penny saved is a penny earned.
   c. Don't put off until tomorrow what you can do today.
   d. A stitch in time saves nine.

C. Words to Know. Write the letter of the best answer. (4 points each)

_____ 1. When food supplies <u>dwindle</u>, they become
   a. rotten.　　　　　　b. less.　　　　　　c. expensive.

_____ 2. Money that is <u>allotted</u> to three sons is
   a. given out.　　　　b. spent quickly.　　c. saved up.

_____ 3. If two tennis players reach a <u>stalemate</u>, neither player is
   a. willing to quit.　　b. able to continue.　c. able to win.

_____ 4. A person in a state of <u>lethargy</u> is likely to be
   a. inactive.　　　　　b. healthy.　　　　　c. happy.

_____ 5. To <u>divulge</u> a secret means to
   a. protect it.　　　　b. reveal it.　　　　c. improve it.

D. Answer **one** of the following questions based on your understanding of the story. Write your answer on a separate sheet of paper. (20 points)

1. Why did Jerry sell the Grover Cleveland card to Rollie Tremaine? Explain the reasons that led to his decision.

2. Did Jerry do something "fine and noble" when he sold the Grover Cleveland card, or was Jerry a "traitor"? Why?

E. Linking Literature to Life. Answer the following question based on your own experience and knowledge. Write your answer on a separate sheet of paper. (15 points)

Do you think love is an "unnecessary waste of time," as Jerry thinks in the story, or is it something important? Why?

Scout's Honor (page 52)

Selection Test

A. Write details from the story to describe the setting: when the story takes place, where the boys live, and where the boys go. In the box at the bottom, write notes explaining how the story is affected by the setting. (6 points each)

Task	Details
1. Tell when the story takes place.	
2. Describe where the boys live.	
3. Describe where the boys go.	
4. Explain how the story is affected by the setting.	

B. Write the letter of the best answer. This exercise is continued on the next page. (5 points each)

_____ 1. The narrator joined the Boy Scouts because he wanted to
   a. go camping.
   b. become tough.
   c. make new friends.
   d. see the world.

_____ 2. It was difficult for the boys to do any "real camping" because they
   a. did not have any money.
   b. could not read maps.
   c. did not have sleeping bags.
   d. lived in the city.

_____ 3. Which word best describes how the boys felt as they crossed the George
Washington Bridge?
   a. afraid   c. cautious
   b. excited   d. silly

_____ 4. In this story, "Scout's honor" refers to the idea that
   a. scouts are tough.
   b. a scout never lies.
   c. camping is fun.
   d. a compass always points north.

C. Words to Know. Write the letter of the best answer. (4 points each)

_____ 1. A person who <u>bellowed</u> would be
   a. walking.   b. shouting.   c. laughing.

_____ 2. Which of these would most likely be <u>immense</u>?
   a. a rock   b. a pebble   c. a boulder

_____ 3. A boy would be most likely to <u>straddle</u> a
   a. fence.   b. book.   c. baseball.

_____ 4. Which of the following are <u>rivals</u>?
   a. musicians   b. competitors   c. teachers

_____ 5. A <u>vent</u> would most often be used to get rid of
   a. trash.   b. money.   c. smoke.

D. Answer **one** of the following questions based on your understanding of the story.
Write your answer on a separate sheet of paper. (20 points)

1. In what ways did the narrator, Max, and Horse try to prove that they were "tough"?
   Do you think they succeeded? Tell why.

2. What parts of "Scout law" did the boys follow, and what parts of the law did they
   break? Give examples from the story to support your answer.

E. Linking Literature to Life. Answer the following question based on your own
experience and knowledge. Write your answer on a separate sheet of paper. (16 points)

   Do you think you would be a good Boy Scout or Girl Scout? What aspects of being
a Scout appeal to you, and what aspects do not?

Nadia the Willful (page 67)

Selection Test

A. In each box on the left, write a theme, or message, that the story expressed. In the boxes on the right, write details from the plot that support or illustrate each theme. (8 points each)

Theme	Details
1.	
2.	
3.	

B. Write the letter of the best answer. This exercise is continued on the next page. (5 points each)

_____ 1. What is Nadia's main reason for disobeying the sheik?
  a. She is angry with him.
  b. She wants to help her people.
  c. She wants to show she does not fear him.
  d. She knows it is the only way she can find peace.

_____ 2. When the sheik repeats his command, the people of the clan obey him because of their feelings of
  a. fear.
  b. guilt.
  c. respect.
  d. sympathy.

_____ 3. The sheik changes his command about speaking Hamed's name because he realizes that
    a. he does not want to punish Nadia.
    b. he was wrong to make the command.
    c. Hamed is dead and will never return.
    d. his people will never obey the command.

_____ 4. At the end of the story, the sheik gives Nadia a new title that honors her
    a. pride.
    b. bravery.
    c. wisdom.
    d. stubbornness.

C. Words to Know. Write the letter of the best answer. (4 points each)

_____ 1. A person who has been <u>banished</u> has been
    a. praised.   b. sent away.   c. given a reward.

_____ 2. Which of the following might be called a <u>clan</u>?
    a. a sad feeling   b. a wise person   c. the Jones family

_____ 3. A <u>decree</u> is an official
    a. request.   b. order.   c. apology.

_____ 4. At a <u>bazaar</u>, you would most expect to see people who were
    a. selling things.   b. playing games.   c. giving speeches.

_____ 5. A wise man would be most likely to <u>ponder</u> a
    a. question.   b. robe.   c. vegetable.

D. Answer **one** of the following questions based on your understanding of the story. Write your answer on a separate sheet of paper. (20 points)

1. Why might the sheik have thought that it was a good idea to forbid people to talk about Hamed? Explain your answer.

2. Think about the setting of this story, including the Bedouin culture and way of life. How do the setting and the Bedouin way of life affect what happens in the story?

E. Linking Literature to Life. Answer the following question based on your own experience and knowledge. Write your answer on a separate sheet of paper. (16 points)

What do you think are the main purposes of having laws? Do you think that people have the right to break laws that they disagree with? Explain.

Unit One: The Courage to Be Me

Part One Open-Book Test

A. Answer each question. (5 points each)

1. In "Nadia the Willful," why did the sheik change his daughter's title to Nadia the Wise?

_____

_____

2. What was the main conflict in the story "Eleven"?

_____

_____

3. In "President Cleveland, Where Are You?" why was Jerry trying to find a President Cleveland card?

_____

_____

4. Why did the boys in "Scout's Honor" decide to go camping?

_____

_____

B. In each selection, a character must struggle against something. Circle the letter of one character. Then answer the question. (20 points)

a Rachel in "Eleven"
b. Jerry in "President Cleveland, Where Are You?"
c. the narrator in "Scout's Honor"
d. Nadia in "Nadia the Willful"

1. Who or what does the character struggle against?

_____

2. Does he or she win the struggle?

_____

3. What are the main reasons the character wins or loses the struggle?

_____

_____

_____

C. Answer **two** of the following essay questions. Write your answers on a separate sheet of paper. (20 points each)

1. Many of the characters in these selections are driven to take risks. Which one do you think risks the most, and which one do you think risks the least? Would you describe their risky actions as courageous, reckless, or both? Support your answers with details from the selections and your own ideas about taking risks.

2. Eleanor Roosevelt once said, "You must do the thing you think you cannot do." Choose **two** characters from these selections who would agree with this statement. Give reasons why they would agree.

3. Choose a selection from this part in which the setting is important to the plot and one in which the setting is not important to the plot. Give at least **two** reasons for each of the selections that you choose.

D. Sometimes it takes courage to stay true to yourself. Choose a character from a selection in this part. Write the name of the character and the selection. Then describe the challenges the character faced and why you think the character stayed true to himself or herself—or not. (20 points)

Character/Selection
What challenges did the character face?
Do you think the character stayed true to himself or herself? Why?

Matthew Henson at the Top of the World (page 101)

Selection Test

A. Three sources of information that a biographer might use to gather information about Matthew Henson's life are listed below. Write an important question that a biographer might try to answer about Henson's life from each source of information. (8 points each)

1. Captain Childs's diaries
2. Robert Peary's autobiography
3. Interviews with Matthew Henson's friends

B. Write the letter of the best answer. This exercise is continued on the next page. (5 points each)

_____ 1. Henson decided to get a job as a sailor mainly because he
    a. was looking for adventure.
    b. thought it would be an easy job.
    c. hadn't found any other work.
    d. wanted a steady, well-paying job.

_____ 2. Robert Peary first hired Henson to work as
    a. an engineer.   c. a skipper.
    b. a guide.   d. a servant.

_____ 3. What problem did Peary face when he returned from his successful expedition to the North Pole?
    a. Peary's men criticized the way he led the expedition.
    b. Experts said the expedition had not reached the North Pole.
    c. Another explorer said he had reached the North Pole first.
    d. Peary lost the readings he took to prove he had been to the North Pole.

_____ 4. The selection says, "Because Henson was black, his contributions to the expedition were not recognized for many years." This means that
a. no one in the expedition appreciated Henson's contribution.
b. Henson was not publicly honored for the important role he played in the expedition.
c. people ignored the expedition's success because a black man took part in it.
d. Henson was too modest to recognize what he did to make the expedition a success.

C. Words to Know. Write the letter of the best answer. (4 points each)

_____ 1. Stamina is something that is most needed when you are
a. resting.   b. struggling.   c. wondering.

_____ 2. People who live under tyranny would most likely be
a. treated unfairly.   b. well paid.   c. very popular.

_____ 3. An apt student is one who
a. works hard.   b. learns quickly.   c. shows off.

_____ 4. To call someone an ardent golfer means that the golfer
a. is skillful.   b. is a beginner.   c. loves to play.

_____ 5. A person who suffers from sleep deprivation would be most likely to
a. feel exhausted.   b. snore.   c. have nightmares.

D. Answer **one** of the following questions based on your understanding of the selection. Write your answer on a separate sheet of paper. (20 points)

1. Discuss how Henson benefited from working for Captain Childs on the *Katie Hines*. How did this experience prepare Henson for his expedition to the North Pole?

2. Why was trying to reach the North Pole so dangerous and difficult? Give at least two reasons and explain the problems they caused.

E. Linking Literature to Life. Answer the following question based on your own experience and knowledge. Write your answer on a separate sheet of paper. (16 points)

   Imagine that you have been overlooked for an honor you truly deserve. How would you react, and why would you react that way?

Summer of Fire (page 114)

Selection Test

A. Think about the factual information given in this selection and how it is organized. In the boxes below, describe the most important things that happened in Yellowstone during each month. (6 points each)

1. June	**3. August**
2. July	**4. September**

B. Write the letter of the best answer. This exercise is continued on the next page. (5 points each)

_____   1. Before 1988, the policy about wildfires in Yellowstone was to
       a. put them out immediately.
       b. make them turn north.
       c. keep them from spreading.
       d. let them burn.

_____   2. Fires became a serious problem in Yellowstone Park in 1988 mainly
       as a result of
       a. frequent lightning strikes.
       b. untended campfires.
       c. poor fire fighting.
       d. inexperienced rangers.

_____   3. In the North Fork fire, fire fighters concentrated mostly on
       a. extinguishing the fire.
       b. rescuing wildlife.
       c. saving park buildings.
       d. conserving water.

_____ 4. Television news coverage of the fires suggested that
      a. most of Yellowstone Park had been destroyed.
      b. the fires were easily controlled.
      c. the fires should have been allowed to burn.
      d. Old Faithful was harmed by the fire.

C. Words to Know. Write the letter of the best answer. (4 points each)

_____ 1. When storms <u>threaten</u> a town, the storms are likely to
      a. turn away from it.   b. cause damage.   c. weaken.

_____ 2. Plants that are <u>withering</u> in the sun are most likely to be
      a. green.   b. blooming.   c. shriveled.

_____ 3. When two paths <u>merge</u>, they
      a. stop suddenly.   b. become one.   c. change direction.

_____ 4. An entrance that has a <u>canopy</u> is
      a. paved.   b. locked.   c. covered.

_____ 5. A car is said to <u>veer</u> when it
      a. turns sharply.   b. slows down.   c. goes uphill.

D. Answer **one** of the following questions based on your understanding of the selection. Write your answer on a separate sheet of paper. (20 points)

1. Explain why no one tried to put out the first fires in Yellowstone Park early in the summer of 1988. Give at least two reasons.

2. What lessons did park officials and fire fighters probably learn from the Yellowstone fires?

E. Linking Literature to Life. Answer the following question based on your own experience and knowledge. Write your answer on a separate sheet of paper. (16 points)

Think of a time when you faced a force of nature, such as fire, drought, or extreme heat or cold. How did your experience affect the way you feel about nature? Why?

Ghost of the Lagoon (page 124)

Selection Test

A. Think of one *external* and one *internal* conflict Mako faces in the story. In the box on the left, describe the conflict that Mako faces. In the box on the right, tell how the conflict is resolved. (12 points each)

1. External Conflict	How Conflict Is Resolved
2. Internal Conflict	How Conflict Is Resolved

B. Write the letter of the best answer. This exercise is continued on the next page. (5 points each)

_____ 1. What was the main reason Mako was afraid of Tupa?
  a. He had seen Tupa in the lagoon.
  b. His grandfather had been killed by Tupa.
  c. He had heard fishermen's tales about Tupa.
  d. His mother often warned him about Tupa.

_____ 2. Mako paddled off in his canoe to
  a. go fishing.
  b. find fruit on a nearby island.
  c. swim with Afa.
  d. look for Tupa near the reef.

_____ 3. Mako was able to kill Tupa because
  a. he had often practiced on the reef that looked like a shark.
  b. Tupa was weak from hunger.
  c. he was not afraid of Tupa.
  d. Tupa was distracted by Afa's barking and splashing.

_____ 4. You can predict that on the next day, Mako probably will
   a. scold Afa.
   b. collect his reward.
   c. swim back to the reef.
   d. look for his father.

C. Words to Know. Write the letter of the best answer. (4 points each)

_____ 1. A <u>harpoon</u> is most similar to a
   a. spear.   b. club.   c. net.

_____ 2. <u>Phosphorus</u> is a substance that
   a. smells awful.   b. glows.   c. produces smoke.

_____ 3. A trip is called an <u>expedition</u> if it
   a. is dangerous.   b. has a purpose.   c. happens at night.

_____ 4. A <u>lagoon</u> is always found near a
   a. tropical island. b. coastal city.   c. larger body of water.

_____ 5. An ocean <u>reef</u> is always
   a. near the surface. b. brightly colored. c. far from shore.

D. Answer **one** of the following questions based on your understanding of the story. Write your answer on a separate sheet of paper. (20 points)

1. Why does Mako want to kill Tupa? Give at least three reasons you think he has for doing this.

2. Explain how Tupa became a fearsome legend to the people of Bora Bora.

E. Linking Literature to Life. Answer the following question based on your own experience and knowledge. Write your answer on a separate sheet of paper. (16 points)

   Describe a situation in which you would be willing to take a risk. What would be the rewards of taking the risk in this situation? If things didn't work out as you had planned, would there still have been any value in having taken the risk? Explain.

from **The Fun of It (page 135)**

Selection Test

A. Think about the kinds of information presented in this selection. In the boxes on the left, write three details of Earhart's flight that would have been included in newspaper accounts. In the boxes on the right, add information about each detail that would appear only in her autobiography. (8 points each)

Newspaper Account	Autobiography
1.	
2.	
3.	

B. Write the letter of the best answer. This exercise is continued on the next page. (5 points each)

_____ 1. What part of Earhart's plane failed while she was flying at 12,000 feet?
    a. the altimeter
    b. the engine
    c. the propeller
    d. the gyro compass

_____ 2. Earhart knew that to get rid of the ice on her plane, she had to fly at a
    a. faster speed.
    b. lower altitude.
    c. slower speed.
    d. higher altitude.

_____ 3. To fly safely through fog, Earhart depended on
    a. instructions radioed from other planes.
    b. her own senses and judgment.
    c. her plane's instruments.
    d. brief glimpses of the ocean or the moon.

_____ 4. Where did Earhart end her transatlantic flight?
   a. Newfoundland
   b. France
   c. New York
   d. Ireland

C. Words to Know. Write the letter of the best answer. (4 points each)

_____ 1. If you have a <u>sufficient</u> amount of something, you have
   a. much left over.   b. enough.   c. less than needed.

_____ 2. You would most likely take a <u>fleeting</u> look at something that is
   a. passing by.   b. very large.   c. colorful.

_____ 3. If snow is <u>accumulating</u>, it is
   a. melting.   b. turning to rain.   c. piling up.

_____ 4. Which of these is a <u>vessel</u>?
   a. harbor   b. lighthouse   c. ship

_____ 5. To show <u>hospitality</u> to someone is to make that person feel
   a. welcome.   b. clever.   c. nervous.

D. Answer **one** of the following questions based on your understanding of the selection. Write your answer on a separate sheet of paper. (20 points)

1. Which details from Earhart's account of her flight show that she was a skillful pilot?

2. Based on Earhart's account, what kind of personal traits do you think it is important for a pilot to have? Why are these traits important?

E. Linking Literature to Life. Answer the following questions based on your own experience and knowledge. Write your answer on a separate sheet of paper. (16 points)

Amelia Earhart became famous for her feats as an airplane pilot. If you could become famous for some accomplishment, what would it be? Why is this accomplishment important to you?

Older Run (page 154)

Selection Test

A. Paulsen's anecdote is amusing because he dares to make fun of himself and his troubles. Think of two events from the anecdote in which Paulsen does this. Write a brief description of the event. Then tell how Paulsen makes it funny. (12 points each)

What Happens	What Makes It Funny
1.	
2.	

B. Write the letter of the best answer. This exercise is continued on the next page. (5 points each)

_____ 1. At the beginning of the run, Paulsen mistakenly believed that
    a. the weather would be clear.
    b. he had brought along enough food for the dogs.
    c. ten dogs was the perfect number for the run.
    d. he was fully in control of his dog team.

_____ 2. Why did the dogs suddenly stop in the middle of the railroad trestle?
    a. Its tracks were covered with deep snow.
    b. It sagged dangerously in the middle.
    c. Its plywood base had been removed.
    d. It was too narrow for the team.

_____ 3. What did Paulsen do when the dogs ran off?
    a. He called for them.
    b. He followed their tracks.
    c. He put food out and waited for them.
    d. He began pulling the sled home.

_____ 4. The dogs probably returned because
        a. Cookie rounded them up.
        b. they missed Paulsen.
        c. they were hungry.
        d. a wild animal had chased them.

C. Words to Know. Write the letter of the best answer. (4 points each)

_____ 1. The main activity of a <u>spectator</u> is
        a. talking.   b. watching.   c. helping.

_____ 2. What does a <u>seasoned</u> performer have?
        a. talent   b. enthusiasm   c. experience

_____ 3. A <u>maneuver</u> is a
        a. polite person.   b. pleasing scene.   c. skillful movement.

_____ 4. When you <u>marvel</u> at something, you feel
        a. amazement.   b. sorrow.   c. boredom.

_____ 5. Which of these is most likely to <u>ricochet</u>?
        a. a shadow   b. a ball   c. a flower

D. Answer **one** of the following questions based on your understanding of the selection. Write your answer on a separate sheet of paper. (20 points)

1. Cookie is an important character in this story. Describe two of her traits, and explain how she demonstrates each one.

2. Were Paulsen's troubles more a result of bad luck or bad decisions? Give reasons for your answer.

E. Linking Literature to Life. Answer the following questions based on your own experience and knowledge. Write your answer on a separate sheet of paper. (16 points)

Describe a time when you were in charge of something that went very wrong. How did you respond, and how did others respond to you?

from Woodsong (page 165)

Selection Test

A. Choose two interesting events from the selection. In the box on the left, describe each event the way an outside observer might describe it. In the box on the right, add the details that only Paulsen could supply. (12 points each)

An Observer's Version	Paulsen's Version
1.	
2.	

B. Write the letter of the best answer. This exercise is continued on the next page. (5 points each)

_____ 1. Bears came to Paulsen's area mainly to
      a. find food.
      b. escape from hunters.
      c. look for mates.
      d. enjoy human companionship.

_____ 2. According to Paulsen, naming the wild bears led him to
      a. become too fond of bears.
      b. realize that humans and bears are equal.
      c. make the bears depend on him.
      d. forget how dangerous bears can be.

_____ 3. Scarhead most likely threatens to attack Paulsen because Scarhead
      a. is hungry.
      b. does not recognize Paulsen.
      c. feels threatened.
      d. has been badly wounded by Paulsen.

_____ 4. Why does Paulsen finally decide not to shoot Scarhead?
    a. The bear had not harmed him after all.
    b. He might miss and anger the bear more.
    c. Having bears around was useful.
    d. Other bears might react badly.

C. Words to Know. Write the letter of the best answer. (4 points each)

_____ 1. Which of these is a <u>predator</u>?
    a. wolf   b. sheep   c. goat

_____ 2. If you think something is a <u>menace</u>, what is your most likely reaction?
    a. delight   b. curiosity   c. fear

_____ 3. A person who is <u>rummaging</u> in an attic probably wants to
    a. hide something.   b. clean something.   c. find something.

_____ 4. If something is a <u>novelty</u> to you, it is
    a. unusual.   b. comforting.   c. admirable.

_____ 5. Someone who is <u>scavenging</u> for food is
    a. buying groceries.   b. looking for scraps.   c. cooking a meal.

D. Answer **one** of the following questions based on your understanding of the selection. Write your answer on a separate sheet of paper. (20 points)

1. How did Paulsen's attitude toward wild bears change from the beginning of the selection to the end?

2. Paulsen felt a range of emotions from the moment he threw the stick at Scarhead to the moment he put his gun away. Describe the emotions he felt and explain how each one made him behave.

E. Linking Literature to Life. Answer the following question based on your own experience and knowledge. Write your answer on a separate sheet of paper. (16 points)

Do you think a person ever has the right to kill a wild animal? Give reasons for your opinion.

Unit One: Tests of Courage

Part Two Open-Book Test

A. Write the letter of the best answer to each question. (5 points each)

_____ 1. Which selection in this part is an example of biography?
   a. *The Fun of It*
   b. "Matthew Henson at the Top of the World"
   c. "Ghost of the Lagoon"
   d. "Older Run"

_____ 2. "Summer of Fire" describes events that occurred mainly in
   a. Minnesota.   c. the wilderness of Alaska.
   b. Newfoundland.   d. Yellowstone National Park.

_____ 3. "Ghost of the Lagoon" focuses on a struggle between a boy and
   a. a shark.   c. his father.
   b. his dog.   d. an eel.

_____ 4. All the selections in this part concern people or characters who
   a. travel long distances.   c. save someone else's life.
   b. face danger.   d. depend on animals.

B. People in several of these selections face similar kinds of conflicts or problems, even though their experiences are quite different. In the boxes below, write the titles of **two** selections in which people face similar conflicts or problems. Describe the conflict or problem that each person faces and tell how the situations in the two selections are similar. (20 points)

Selection	Selection
Conflict or Problem	**Conflict or Problem**
How the Two Situations Are Similar	

C. Answer **two** of the following essay questions based on your understanding of the selections. Write your answers on a separate sheet of paper. (20 points each)

1. The selections in this part contain some important lessons about life. Choose **one** selection that you think communicates an important lesson. Explain what that lesson is and why you think it is an important one.

2. Many of the people in these selections take risks and hope to gain some kind of reward. Choose people from **two** of these selections and describe the risks they took and what reward they hoped to gain. Tell which of the two rewards you think was greater, and why.

3. Of all the people or characters in these selections, whom do you admire most? Why do you admire this person? Give at least **two** reasons.

4. In several selections in this part, a person or character does something that might be considered foolish. Choose **one** person or character from a selection you wish to discuss. Tell what the person did and why it could be considered foolish.

D. Many of the people and characters in these selections showed "courage in action," but they had different reasons for doing what they did. Choose **two** of the selections in this part. For each selection, name one person and describe what you think was the person's most courageous act. Then tell why you think he or she acted that way. (20 points)

1. Selection/Person	
The Person's Most Courageous Act	**Why the Person Did It**
2. Selection/Person	
The Person's Most Courageous Act	**Why the Person Did It**

I'm Nobody! Who Are You?/It Seems I Test People/ Growing Pains (page 194)

Selection Test

A. In the boxes on the left are examples of figurative language from the poems. In the boxes on the right, rewrite each example in your own words to tell what it means. (6 points each)

Examples of Figurative Language	Your Interpretation
1. from "I'm Nobody! Who Are You?" "How public—like a Frog— / To tell one's name— / the livelong June— / To an admiring Bog!"	
2. from "It Seems I Test People" "My skin sun-mixed like basic earth"	
3. "my eyes packed with hellos behind them"	
4. from "Growing Pains" "She said my room was a pigsty."	

B. Write the letter of the best answer. This exercise is continued on the next page. (6 points each)

_____ 1. In "I'm Nobody! Who Are You?" the speaker is addressing
   a. another nobody.
   b. somebody important.
   c. herself.
   d. the general public.

_____ 2. In "I'm Nobody! Who Are You?" the speaker suggests that being "Somebody" is
   a. enjoyable.
   b. meaningless.
   c. natural.
   d. dangerous.

_____ 3. In "It Seems I Test People," the speaker wants other people to
        a. ignore him.
        b. help him.
        c. test him.
        d. notice him.

_____ 4. In "Growing Pains," the speaker is having trouble with her mother
       mainly because
        a. the mother is harsh.
        b. they are both moody people.
        c. the mother ignores the child.
        d. the mother is sharing her troubles.

_____ 5. In "Growing Pains," the speaker finds it most difficult to accept
       the mother's
        a. anger.
        b. sadness.
        c. apology.
        d. politeness.

C. Answer **one** of the following questions based on your understanding of the poems. Write your answer on a separate sheet of paper. (26 points)

  1. In both "I'm Nobody! Who Are You?" and "It Seems I Test People," the speaker has a sense of not quite fitting into the world. What are the factors that affect each speaker's sense of not quite belonging? Do the speakers seem comfortable or uncomfortable with their position in the world? Explain your answer.

  2. Why do you think Jean Little titled her poem "Growing Pains"? Give at least two reasons.

D. Linking Literature to Life. Answer the following question based on your own experience and knowledge. Write your answer on a separate sheet of paper. (20 points)

  How important is it to you to feel that you "belong," or fit into, your world, your community, or your group of friends? Explain your answer.

Three Haiku (page 205)

Selection Test

A. Each of these haiku suggests a certain feeling or mood and expresses an idea. For each poem write notes in the boxes below to describe the feeling it suggests and an idea that it expresses. (10 points each)

Haiku by	Feeling It Suggests	Idea(s) It Expresses
1. Bashō		
2. Issa		
3. Patterson		

B. Write the letter of the best answer. (10 points each)

_____ 1. The haiku by Issa appeals mainly to the sense of
   a. sight.
   b. touch.
   c. hearing.
   d. smell.

_____ 2. The haiku by Bashō focuses mainly on
   a. the beauty of nature.
   b. how to live one's life.
   c. the importance of family.
   d. how the speaker feels about himself.

_____ 3. The haiku by Patterson suggests a mood of
   a. sadness.
   b. excitement.
   c. love.
   d. grief.

C. Answer **one** of the following questions based on your understanding of the haiku. Write your answer on a separate sheet of paper. (20 points)

1. After reading these poems, what can you tell about the type of poetry known as haiku?

2. Choose one of the haiku. Use your imagination and your own words to describe what you "see" in your mind when you read the poem.

D. Linking Literature to Life. Answer the following question based on your own experience and knowledge. Write your answer on a separate sheet of paper. (20 points)

Describe a time when you really noticed something in nature—something worth remembering. Which of your senses were involved in your appreciation of the scene or object? Why do you think you were so struck by this particular scene at this particular moment?

All Summer in a Day (page 209)

Selection Test

A. In science fiction, many details are different from what we are familiar with, but the human elements of the story are familiar. In the boxes below, write four details from the story that are different from life on Earth. Then write four details telling how the story is similar to what might happen on Earth in a familiar classroom. (12 points each)

1. Differences	2. Similarities

B. Write the letter of the best answer. This exercise is continued on the next page. (5 points each)

_____ 1. Why does Margot remember the sun?
   a. She is smarter than the other children.
   b. She is older than the other children.
   c. She has been on Venus longer than the other children.
   d. She saw it before moving to Venus.

_____ 2. The beginning of this story takes place in a
   a. spaceship.
   b. schoolroom.
   c. laboratory.
   d. closet.

_____ 3. Margot's parents are planning to move to Earth because
   a. they want to make more money.
   b. Margot is wasting away.
   c. the students in her school dislike Margot.
   d. Margot is forgetting what the sun is like.

_____ 4. When the sun comes out, Margot does not see it because
        a. the other children locked her in the closet.
        b. she is being punished by the teacher.
        c. no one is allowed to look at the sun.
        d. she does not want to be with the other children.

C. Words to Know. Write the letter of the best answer. (4 points each)

_____ 1. You might well feel a <u>concussion</u> from
        a. a hot bath.   b. a spring breeze.   c. an earthquake.

_____ 2. The <u>apparatus</u> for a tightrope walker includes the
        a. tightrope.   b. fear of falling.   c. other circus acts.

_____ 3. Which group of people would be most likely to behave <u>tumultuously</u>?
        a. rioters   b. choir members   c. chess players

_____ 4. Which of the following things is most <u>resilient</u>?
        a. wood   b. steel   c. rubber

_____ 5. If you say that you <u>savor</u> an experience, you mean that you find it
        a. frightening.   b. enjoyable.   c. boring.

D. Answer **one** of the following questions based on your understanding of the story. Write your answer on a separate sheet of paper. (20 points)

1. What might be some reasons that the children get angry when Margot talks about the sun? Support your ideas with reference to the story.

2. Do you think that, after this experience, the children will be more accepting of Margot? Why or why not?

E. Linking Literature to Life. Answer the following question based on your own experience and knowledge. Write your answer on a separate sheet of paper. (16 points)

Do you think children are sometimes cruel to one another? Do you think they mean to be cruel? Explain your answer.

Chinatown *from* The Lost Garden (page 219)

Selection Test

A. In "Chinatown," Laurence Yep recounts firsthand memories of growing up in San Francisco. In the boxes on the left, write three specific details that Yep remembers about the locations and/or the people he knew in Chinatown. In the boxes on the right, tell how each of the details made Yep feel about Chinatown or about himself. (8 points each)

Details About Chinatown	How Laurence Yep Felt
1.	
2.	
3.	

B. Write the letter of the best answer. This exercise is continued on the next page. (5 points each)

_____ 1. During Yep's childhood, Chinese people lived in Chinatown mainly because they
     a. liked the grassy open lots that dotted the neighborhood.
     b. feared living in areas where people mostly spoke English.
     c. could not afford the housing in other neighborhoods.
     d. were refused housing in other neighborhoods.

_____ 2. Yep believes that his schoolmate Paul had trouble learning English and social skills because he
     a. went to school in Chinatown.
     b. hung around with a rough group of boys.
     c. was busy with work and family responsibilities.
     d. was unusually tall and strong.

_____ 3. What attitude did Yep and his friends have toward the world inhabited by wealthy white people?
   a. They never saw this world.
   b. They expected to become a part of this world someday.
   c. They saw this world but felt they could never join it.
   d. They felt their world was superior to the white world in every way.

_____ 4. What is the main reason that Yep feels he disappointed his family?
   a. He is unskilled in playing sports.
   b. He cannot speak Chinese.
   c. He is a poor student.
   d. He refuses to help out in the family store.

C. Words to Know. Write the letter of the best answer. (4 points each)

_____ 1. Which would most likely be described as gaudy?
   a. a dark corridor   b. a large, shiny necklace   c. a delicate flower

_____ 2. The conditions in a tenement are
   a. rundown.   b. luxurious.   c. cozy.

_____ 3. A subject that is taboo is something to be
   a. avoided.   b. studied.   c. discussed.

_____ 4. Which person would most likely be shunned?
   a. a teacher   b. a close friend   c. an enemy

_____ 5. Which would most likely be palatial?
   a. a coffee shop   b. an expensive hotel   c. a post office

D. Answer **one** of the following questions based on your understanding of the selection. Write your answer on a separate sheet of paper. (20 points)

1. At the end of the selection Yep says, "In trying to find solutions, I had created more pieces to the puzzle." What puzzle is Yep talking about? Why is he having a hard time putting the puzzle together?

2. What separates Yep from his classmates and friends, and what ties him to them?

E. Linking Literature to Life. Answer the following question based on your own experience and knowledge. Write your answer on a separate sheet of paper. (16 points)

Which do you think is worse—for people to expect you to have more skills than you really have or for people to think you have fewer skills and not give you a chance? Explain your answer.

Unit Two: Growth and Change

Part One Open-Book Test

A. Write the letter of the best answer. (5 points each)

_____ 1. Which poem in this part suggests how difficult it is for children
to understand their parents?
a. "I'm Nobody! Who Are You?"
b. "Growing Pains"
c. "It Seems I Test People"
d. the haiku by Patterson

_____ 2. You know that "All Summer in a Day" is science fiction because it
a. takes place on Venus.
b. tells a story about the sun.
c. takes place during a rainstorm.
d. involves a school teacher.

_____ 3. In "Chinatown," Laurence Yep reveals that as a child he often felt
a. confident.   c. excited.
b. popular.   d. confused.

_____ 4. In "It Seems I Test People," the speaker seems to feel that he is
a. unwelcome.   c. gloomy.
b. famous.   d. too honest.

B. Think about the imagery in the poems in this part. Choose **one** poem that you want
to discuss and write the title on the line. In the boxes below, note an image from the
poem that you think is effective. Then write notes telling what senses the image
appeals to and why you think the image is effective. (20 points)

Title	
The image of	**appeals to the sense(s) of**
and is effective because	

C. Answer **two** of the following essay questions based on your understanding of the selections. Write your answers on a separate sheet of paper. (20 points each)

1. In some of the poems in this part, the speaker has a problem with the way a person or people respond to him or her. Choose **one** poem in this part. Explain what problem the speaker has and how he or she feels about it.

2. In several of the selections in this part, people do not come right out and tell other people what is on their minds. Choose **one** selection in which it might have helped a person to "talk straight," and tell how you think this might have helped.

3. Which **one** of the selections in this part did you enjoy most? Why?

4. Several selections in this part involve a place that is special in some way. Choose **one** of those places and explain what makes it special.

D. The theme of this part is "The Need to Belong." The selections present a number of people who feel they do not fit in. Choose two people from the selections and write their names in the boxes below. Beneath each name, write notes telling why the person feels out of place. At the bottom, suggest ways in which the person could either change and better fit in or simply come to feel better about the situation. (20 points)

Person	**Person**
Why the Person Feels Out of Place	**Why the Person Feels Out of Place**
Ways the Person Could Feel Better	**Ways the Person Could Feel Better**

Aaron's Gift (page 248)

Selection Test

A. Listed below are three techniques that authors use to develop characters. Next to each technique, give an example of how Myron Levoy uses it in "Aaron's Gift." (8 points each)

Type of Characterization	Example
1. Presenting a character's words or actions	
2. Presenting what other characters think or say about the character	
3. Commenting directly on the character	

B. Write the letter of the best answer. This exercise is continued on the next page. (5 points each)

_____ 1. Aaron captures the pigeon in the park because he wants to
   a. help it.
   b. practice his medical skills.
   c. use it to get into a boys' club.
   d. give it to his grandmother.

_____ 2. When Aaron's father sees the pigeon, he is
   a. irritated with his son for acting without permission.
   b. pleased that the family will finally have a pet.
   c. proud of his son's skill in setting the bird's wing.
   d. worried that his son is going to get into trouble.

_____ 3. Aaron manages to go to a club meeting by
          a. persuading his mother to change her mind.
          b. lying about where he is going.
          c. openly refusing to obey his mother.
          d. sneaking out of the house.

_____ 4. Aaron calls the boys "Cossacks" as a way of showing that he
          a. is afraid of them.
          b. wants to join them.
          c. thinks they are from the Ukraine.
          d. thinks they are cruel bullies.

C. Words to Know. Write the letter of the best answer. (4 points each)

_____ 1. To <u>assassinate</u> a political leader is to
          a. elect him.   b. criticize him.   c. kill him.

_____ 2. Which of the following would you most likely do on a <u>stoop</u>?
          a. cook dinner   b. sit down   c. take a ride

_____ 3. Students behaving in a <u>frenzied</u> way would most likely be told to
          a. calm down.   b. speak up.   c. join in.

_____ 4. A football team's <u>mascot</u> would come on the field to
          a. throw the ball.   b. lead a cheer.   c. settle an argument.

_____ 5. A person would be most likely to start <u>thrashing</u> during a
          a. nightmare.   b. meal.   c. test.

D. Answer **one** of the following questions based on your understanding of the story. Write your answer on a separate sheet of paper. (20 points)

1. What can you tell about the kind of person Aaron's grandmother is, and how can you tell what she is like?

2. What is Aaron's gift to his grandmother? How is the face she shows him in the mirror a part of that gift?

E. Linking Literature to Life. Answer the following question based on your own experience and knowledge. Write your answer on a separate sheet of paper. (16 points)

Can a person "make up" for terrible things that have happened to someone else? Explain your answer.

Name _____   Date _____

The Circuit (page 264)

Selection Test

A. In this story, the writer uses sensory details to describe places and people. In the boxes below, write a detail from the story that appeals to each of the senses listed. Then tell who or what the detail describes. (8 points each)

Sense	Detail	Who or What It Describes
1. Sight		
2. Hearing		
3. Touch		

B. Write the letter of the best answer. This exercise is continued on the next page. (5 points each)

_____ 1. Why do Panchito and his family move so often?
a. They must go where the crops are.
b. They enjoy traveling and living in new places.
c. They are frequently forced to move by the authorities.
d. They are trying to hide the fact that the children are not in school.

_____ 2. What can you infer from Panchito's little brothers' and sisters' reactions to the preparations for leaving a place?
a. They are nervous and insecure from so much traveling.
b. They are too young to worry about the future.
c. They are desperate to go somewhere that has good schools.
d. They don't realize that the family will be moving again.

_____ 3. Why do Panchito and Roberto hide from the school bus?
    a. They hate school and don't want to be forced to go.
    b. They are ashamed of being migrant workers.
    c. They don't want their parents to get into trouble.
    d. They don't want to be forced to move to the next town.

_____ 4. When Panchito goes to school in Fresno for the first time, his behavior shows that he is
    a. extremely sure of his ability to succeed.
    b. nervous but determined to do well.
    c. overwhelmed by his fears of failure.
    d. eager to fail at school and return to the fields.

C. Words to Know. Write the letter of the best answer. (4 points each)

_____ 1. What would a person do with a jalopy?
    a. drive it   b. wear it   c. eat it

_____ 2. A surplus at a restaurant would be made up of
    a. minutes.   b. leftovers.   c. coins.

_____ 3. You would go to a vineyard to pick
    a. berries.   b. vegetables.   c. grapes.

_____ 4. A move you made by instinct would seem
    a. learned.   b. natural.   c. abnormal.

_____ 5. A person who speaks hesitantly most likely feels
    a. confident.   b. excited.   c. uncertain.

D. Answer **one** of the following questions based on your understanding of the story. Write your answer on a separate sheet of paper. (20 points)

1. Panchito does not say how he feels when, at the end of the story, he sees the cardboard boxes packed. How do you think he feels? What details from the story help you infer Panchito's emotions, even though they are never stated directly?

2. Do you think Panchito will lead a life like his parents', or do you think he will live a different sort of life? Give evidence from the story to support your point of view.

E. Linking Literature to Life. Answer the following question based on your own experience and knowledge. Write your answer on a separate sheet of paper. (16 points)

Do you and your classmates tend to view going to school as a privilege, or do you take it for granted? Give at least three reasons for your answer.

Oh Broom, Get to Work (page 275)

Selection Test

A. In this selection, the narrator reveals much about herself and her family by what she chooses to describe and how she describes it. Read each excerpt below and write notes telling what it reveals about Yoshiko and her family. (8 points each)

Excerpt	What It Reveals About Yoshiko and Her Family
1. "Look, Mama! I found a dead sparrow!" But Mama was busy. She was sitting in the easy chair, knitting quietly. Sitting across from her on the sofa was a squat blob of a man—balding and gray—as silent as a mushroom.	
2. One pompous minister from Japan not only stayed overnight, which was bad enough, but left his dirty bathwater in the tub for Mama to wash out. "What nerve!" Keiko fumed.	
3. "I'm sorry," he murmured, "but it was so warm I had to remove my winter undershirt." He wiped his face with a big handkerchief and added, "I feel much better now." I knew if I looked at Keiko we would both explode. But I did. And we did. We laughed so hard we had to leave the table.	

B. Write the letter of the best answer. This exercise is continued on the next page. (5 points each)

_____ 1. Yoshiko wishes that the visitors would
   a. show their appreciation.
   b. ask her father for advice.
   c. include her and her sister in their conversations.
   d. leave her family alone.

_____ 2. Yoshiko's parents treat the meals with visitors as
   a. festive celebrations.
   b. normal, everyday events.
   c. irritating events that they try to hurry through.
   d. formal occasions that make them shy and nervous.

_____ 3. Yoshiko's mother thinks the worst fault someone can have is to
    a. bore other people.
    b. stay too long during a visit.
    c. not care about other people.
    d. visit someone without an invitation.

_____ 4. At the end of the story, the visitor most likely leaves because he
    a. knows the broom is magical.
    b. remembers he has something else to do.
    c. hears Yoshiko tell him to go away.
    d. sees the broom and realizes he is not wanted.

C. Words to Know. Write the letter of the best answer. (4 points each)

_____ 1. You could show that you are <u>indifferent</u> by
    a. shrugging.   b. nodding.   c. crying.

_____ 2. Something that is used to prevent an <u>intrusion</u> is a
    a. door lock.   b. smoke alarm.   c. safety pin.

_____ 3. It is <u>audacious</u> to
    a. avoid trouble.   b. break rules.   c. accept criticism.

_____ 4. You are most likely to <u>dread</u> receiving a
    a. gift.   b. suggestion.   c. scolding.

_____ 5. A police officer would be most likely to <u>dispense</u>
    a. criminals.   b. handcuffs.   c. tickets.

D. Answer **one** of the following questions based on your understanding of the selection. Write your answer on a separate sheet of paper. (20 points)

1. Why doesn't Yoshiko like having visitors? Give at least three reasons.

2. What positive things happen to Yoshiko because of her parents' attitudes toward visitors? Support your answer with details from the story.

E. Linking Literature to Life. Answer the following question based on your understanding of the story. Write your answer on a separate sheet of paper. (16 points)

What do you think are some good things and some bad things about having company in your home? Explain.

Western Wagons/Night Journey (page 284)

Selection Test

A. Think about the use of rhythm, rhyme, and repetition in the poems. Read the quotations from "Western Wagons" and "Night Journey." First use the symbols ´ and ˘ to mark the stressed and unstressed syllables in each line. Check the box for each technique used in the line or lines. (8 points each)

from "Western Wagons"	Rhyme	Repetition
1. They went with axe and rifle, when the trail was still to blaze, They went with wife and children, in the prairie-schooner days		
2. We shall starve and freeze and suffer. We shall die, and tame the lands.		

from "Night Journey"	Rhyme	Repetition
3. Now as the train bears west, / Its rhythm rocks the earth, / And from my Pullman berth		
4. I watch a beacon swing / From dark to blazing bright, / We thunder through ravines / And gullies washed with light.		

B. Write the letter of the best answer. This exercise is continued on the next page.
(6 points each)

_____ 1. Both "Western Wagons" and "Night Journey" express a love of
  a. security.   c. wealth.
  b. movement.   d. conversation.

_____ 2. Most of "Western Wagons" is written from the point of view of
  a. a historian looking back at America's frontier days.
  b. a person in the East saying farewell to people going west.
  c. the ghost of someone who died going west in a wagon.
  d. a pioneer setting out to travel to a new frontier.

_____ 3. Why does the speaker in "Night Journey" stay up half the night?
  a. He is uncomfortable and cannot get to sleep.
  b. He is talking to a fellow passenger.
  c. He wants to see the changing landscape.
  d. He is awakened by a rainstorm.

_____ 4. What is the mood of "Night Journey"?
        a. tense
        b. alert
        c. sleepy
        d. sad

_____ 5. How is the scene described in "Night Journey" similar to the scene described in "Western Wagons"?
        a. Both are descriptions of traveling west.
        b. Both describe starting an unknown new life.
        c. Both describe traveling by train.
        d. Both describe traveling alone.

C. Answer **one** of the following questions based on your understanding of the poems. Write your answer on a separate sheet of paper. (22 points)

1. According to "Western Wagons," what are some of the possible reasons that people moved west? Do you think they totally understood their reasons for going? Explain your answer.

2. How does Theodore Roethke convey the feeling of movement in "Night Journey"? Use specific examples from the poem in your answer.

D. Linking Literature to Life. Answer the following question based on your own experience and knowledge. Write your answer on a separate sheet of paper. (16 points)

How do you feel about long trips? Which is better, the traveling itself or reaching your destination? Explain.

Unit Two: Growth and Change

Part Two Open-Book Test

A. Write the answer to each question on the lines. (5 points each)

1. From what point of view is "The Circuit" written, and who is the narrator?

   _____

   _____

2. What is the gift that Aaron plans to give to his grandmother in "Aaron's Gift"?

   _____

3. Which selection in this part is about the pioneers who settled America?

   _____

4. In "Oh Broom, Get to Work," what does the title refer to?

   _____

   _____

B. All the selections in this part involve journeys of one kind or another. Some of the reasons for and descriptions of these journeys are positive, but others are negative. Choose one selection in which the journey seems positive and one in which the journey seems negative. In the chart below, write the titles of the selections you choose, brief descriptions of the journeys, and why you think they are positive or negative. (20 points)

Selection	Selection
Description of Journey	**Description of Journey**
Why It Is Positive	**Why It Is Negative**

C. Answer **two** of the following essay questions based on your understanding of the selections. Write your answers on a separate sheet of paper. (20 points each)

1. Choose **one** selection from this part that you think deals with an interesting test of endurance. Tell what is tested and whether the test is passed.

2. The authors of the selections in this part use description to make their settings and characters come alive to the reader. In your opinion, which writer created the most vivid and memorable descriptions? Choose **one** selection, give examples of your favorite descriptions, and tell why they are so effective.

3. Several selections in this part are told from the first-person point of view. Choose **one** of these selections and discuss how the use of the first person affects the way the story is told.

4. In most of these selections, a single object or figure serves as a symbol—a strong image that represents something important. Choose **two** selections in this part. Describe one symbol in each selection and explain its meaning within the story.

D. All the selections in this part are linked by the theme of "Home and Heritage." Choose **two** of the selections in this part. In the boxes below, write notes telling what you think the main theme or message of the selection is and how it relates to the theme of "Home and Heritage." (20 points)

Selection	Selection Theme	How It Relates to "Home and Heritage" Theme
1.		
2.		

Damon and Pythias (page 322)

Selection Test

A. Look at the stage directions in the chart below. In the boxes on the right, write notes explaining what the direction tells you about the setting, action, or character. (10 points each)

Stage Direction	What the Direction Tells You
1. At the beginning of the play: *(Sound: Iron door opens and shuts. Key in lock.)*	
2. **Pythias.** No, no, Damon! You must not do such a foolish thing! . . . Don't go! *(to himself)* Damon, my friend! You may find yourself in a cell beside me!	
3. **Damon** *(quiet, sincere)*. I would have died for you gladly, my friend. **Crowd Voices** *(loud, demanding)*. Set them free! Set them both free!	

B. Write the letter of the best answer. This exercise is continued on the next page. (5 points each)

_____ 1. Why did the people of Sicily obey the king?
     a. They thought he was strict but just.
     b. They feared his army.
     c. They were not aware of his cruelty.
     d. They knew he would die soon.

_____ 2. What crime was Pythias accused of?
     a. robbing travelers
     b. plotting to hurt the king
     c. being friends with Damon
     d. speaking out against a law

_____ 3. The king allowed Pythias to leave because the king
     a. was curious to see if Pythias would return.
     b. pitied Pythias.
     c. wanted to look merciful in the eyes of the public.
     d. didn't realize that Damon had taken the place of his friend.

_____ 4. As time passed and Pythias did not return, Damon felt
    a. confident that Pythias would appear in time.
    b. fearful that Pythias had changed his mind.
    c. angry that he had put his own life at risk.
    d. that Pythias was being selfish.

_____ 5. Who prevented Pythias from returning when he expected to?
    a. his mother
    b. his sister
    c. the king
    d. robbers

_____ 6. When Pythias showed up at the last moment, the king felt
    a. frustrated that he could not execute Damon.
    b. glad that he could execute Pythias.
    c. awe at Damon and Pythias's friendship.
    d. embarrassed that he had been wrong about Pythias.

C. Answer **one** of the following questions based on your understanding of the play. Write your answer on a separate sheet of paper. (20 points)

1. What values do Damon and Pythias represent in this play? Use details from the play to support your answer.

2. In what way does the king change in this play, and why does he change? Explain your answer.

D. Linking Literature to Life. Answer the following question based on your own experience and knowledge. Write your answer on a separate sheet of paper. (20 points)

Risking one's life for a friend is unusual, but often friends are willing to make sacrifices for each other. What kinds of things would you expect a close friend to be willing to do for you? Would you be willing to do the same kinds of things for your friend?

Name _____ Date _____

Cricket in the Road (page 333)

Selection Test

A. The children in "Cricket in the Road" speak Trinidad English. Read each piece of dialogue from the story, listed below. Then tell what the dialogue reveals about the character who is speaking. (8 points each)

Dialogue	What It Reveals
1. "Toss for it," he [Vern] said. "What you want?"	
2. "Tell on him," Amy cried. "He throw them away."	
3. "Selo, here—*you* first bat," he [Vern] said gleefully.	

B. Write the letter of the best answer. This exercise is continued on the next page. (5 points each)

_____ 1. At the beginning of the story, what puts Selo in such a bad mood?
   a. He has lost a game of cricket.
   b. He has gotten in trouble for tracking mud into the house.
   c. His friends have run away from him.
   d. He is frightened by the thunderstorm.

_____ 2. Vern and Amy react to the rainy season with
   a. patient acceptance.
   b. angry pouting.
   c. cheerful excitement.
   d. terror and disappointment.

_____ 3. The three friends have an argument about
   a. who will bat second.
   b. who will bat first.
   c. whose bat to use.
   d. where to play cricket.

_____ 4. Why does Selo sometimes whistle outside Amy and Vern's house?
   a. He wants to show he is not afraid of the thunder.
   b. He wants them to forgive him and come play.
   c. He wants to fight with them.
   d. He wants to drown out the sound of their voices.

C. Words to Know. Write the letter of the best answer. (4 points each)

_____ 1. The best protection from a <u>torrent</u> would be a
   a. roof.   b. medicine.   c. net.

_____ 2. When directed to <u>fume</u> silently, an actor would most likely
   a. grin.   b. yawn.   c. frown.

_____ 3. You would be most likely to hear a <u>peal</u> of laughter from a person
   who heard something
   a. embarrassing.   b. confusing.   c. really funny.

_____ 4. To protect yourself from the <u>tumult</u> of a storm, you could use
   a. earplugs.   b. galoshes.   c. a rowboat.

_____ 5. If you were <u>dumbfounded</u> by something, you would most likely
   a. complain.   b. applaud.   c. stare.

D. Answer **one** of the following questions based on your understanding of the story. Write your answer on a separate sheet of paper. (20 points)

1. Tell what you think Selo's main internal conflict is in this story. Does he resolve it? If so, how?

2. If the author were to continue this story, what do you predict would happen next? Back up your prediction with information from the story.

E. Linking Literature to Life. Answer the following question based on your own experience and knowledge. Write your answer on a separate sheet of paper. (16 points)

Why do you think people sometimes find it difficult to apologize when they have misbehaved or done something they regret?

Name _____   Date _____

The Quarrel/Fable (page 343)

Selection Test

A. "The Quarrel" and "Fable" are both narrative poems. Complete the Venn diagram below by listing similarities and differences between the plots of the two poems. (30 points)

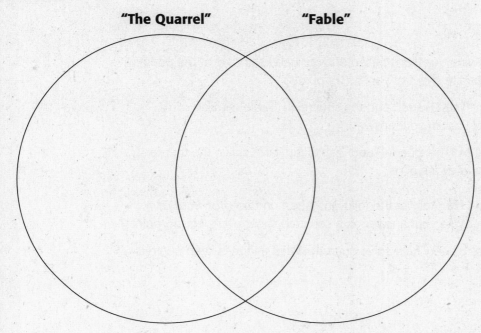

"The Quarrel"   **"Fable"**

B. Write the letter of the best answer. This exercise is continued on the next page. (5 points each)

_____ 1. What does the speaker in "The Quarrel" say about its cause?
   a. She started it.
   b. Her brother started it.
   c. They were equally responsible for starting it.
   d. She doesn't know how it began.

_____ 2. How did the speaker feel about the quarrel?
   a. She enjoyed it.
   b. She was disturbed by it.
   c. She forgot about it.
   d. She ended it.

_____ 3. In "Fable," who is Bun?
   a. a tree
   b. the squirrel
   c. a nut
   d. the mountain

_____ 4. In "Fable," when Bun says, "But all sorts of things and weather / Must be taken in together, / To make up a year / And a sphere," he or she is praising
   a. variety.
   b. hard work.
   c. kindness.
   d. travel.

C. Answer **one** of the following questions based on your understanding of the poems. Write your answer on a separate sheet of paper. (25 points)

1. How are the brother in "The Quarrel" and the squirrel in "Fable" similar? How are they different? Explain your answer.

2. How are the messages of "The Quarrel" and "Fable" similar? Explain the theme of each poem and how they are alike.

D. Linking Literature to Life. Answer the following question based on your own experience and knowledge. Write your answer on a separate sheet of paper. (25 points)

   What qualities and points of view help solve quarrels? What attitudes keep quarrels going? Give examples.

Unit Three: A Sense of Fairness
Part One Open-Book Test

A. Write your answer to each question on the lines. (5 points each)

1. Which selection stresses the theme that there is nothing more valuable than friendship?

   _____

2. Who is arguing in "The Quarrel"?

   _____

3. In "Cricket in the Road," why does Selo discard the bat and ball?

   _____

   _____

   _____

4. Who is arguing in "Fable"?

   _____

B. In several selections in this part, there is a character who cares enough about another person to act unselfishly. Next to each character listed below, write the name of the person the unselfish character cares about. Then describe the unselfish action. (20 points)

Unselfish Character	Person He Cares About	What He Does
Damon (in *Damon and Pythias*)		
Vern (in "Cricket in the Road")		
the brother (in "The Quarrel")		

C. Answer **two** of the following essay questions based on your understanding of the selections. Write your answers on a separate sheet of paper. (20 points each)

1. In your opinion, which character in these selections changes the most? How and why does that character change?

2. Each selection in this part teaches a slightly different lesson. Which lesson do you think is most important for you to learn and apply to your own life? Why?

3. In each selection, a character faces a problem and has to solve it. Who do you think is most successful in solving his or her problem, and who is least successful? Explain your views.

D. In each selection in this part, characters have conflicts that raise questions about fairness. Some of the characters are clearly in the right, whereas others clearly are not. Other characters act in ways that are a little more difficult to judge. Choose characters from **two** selections that you want to discuss. In the boxes below, write the name of each character you choose. Then write notes describing how that character behaved in a conflict, your judgment of the character's fairness, and the reason for your judgment. (20 points)

1. Character/Selection	2. Character/Selection
Behavior in Conflict	**Behavior in Conflict**
Character's Sense of Fairness	**Character's Sense of Fairness**

Abd al-Rahman Ibrahima (page 365)

Selection Test

A. Read the following details from "Abd al-Rahman Ibrahima." Beside each detail, write *primary* or *secondary* to indicate the kind of source each fact most likely came from. (4 points each)

Detail	Source
1. Guinea is a land of green mountains and rich minerals.	
2. Islam was the religion of much of Africa.	
3. Dr. Cox, an Irishman, told of being separated from a hunting party.	
4. "We could not see them," Ibrahima wrote.	
5. Timbuktu was a large city in the Songhai Empire.	
6. Ibrahima sensed that things would not go well for him.	

B. Write the letter of the best answer. This exercise is continued on the next page. (5 points each)

_____ 1. As a young man, Ibrahima went to Timbuktu in order to
   a. get a job.
   b. get an education.
   c. fight against the Mandingo.
   d. fight against the Europeans.

_____ 2. The Mandingo were able to defeat the Fula because
   a. the Mandingo were better armed.
   b. Europeans were fighting alongside the Mandingo.
   c. the Fula were badly nourished and sick.
   d. the Fula were scholars who did not know how to fight.

_____ 3. What was it about Ibrahima that Thomas Foster valued most?
   a. his attitude
   b. his education
   c. his physical strength
   d. his royal background

_____ 4. Why did Dr. Cox try to help Ibrahima?
   a. Ibrahima's people had once helped Dr. Cox.
   b. Dr. Cox wanted Ibrahima to be his guide back to Africa.
   c. Foster had long been an enemy of Dr. Cox.
   d. Dr. Cox spent his life trying to free slaves.

C. Words to Know. Write the letter of the best answer. (4 points each)

_____ 1. An inhabitant of Africa is someone who
   a. visits there.   b. lives there.   c. studies it.

_____ 2. A trek across a country is a
   a. major river.   b. long trip.   c. line on a map.

_____ 3. A person who has a reservation about swimming in a lake would be most
   likely to
   a. hesitate.   b. jump right in.   c. run away.

_____ 4. Which event always involves chaos?
   a. a graduation   b. a riot   c. a party

_____ 5. Which of the following always has a premise?
   a. a painting   b. a recipe   c. an argument

D. Answer **one** of the following questions based on your understanding of the selection. Write your answer on a separate sheet of paper. (20 points)

1. What dangers and humiliations did Ibrahima suffer after he was captured, and how did his experiences change his attitudes toward life?

2. How was Ibrahima's life in Africa different from the way slave owners, such as Thomas Foster, imagined it to be?

E. Linking Literature to Life. Answer the following question based on your own experience and knowledge. Write your answer on a separate sheet of paper. (16 points)

Do you think people around the world are much the same in what they want or how they feel, or are people really quite different from one another? Explain.

from The Story of My Life (page 381)

Selection Test

A. Read each sentence from *The Story of My Life* and note the sensory details.
Put a check under each sense to which the sentence appeals. (4 points each)

	Sight	Hearing	Smell	Taste	Touch
1. "My fingers lingered almost unconsciously on the familiar leaves and blossoms."					
2. "Have you ever been at sea in a dense fog, when it seemed as if a tangible white darkness shut you in . . . ?"					
3. "I felt approaching footsteps."					
4. "We walked down the path to the well-house, attracted by the fragrance of the honeysuckle with which it was covered."					
5. "As the cool stream gushed over one hand she spelled into the other the word *water*, first slowly, then rapidly."					

B. Write the letter of the best answer. This exercise is continued on the next page.
(5 points each)

_____ 1. Helen Keller felt like a ship in a fog before Miss Sullivan arrived
because she was
a. in terrible danger.
b. large and awkward.
c. ready for a new adventure.
d. confused.

_____ 2. When Miss Sullivan first spelled the word *doll* into Helen's hand,
Helen responded by
a. breaking an actual doll.
b. mimicking Miss Sullivan's hand movements.
c. struggling roughly with Miss Sullivan.
d. connecting the word *doll* with the object.

_____ 3. Miss Sullivan seems to have had what sort of personality?
   a. impatient
   b. distant and formal
   c. silly
   d. calm and determined

_____ 4. How did Helen feel at the end of the day when she first understood
   what language meant?
   a. sad at how much she had missed of life
   b. too tired to want to learn anything more
   c. eager for the next day to begin
   d. angry that her parents had never taught her the names of things

C. Words to Know. Write the letter of the best answer. (4 points each)

_____ 1. You would most likely feel <u>bitterness</u> over a
   a. lost puppy.   b. nice present.   c. friend's cruelty.

_____ 2. Which of the following things is <u>tangible</u>?
   a. a secret   b. a noise   c. a blanket

_____ 3. You would most likely feel <u>repentance</u> for
   a. breaking a rule.   b. winning a prize.   c. asking a question.

_____ 4. In a typical day, what <u>succeeds</u> supper?
   a. breakfast   b. tableware   c. bedtime

_____ 5. You could <u>reveal</u> a problem by
   a. describing it.   b. denying it.   c. ignoring it.

D. Answer **one** of the following questions based on your understanding of the selection.
Write your answer on a separate sheet of paper. (20 points)

1. Compare Helen's mental and emotional states before and after she learns the
   "mystery of language." What does her experience tell you about the importance
   of language to human beings?

2. What conclusions can you draw about Anne Sullivan from this selection?
   Describe her personality, her background, and her teaching methods.
   Support your conclusions with details from the selection.

E. Linking Literature to Life. Answer the following question based on your own
experience and knowledge. Write your answer on a separate sheet of paper. (20 points)

   Which of your senses is the most important to you? Why?

Street Corner Flight/Words Like Freedom (page 391)

Selection Test

A. Read these lines from the two poems. Then, next to each set of lines, write down what you can infer about the speaker of the poem. (8 points each)

Lines	What You Can Infer
From "Street Corner Flight": 1. "From this side . . . of their concrete barrio"	

2. "They were free
  to fly
  toward the other side . . .
  a world away."	

From "Words Like Freedom": 3. "On my heartstrings freedom sings All day everyday."	
4. "If you had known what I know You would know why."	

B. Write the letter of the best answer. This exercise is continued on the next page. (5 points each)

_____ 1. Where are the boys in "Street Corner Flight"?
  a. in a city
  b. at an airport
  c. in a field
  d. in a prison

_____ 2. Why did the boys let the birds go?
  a. The boys were bored with the birds.
  b. The birds were poorly fed and sick.
  c. The boys wanted the birds to be free.
  d. The birds could no longer fly.

_____ 3. What can you infer about the boys?
  a. They are rough.
  b. They are clever.
  c. They are lost.
  d. They are poor.

_____ 4. What sound device is *not* used in "Words Like Freedom"?
  a. repetition
  b. rhyme
  c. rhythm
  d. onomatopoeia

_____ 5. What does the speaker imply about the word *freedom*?
  a. The word means nothing to him personally.
  b. The concept is very important to him.
  c. He only thinks about freedom when he is in trouble.
  d. He thinks people are better off without freedom.

_____ 6. What does the speaker imply about his life?
  a. He can't remember much about it.
  b. He has seen suffering.
  c. He lives only for fun and pleasure.
  d. He has had total liberty to do what he pleased.

C. Answer **one** of the following questions based on your understanding of the poems. Write your answer on a separate sheet of paper. (20 points)

1. Analyze the use of images in "Street Corner Flight" to convey ideas of freedom and the lack of freedom.

2. In "Words Like Freedom," Langston Hughes uses very small, simple words to get across very big, important ideas. What do you think Hughes's overall message is, and how does he suggest it?

D. Linking Literature to Life. Answer the following question based on your own experience and knowledge. Write your answers on a separate sheet of paper. (18 points)

What best symbolizes freedom to you? It might be an animal, a person, an object, or something else. Explain why this symbol means something special to you.

The School Play (page 402)

Selection Test

A. The tone of a story can vary. Next to each excerpt below, write one or more adjectives to describe the tone. (5 points each)

Excerpt	Tone
1. "She was known to slap boys and grind their faces into the grass so that they bit into chunks of wormy earth."	
2. "Mrs. Bunnin threw him a wrinkled shirt. Ruben raised it to his chest and said, 'My dad could wear this. Can I give it to him after the play is done?' Mrs. Bunnin turned away in silence."	
3. "He thought about how full he was and how those poor people had had nothing to eat but snow."	
4. "'How are we going to get through?' she boomed, wringing her hands together at the audience, some of whom had their mouths taped shut because they were known talkers."	

B. Write the letter of the best answer. This exercise is continued on the next page. (8 points each)

_____ 1. During rehearsal, Belinda says a line wrong several times because she
   a. is nervous.
   b. is trying to impress her teacher.
   c. can't remember the correct line.
   d. wants to act tough.

_____ 2. Robert likes the beard he wears mainly because
   a. it feels comfortable.
   b. nobody will know who he is when he performs.
   c. he thinks it looks good on him.
   d. it protects him from Belinda.

_____ 3. Robert says his line incorrectly during the performance because he
a. is nervous.
b. has not practiced it.
c. wants to show off.
d. got his line confused with one of Belinda's.

C. Words to Know. Write the letter of the best answer. (4 points each)

_____ 1. If the supply of groceries were <u>depleted</u>, food would be
a. scarce.　　　　b. stale.　　　　c. cheap.

_____ 2. A person who <u>smirks</u> is showing that he or she feels
a. timid.　　　　b. depressed.　　　　c. superior.

_____ 3. A <u>communal</u> park is one that is
a. very large.　　　　b. public property.　　　　c. run down.

_____ 4. On a windy day, which would most likely <u>quiver</u>?
a. smoke　　　　b. clouds　　　　c. leaves

_____ 5. A <u>relentless</u> enemy is one who
a. won't give up.　　　　b. is very clever.　　　　c. is hard to identify.

D. Answer **one** of the following questions based on your understanding of the story. Write your answer on a separate sheet of paper. (20 points)

1. From this short story, you learn a lot about Robert's personality, his dreams and fears, and his environment. Write a short character sketch of Robert. Use details from the story to support your views.

2. What message or theme do you think the author is trying to get across in "The School Play"?

E. Linking Literature to Life. Answer the following question based on your own experience and knowledge. Write your answer on a separate sheet of paper. (16 points)

In this story, Robert tries a new experience and enjoys it, even though it makes him very nervous. What do you think are the benefits of trying new things? What are the drawbacks?

Ode to My Library (page 411)

Selection Test

A. "Ode to My Library" contrasts images of power and beauty with images
of ordinariness, poverty, and smallness. Find three examples of each type
of image and write them in the correct boxes. (15 points each)

1. Images of Power	2. Images of the Small and Ordinary

B. Write the letter of the best answer. This exercise is continued on the next page.
(6 points each)

_____ 1. Who is the speaker in this poem?
    a. a librarian
    b. a grandmother or grandfather
    c. a student
    d. an imaginary warrior

_____ 2. The speaker suggests that the library is what kind of place?
    a. cramped and uncomfortable
    b. luxurious and attractive
    c. small but full of resources
    d. large but shabby

_____ 3. The speaker's reaction to the broken phonograph shows his or her
   a. imagination.
   b. impatience.
   c. technical skill.
   d. laziness.

_____ 4. The mural in the library shows
   a. a fish in a tank.
   b. an Aztec warrior.
   c. a dusty ranch.
   d. a mountain scene in California.

_____ 5. What does the speaker have in common with the warrior?
   a. ethnic background
   b. physical strength
   c. an aggressive personality
   d. a loving nature

C. Answer **one** of the following questions based on your understanding of the poem. Write your answer on a separate sheet of paper. (20 points)

1. Why is "Ode to My Library" an appropriate name for this poem? Define an ode and then explain how the poem fits the definition.

2. Although "Ode to My Library" is primarily about a place, the poem also conveys a lot of information about the speaker. Describe what you learn about the speaker. Use details from the poem to support your views.

D. Linking Literature to Life. Answer the following question based on your own experiences and knowledge. Write your answer on a separate sheet of paper. (20 points)

   If you had to describe a place that is special to you, what place would it be? Explain why the place is special to you, and list some images you might use to describe it.

Name _____ Date _____

The Jacket (page 418)

Selection Test

A. In this memoir, Gary Soto uses humor to amuse the reader, but the humor also helps to reveal his true feelings. For each example below, write notes telling what the exaggeration or unusual comparison reveals about how the narrator felt. (6 points each)

Example of Humor	What It Reveals
1. "I discovered draped on my bedpost a jacket the color of day-old guacamole."	
2. "Even the girls who had been friendly blew away like loose flowers to follow the boys in neat jackets."	
3. "I wore that thing for three years until the sleeves grew short and my forearms stuck out like the necks of turtles."	
4. "We saw girls walk by alone, saw couples, hand in hand, their heads like bookends pressing air together."	
5. That jacket "had become the ugly brother who tagged along wherever I went."	

B. Write the letter of the best answer. This exercise is continued on the next page. (5 points each)

_____ 1. What was the main problem with the new jacket?
   a. It was too small.
   b. It was not warm.
   c. It was ugly.
   d. It looked like something a biker would wear.

_____ 2. How did the narrator respond to his mother when he received the new jacket?
   a. He cried to show her how upset he was.
   b. He smiled to pretend he liked it.
   c. He deliberately ripped it, hoping she would throw it away.
   d. He yelled at her because he was so angry.

_____ 3. During the period of his life covered in this selection, the narrator's main
       hope seemed to be
       a. finding a girlfriend.
       b. getting a job.
       c. earning good grades.
       d. making a sports team.

C. Words to Know. Write the letter of the best answer. (4 points each)

_____ 1. Something made of <u>vinyl</u> would most likely be
       a. shiny.   b. soft.   c. fragile.

_____ 2. To show you his <u>profile</u>, a boy would have to stand
       a. upside down.   b. sideways.   c. very straight.

_____ 3. When a bird <u>swoops</u>, it moves
       a. awkwardly.   b. suddenly.   c. slowly.

_____ 4. What would a <u>terrorist</u> most likely do to get his way?
       a. complain   b. plead   c. threaten

_____ 5. People who <u>mope</u> are most likely feeling
       a. depressed.   b. excited.   c. nervous.

D. Answer **one** of the following questions based on your understanding of the selection.
Write your answer on a separate sheet of paper. (20 points)

1. Although "The Jacket" is written in a humorous way, many of the experiences Soto
   describes were actually quite painful. Tell why he was unhappy during the period
   of his life described in this memoir.

2. Soto makes his writing vivid with details that appeal to different senses. Choose
   a particular scene from "The Jacket" and analyze the different senses to which
   it appeals.

E. Linking Literature to Life. Answer the following question based on your
own experience and knowledge. Write your answer on a separate sheet of paper.
(15 points)

   Have you ever had a piece of clothing that you especially loved or hated?
Tell how you got it and what it looked like. Then tell why you loved or hated
it so much.

Unit Three: A Sense of Fairness

Part Two Open-Book Test

A. Write the letter of the best answer. (5 points each)

_____ 1. Which selection is concerned mainly with historical events?
   a. "The Jacket"
   b. "Words Like Freedom"
   c. "Street Corner Flight"
   d. "Abd al-Rahman Ibrahima"

_____ 2. The speaker in "Words Like Freedom" suggests that the words *freedom* and *liberty* fill him with
   a. bitterness and rage.
   b. awe and excitement.
   c. scornful amusement.
   d. confusion and boredom.

_____ 3. The overall tone of "The School Play" is
   a. melancholy.
   b. humorous.
   c. bitter.
   d. eerie.

_____ 4. Which selection focuses on a person's sudden understanding of language?
   a. "The School Play"
   b. "Ode to My Library"
   c. *The Story of My Life*
   d. "Street Corner Flight"

B. In this part, many of the selections deal with the power of words. Choose **two** characters: one who has a positive experience with words and one who has a negative experience. Write the name of each character. Then write notes describing each person's experience with words and why it was positive or negative. (20 points)

Positive Experience

Character/Selection	
What the Person Experienced	**Why It Was Positive**

Negative Experience

Character/Selection	
What the Person Experienced	**Why It Was Negative**

C. Answer **two** of the following essay questions based on your understanding of the selections. (20 points each)

1. Which character in this part do you think does the most to help one or more other people? Explain what the person does and why it was so helpful.

2. Compare the tone in **two** selections that have very different tones. Then analyze why the difference in subject matter makes the difference in tone appropriate.

3. A character in "The School Play" says, "You gotta suck it up in bad times." Choose at least one other selection to which this idea applies. Explain what the statement means and how it applies to the selection(s) you choose.

4. From the selections in this part, choose the person or character you think was the victim of the greatest misfortune and the one you think won the greatest victory. (You may decide that both things are true of one person.) Support your choice with details from the selections.

D. Each selection in this part concerns the theme of breaking barriers. Choose **two** selections from this part that you want to discuss. For each selection, describe the barrier that a person faces and at least one goal that the barrier stands in the way of. (20 points)

Selection	Selection
Barrier That a Person Faces	**Barrier That a Person Faces**
Goal(s)	**Goal(s)**

The Language of Literature: Grade 6

Mid-Year Test

Directions: Read the selection below. Then answer the questions that follow.

The Southpaw
Judith Viorst

Dear Richard,

Don't invite me to your birthday party because I'm not coming. And give back the Disneyland sweat shirt I said you could wear. If I'm not good enough to play on your team, I'm not good enough to be friends with.

Your former friend, Janet

P.S. I hope when you go to the dentist he finds twenty cavities.

Dear Janet,

Here is your stupid Disneyland sweat shirt, if that's how you're going to be. I want my comic books now—finished or not. No girl has ever played on the Mapes Street baseball team, and as long as I'm captain, no girl ever will.

Your former friend, Richard

P.S. I hope when you go for your checkup you need a tetanus shot.

Dear Richard,

I'm changing my goldfish's name from Richard to Stanley. Don't count on my vote for class president next year. Just because I'm a member of the ballet club doesn't mean I'm not a terrific ballplayer.

Your former friend, Janet

P.S. I see you lost your first game, 28–0.

Dear Janet,

I'm not saving any more seats for you on the bus. For all I care you can stand the whole way to school. Why don't you forget about baseball and learn something nice like knitting?

Your former friend, Richard

P.S. Wait until Wednesday.

Dear Richard,

My father said I could call someone to go with us for a ride and hot-fudge sundaes. In case you didn't notice, I didn't call you.

Your former friend, Janet

P.S. I see you lost your second game, 34–0.

Dear Janet,

Remember when I took the laces out of my blue-and-white sneakers and gave them to you? I want them back.

Your former friend, Richard

P.S. Wait until Friday.

Dear Richard,

Congratulations on your unbroken record. Eight straight losses, wow! I understand you're the laughingstock of New Jersey.

Your former friend, Janet

P.S. Why don't you and your team forget about baseball and learn something nice like knitting, maybe?

Dear Janet,

Here's the silver horseback-riding trophy that you gave me. I don't think I want to keep it anymore.

Your former friend, Richard

P.S. I didn't think you'd be the kind who'd kick a man when he's down.

Dear Richard,

I wasn't kicking exactly. I was kicking back.

Your former friend, Janet

P.S. In case you were wondering my batting average is .345.

Dear Janet,

Alfie is having his tonsils out tomorrow. We might be able to let you catch next week.

Richard

Dear Richard,

I pitch.

Janet

Dear Janet,

Joel is moving to Kansas and Danny sprained his wrist. How about a permanent place in the outfield?

Richard

Dear Richard,

I pitch.

Janet

Dear Janet,

Ronnie caught the chicken pox and Leo broke his toe and Elwood has these stupid violin lessons. I'll give you first base. That's my final offer.

Richard

Dear Richard,

Susan Reilly plays first base, Marilyn Jackson catches, Ethel Kahn plays center field, I pitch. It's a package deal.

Janet

P.S. Sorry about your 12-game losing streak.

Dear Janet,

Please! Not Marilyn Jackson.

Richard

Dear Richard,

Nobody ever said that I was unreasonable. How about Lizzie Martindale instead?

Janet

Dear Janet,

At least could you call your goldfish Richard again?

Your friend, Richard

Name _____   Date _____

A. The following items test your understanding of the selection. Circle the letter of the response that best completes the sentence or answers the question.

1. In this selection, what does Janet want to do?
   a. go to Richard's birthday party
   b. get back some comic books
   c. play on the baseball team
   d. go to Disneyland

2. You can tell that Richard is the
   a. catcher.
   b. captain of the team.
   c. coach.
   d. best hitter on the team.

3. As used in both Richard's and Janet's letters, the word *former* means
   a. in the past.
   b. best.
   c. one and only.
   d. closest.

4. Richard suggests that Janet should forget baseball and take up
   a. dancing.
   b. horseback riding.
   c. knitting.
   d. field hockey.

5. What can you tell about the Mapes Street baseball team from Janet's "P.S." notes?
   a. It has lost every game.
   b. The team is in first place.
   c. It was a better team last year.
   d. The team scores a lot of runs.

6. In his "final offer," Richard says that Janet can
   a. be the captain.
   b. sit on the bench.
   c. be the catcher.
   d. play first base.

B. The following items check your understanding of literary elements in the story. Circle the letter of the response that best completes each sentence.

7. Both Richard and Janet can best be described as
   a. stubborn.
   b. talented.
   c. selfish.
   d. angry.

8. The tone of Janet's letters is best described as
   a. sad.
   b. friendly.
   c. respectful.
   d. sarcastic.

9. To "kick a man when he's down" means to
   a. injure a player.
   b. insult someone who already feels bad.
   c. take away his job.
   d. help someone who can't help himself.

10. "I understand you're the laughingstock of New Jersey" is an example of
    a. a simile.
    b. symbolism.
    c. exaggeration.
    d. an anecdote.

C. The following items check your understanding of literary elements in the story. Write your response after each item.

11. Explain the main conflict in this story.

_____

_____

_____

_____

12. Write a brief description of Janet's character based on what she says in her letters.

_____

_____

_____

_____

_____

13. Explain how the author creates humor in this selection.

_____

_____

_____

_____

_____

D. The following items check your ability to analyze and evaluate the selection. Circle the letter of the response that best completes the sentence or answers the question.

14. What evidence in the story best supports the idea that Richard is a natural leader?
    a. He saves a seat on the bus for Janet each day.
    b. He is confident that his team will get better.
    c. He vows that girls will never play on the Mapes Street team.
    d. He is the team captain and wants to run for class president.

15. Which is the best evidence that Janet is a good baseball player?
    a. Her batting average is .345.
    b. She is a member of the ballet club.
    c. Her favorite position is pitcher.
    d. She won a trophy for horseback riding.

16. What Janet decides to name her goldfish is a good indicator of
    a. why she wants her sweat shirt back.
    b. how she feels about Richard.
    c. where she plans to go on vacation.
    d. how well she plays baseball.

17. You can conclude from the ending of this story that Richard will
    a. quit the team and let Janet take over.
    b. try to find another sport in which he will be more successful.
    c. let Janet and three other girls play on the team.
    d. refuse to talk to Janet ever again.

E. The following items check your ability to analyze and evaluate the selection. Write your response after each item.

18. Name one way Janet and Richard are alike and one way they are different.

_____

_____

_____

_____

_____

19. What reasons does Richard have to change his mind about keeping girls off the team?

_____

_____

_____

_____

_____

20. What techniques does Janet use to convince Richard to let her play?

_____

_____

_____

_____

_____

Writing Exercise The following activity is designed to assess your writing ability. The prompt asks you to express your own views. Think of your audience as being any reader other than yourself.

When scorers evaluate your writing, they will look for evidence that you can

- respond directly to the prompt.

- make your writing thoughtful and interesting.

- organize your ideas so that they are clear and easy to follow.

- develop your ideas thoroughly by using appropriate details and precise language.

- tay focused on your purpose for writing by making sure that each sentence you write contributes to your composition as a whole.

- communicate effectively by using correct spelling, capitalization, punctuation, grammar, usage, and sentence structure.

Prompt: Think about how you reacted to "The Southpaw." For example, did you admire Janet? Did you feel sorry for Richard? Write a short response to the selection telling how you feel about it. You can include your feelings about the plot, the characters, or the author's technique.

Use the bottom of the page to organize your ideas. Then write your essay on a separate sheet of paper.

_____

_____

_____

_____

_____

_____

_____

_____

_____

_____

_____

_____

_____

Revising/Editing The purpose of the following exercise is to check your ability to proofread and revise a piece of writing in order to improve its readability and presentation of ideas. Read the following paragraph. Then, for each underlined section, circle the letter of the revision below that most improves the writing. Or, if the section is best left as it is, circle the letter *d*.

Have you ever played <u>baseball.</u> Last year I decided to try out for a Little

                                  1.

League team. I <u>hadn't never</u> really played baseball before. On the day of the

                      2.

tryouts, I <u>go to the field and see</u> about a thousand kids. <u>Many of them were</u>

                       3.   4.

even <u>badder</u> than I was. <u>Got on a team, though.</u> We all had fun, too!

      5.   6.

1. a. baseball
   b. baseball?
   c. baseball!
   d. correct as is

2. a. had never
   b. haven't never
   c. had not never
   d. correct as is

3. a. gone to the field and seen
   b. go to the field and saw
   c. went to the field and saw
   d. correct as is

4. a. Many of them was
   b. Many of they were
   c. Many of them is
   d. correct as is

5. a. bad
   b. worse
   c. worser
   d. correct as is

6. a. Getting on a team, though.
   b. We get on a team, though.
   c. Everybody got on a team, though.
   d. correct as is

Lob's Girl (page 447)

Selection Test

A. Read each description from the story. Then write notes telling what event was foreshadowed by each description. (8 points each)

Description	Event Foreshadowed
1. "She picked up a bit of driftwood and threw it. Lob, whisking easily out of his master's grip, was after it like a sand-colored bullet. He came back with the stick, beaming, and gave it to Sandy."	
2. "The village was approached by a narrow, steep, twisting hillroad and guarded by a notice that said LOW GEAR FOR 1 $\frac{1}{2}$ MILES, DANGEROUS TO CYCLISTS."	
3. "By that afternoon it became noticeable that a dog seemed to have taken up position outside the hospital, with the fixed intention of getting in."	

B. Write the letter of the best answer. This exercise is continued on the next page. (5 points each)

_____ 1. Where did Sandy first meet Lob?
  a. on the beach
  b. at her house
  c. on a village road
  d. at Mr. Dodsworth's house

_____ 2. Why did Lob insist on returning to the Pengellys' house?
  a. He wanted to live by the ocean.
  b. He was treated cruelly by Mr. Dodsworth.
  c. He loved Sandy.
  d. He enjoyed being around a big family.

_____ 3. Sandy stirred from her coma when
  a. her parents visited her.
  b. the dog whined at her.
  c. the doctors gave her medicine.
  d. Granny Pearce spoke to her.

_____ 4. What does the end of the story reveal about Lob?
   a. He ran away from the Pengellys' home.
   b. He had drowned in the ocean.
   c. He was killed by the truck that hit Sandy.
   d. He had died of old age.

C. Words to Know. Write the letter of the best answer. (4 points each)

_____ 1. A person is most likely to try to <u>atone</u> for
   a. admiring a friend.   b. meeting a friend.   c. hurting a friend.

_____ 2. What is the mood of someone who is <u>melancholy</u>?
   a. scared   b. hopeful   c. sad

_____ 3. A person is most likely to become <u>agitated</u> by
   a. bad news.   b. soft music.   c. sunny weather.

_____ 4. If you <u>conceal</u> an object, you
   a. clean it.   b. hide it.   c. break it.

_____ 5. To <u>inquire</u> means to
   a. demand.   b. explain.   c. ask.

D. Answer **one** of the following questions based on your understanding of the selection. Write your answer on a separate sheet of paper. (20 points)

1. How does the story suggest that Sandy and Lob have an almost magical bond between them? Describe at least two events from the story that demonstrate how Sandy and Lob felt about each other.

2. How do other people in the story respond to the bond between Sandy and Lob? Support your answer with details from the story.

E. Linking Literature to Life. Answer the following question based on your own experience and knowledge. Write your answer on a separate sheet of paper. (16 points)

Do you think there are times when a pet is the best companion of all? Tell why you agree or disagree with this idea, and give examples.

Name _____   Date _____

My First Dive with the Dolphins (page 465)

Selection Test

A. In each box on the left, write notes describing something the writer learns about dolphins from his experiences during his first dive. In each box on the right, write notes telling how he gains that knowledge or understanding. (12 points each)

1. What does the writer learn about dolphins?	→	How does he learn this?
2. What does the writer learn about dolphins?	→	How does he learn this?

B. Write the letter of the best answer. This exercise is continued on the next page. (5 points each)

_____ 1. What is the main point of the lesson that the head diver gives the writer before his first dive?
    a. Most dolphins are sweet and gentle.
    b. Dolphins are intelligent because they are mammals.
    c. Each dolphin behaves differently.
    d. Dolphins are fond of humans.

_____ 2. According to the writer, the biggest part of his job would be
    a. removing algae from the dolphins' tank.
    b. observing the dolphins' movements.
    c. keeping the dolphins entertained.
    d. teaching the dolphins to trust humans.

_____ 3. What experience did the writer have with the dolphin named Ernestine?
    a. She attacked him.
    b. She chased him around the tank.
    c. She stole his brush.
    d. She towed him through the water.

_____ 4. The writer believes that it is important to show Lucky (the "king bull") that the writer
   a. fears him.
   b. respects him.
   c. wants to play with him.
   d. is in the tank to get a job done.

C. Words to Know. Write the letter of the best answer. (4 points each)

_____ 1. A dolphin that is <u>hurtling</u> toward you is moving
   a. very fast.   b. gracefully.   c. very quietly.

_____ 2. Someone who shows <u>aggression</u> toward you is being
   a. friendly.   b. threatening.   c. forgetful.

_____ 3. The <u>dominant</u> person in a group is the one who
   a. takes charge.   b. likes everyone.   c. has good ideas.

_____ 4. A soldier wears <u>camouflage</u> clothing mainly to
   a. keep warm.   b. hide from view.   c. look important.

_____ 5. A <u>luminous</u> object is one that is
   a. very large.   b. dangerous.   c. filled with light.

D. Answer **one** of the following questions based on your understanding of the selection. Write your answer on a separate sheet of paper. (20 points)

1. What do you think the head diver meant when he said that five percent of the writer's job would be magic? Why would he use the word *magic*?

2. What are two purposes the writer had for writing this selection? Why do you think so?

E. Linking Literature to Life. Answer the following question based on your own experience and knowledge. Write your answer on a separate sheet of paper. (16 points)

What would you say is the most important way in which animals are different from people? Explain your answer.

Something Told the Wild Geese/Questioning Faces (page 476)

Selection Test

A. Compare the use of rhyme and repetition in the two poems by circling *Yes* or *No* and giving examples of each. (14 points each)

1. "Something Told the Wild Geese"	2. "Questioning Faces"
Is rhyme used in the poem? Yes No If you answered yes, give an example of rhyme from the poem.	Is rhyme used in the poem? Yes No If you answered yes, give an example of rhyme from the poem.
Is repetition used in the poem? Yes No If you answered yes, give an example of repetition from the poem.	Is repetition used in the poem? Yes No If you answered yes, give an example of repetition from the poem.

B. Write the letter of the best answer. This exercise is continued on the next page. (8 points each)

_____ 1. What season is drawing to a close in "Something Told the Wild Geese"?
　　　　　　　a. summer
　　　　　　　b. fall
　　　　　　　c. winter
　　　　　　　d. spring

_____ 2. The mood of "Something Told the Wild Geese" is best described as
　　　　　　　a. fear.
　　　　　　　b. sadness.
　　　　　　　c. wonder.
　　　　　　　d. melancholy.

_____ 3. In "Questioning Faces," the faces belong to
a. owls.
b. children.
c. reflections in a mirror.
d. an owl's prey.

_____ 4. "Questioning Faces" includes a description of an owl's
a. wings.
b. eyes.
c. beak.
d. claws.

C. Answer **one** of the following questions based on your understanding of the poems. Write your answer on a separate sheet of paper. (20 points)

1. If each poem had another four lines at the end, what action would the lines be likely to describe? Make a prediction that tells how "Something Told the Wild Geese" and "Questioning Faces" would end if another verse were added.

2. Think about the rhythm of each poem. Explain how the rhythm of each poem helps you understand its meaning.

D. Linking Literature to Life. Answer the following question based on your own experience and knowledge. Write your answer on a separate sheet of paper. (20 points)

Wild birds are described in poems, songs, and stories from all around the world. Why do you think wild birds have captured the imaginations of so many writers? What is it about wild birds that might inspire you to write?

Name _____ Date _____

Zlateh the Goat (page 481)

Selection Test

A. Complete this plot diagram with details from "Zlateh the Goat." Begin by describing the main character's conflict. Then briefly describe key events that take place during the rising action, climax, and resolution. (5 points each)

1. Conflict _____

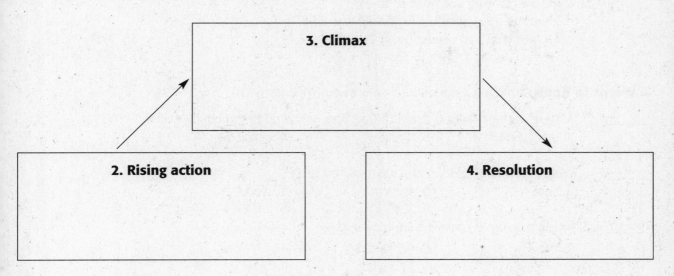

B. Write the letter of the best answer. This exercise is continued on the next page. (5 points each)

_____ 1. Aaron's father decided to sell Zlateh because he
    a. believed she had brought him bad luck.
    b. needed money to buy Hanukkah necessities.
    c. thought his family had grown too fond of her.
    d. wanted to replace her with a goat that gave more milk.

_____ 2. What was Aaron's main reaction when his father told him to bring Zlateh to the butcher?
    a. He was annoyed that he would have to make a long journey.
    b. He was relieved that his father had gotten a good price for the goat.
    c. He was proud to be trusted with such an important errand.
    d. He was sad that the goat he loved would be killed.

_____ 3. Aaron and Zlateh took shelter in a haystack when
    a. they became lost in a blizzard.
    b. a cold wind began to blow.
    c. they were chased by a dog.
    d. the sun went down.

Name _____   Date _____

_____

_____ 4. The haystack was an excellent shelter for Zlateh mostly because it
        a. had a pleasing odor.
        b. was dark.
        c. provided her with food.
        d. was small.

_____ 5. What was Aaron's main reason for returning home instead of taking Zlateh
        to the butcher?
        a. He was starving and needed to eat.
        b. He wanted his parents to know he was alive.
        c. He was cold and needed warmer clothing.
        d. He had decided never to part with Zlateh.

C. Words to Know. Write the letter of the best answer. (4 points each)

_____ 1. A friend is most likely to astonish you if he or she does something that is
        a. unexpected.   b. funny.   c. sensible.

_____ 2. Which material is used to make a thatched roof?
        a. slate   b. straw   c. wood

_____ 3. Which creature is most like an imp?
        a. a giant   b. a dragon   c. a fairy

_____ 4. A person who feels content is most likely to
        a. smile.   b. frown.   c. sneer.

_____ 5. You would need to regain your strength if you had been
        a. resting.   b. sick.   c. eating.

D. Answer **one** of the following questions based on your understanding of the selection. Write your answer on a separate sheet of paper. (20 points)

1. Aaron tells Zlateh, "I need you and you need me." What does Aaron mean? Explain how each character needs the other.

2. Compare how Zlateh is treated at the beginning and at the end of the story. Why is she treated differently?

E. Linking Literature to Life. Answer the following question based on your own experience and knowledge. Write your answer on a separate sheet of paper. (15 points)

Do you think animals feel emotions such as love and gratitude in the same way that people do? Give reasons for your answer.

Unit Four: Wondrous Worlds

Part One Open-Book Test

A. Write the letter of the best answer. (5 points each)

_____ 1. In this part, which animal has a sad and unexpected death?
a. the owl in "Questioning Faces"
b. Lob in "Lob's Girl"
c. Ernestine in "My First Dive with the Dolphins"
d. Zlateh in "Zlateh the Goat"

_____ 2. Which selection is written in the form of an essay?
a. "My First Dive with the Dolphins"
b. "Something Told the Wild Geese"
c. "Questioning Faces"
d. "Lob's Girl"

_____ 3. "Something Told the Wild Geese" tells about the powerful influence of
a. people.   c. instinct.
b. fear.   d. love.

_____ 4. What event from "Zlateh the Goat" occurs during the story's resolution?
a. Aaron and Zlateh find shelter in a haystack.
b. Aaron returns to his family with Zlateh.
c. Aaron's father decides to sell Zlateh.
d. Aaron drinks Zlateh's milk.

B. In several selections in this part, a person has strong feelings about an animal. Choose **two** selections you want to discuss. In the boxes below, indicate the person and the selection, the animal, and the person's feeling toward the animal. Then write notes explaining why the person feels this way. (20 points)

Person/Selection	Person/Selection
Animal	**Animal**
Person's Feeling	**Person's Feeling**
Why the Person Feels This Way	**Why the Person Feels This Way**

C. Answer **two** of the following essay questions based on your understanding of the selections. Write your answers on a separate sheet of paper. (20 points each)

1. Weather plays an important role in several selections in this part. Choose **two** of the selections and discuss what part weather plays in each.

2. What do you think is the difference between a wild animal and a tame animal? Use two animals from the selections to explain the difference between *wild* and *tame*.

3. Sometimes animals do things that make them seem almost human. Which animal from these selections do you think has the most human qualities? Explain why you think so.

4. If you could relive the experience that any person in these selections has with an animal, which experience would you choose? Tell what you think you might gain from the experience.

D. In this part, animals demonstrate remarkable behaviors that are a source of wonder to the people who observe or experience them. Choose animals from **two** of the selections in this part. Write the names of the animals and selections in the boxes below. Then write notes to answer the questions. (20 points)

Animal/Selection	**Animal/Selection**
What remarkable behavior does the animal display?	**What remarkable behavior does the animal display?**
Who observes or experiences the behavior?	**Who observes or experiences the behavior?**
What is the person's reaction?	**What is the person's reaction?**

Name _____ Date _____

The Phantom Tollbooth (page 512)

Selection Test

A. Think about the fantasy elements in *The Phantom Tollbooth*. In the chart below, write notes describing two examples of fantasy in the play's settings, characters, and events. (8 points each)

1. Settings	2. Characters	3. Events

B. Write the letter of the best answer. This exercise is continued on the next page. (5 points each)

_____ 1. When Milo first appears onstage in the play, he seems to be
    a. cheerful and easy to please.
    b. bored by everything.
    c. curious and adventurous.
    d. afraid of everything.

_____ 2. What is most important to Azaz?
    a. noise
    b. numbers
    c. time
    d. words

_____ 3. Before they were banished, Rhyme and Reason used to
    a. settle quarrels between Azaz and Mathemagician.
    b. guard the gates of Dictionopolis.
    c. help travelers escape from the Land of Ignorance.
    d. count the sands and name the stars.

_____ 4. What does Milo discover is the most important thing about learning?
   a. trying never to make mistakes as you learn
   b. learning only what you need to survive
   c. knowing how to use what you have learned
   d. learning more than anyone else

C. Words to Know. Write the letter of the best answer. (4 points each)

_____ 1. You are likely to speak <u>dejectedly</u> when you feel
   a. hopeful.   b. unhappy.   c. amazed.

_____ 2. Which event most often causes people to <u>mourn</u>?
   a. a birth   b. a marriage   c. a death

_____ 3. Which activity usually involves a <u>destination</u>?
   a. traveling   b. talking   c. resting

_____ 4. To <u>pantomime</u> an idea you want to express, you could use
   a. your voice.   b. printed words.   c. facial expressions.

_____ 5. In which direction do you move when you <u>ascend</u>?
   a. up   b. down   c. sideways

D. Answer **one** of the following questions based on your understanding of the selection. Write your answer on a separate sheet of paper. (20 points)

1. Explain the importance of the role played by Rhyme and Reason in the Land of Wisdom. What does their role suggest about different kinds of wisdom and learning?

2. According to Clock, "For some people, an hour seems to last forever. For others, just a moment, and so full of things to do." Which type of person is Milo at the beginning of the story? At the end of the story? What causes him to change?

E. Linking Literature to Life. Answer the following question based on your understanding of the selection. Write your answer on a separate sheet of paper. (16 points)

Of all the things you have learned in your life, what knowledge or skill is most important to you? Give reasons for your answer.

Name _____ Date _____

The Walrus and the Carpenter/Fairy Lullaby (page 555)
Selection Test

A. "The Walrus and the Carpenter" uses setting, characters, and plot to tell a story. Each element has some details that are realistic and some that are imaginary, or fantastic. For each element listed below, describe one detail from the poem that is realistic and one that is fantastic. (10 points each)

	Realistic Detail	**Fantastic Detail**
1. Setting		
2. Character		
3. Plot		

B. Write the letter of the best answer. This exercise is continued on the next page. (6 points each)

_____ 1. In "The Walrus and the Carpenter," the moon is annoyed by the
        a. clouds.   c. sand.
        b. sea.   d. sun.

_____ 2. The Walrus and the Carpenter weep because
        a. they are hungry.
        b. there is so much sand.
        c. they are tired.
        d. there are no birds.

_____ 3. The Walrus and the Carpenter invite the Oysters to
        a. walk with them.
        b. have dinner with them.
        c. swim with them.
        d. tell them stories.

_____ 4. The Walrus and the Carpenter's behavior toward the Oysters is best
described as
a. jealous and resentful.
b. playful and silly.
c. cunning and cruel.
d. sweet and caring.

_____ 5. In "Fairy Lullaby," the First Fairy tells snakes, hedgehogs, newts, and
worms to
a. stay away.
b. cast a spell.
c. sing a song.
d. fall asleep.

C. Answer **one** of the following questions based on your understanding of the poems.
Write your answer on a separate sheet of paper. (20 points each)

1. Do you think most readers feel upset about what happens to the Oysters
in "The Walrus and the Carpenter"? Why or why not?

2. Do you think that "Fairy Lullaby" has the soothing and peaceful qualities
of a lullaby? Why or why not?

D. Linking Literature to Life. Answer the following question based on your own
experience and knowledge. Write your answer on a separate sheet of paper. (20 points)

Do you think people can learn important things from works of fantasy?
Why or why not?

Three Limericks (page 563)

Selection Test

A. Think about what makes each of these limericks funny. In the chart below, write
notes describing the central idea that makes each limerick humorous. (10 points each)

Limerick	What Makes It Funny
1. by Prelutsky	
2. by Nash	
3. by Lear	

B. Write the letter of the best answer. This exercise is continued on the next page.
(8 points each)

_____ 1. In Prelutsky's limerick, what happens to Ben?
   a. He swallows his watch.
   b. He guesses the time.
   c. He buys a clock.
   d. He catches a cold.

_____ 2. In Prelutsky's limerick, Ben is described as
   a. careless.
   b. silly.
   c. old.
   d. clever.

_____ 3. In Nash's limerick, why does Dougal MacDougal learn to sneeze
   in different keys?
   a. He hopes to become famous.
   b. He wants to amuse others with his trick.
   c. He thinks the sounds are pleasant.
   d. He wants to save money on a bugle.

_____ 4. In Lear's limerick, what happens to the old man?
  a. He shaves off his beard.
  b. He keeps pet birds.
  c. He finds birds in his beard.
  d. He looks for a bird's eggs.

C. Answer **one** of the following questions based on your understanding of the selections. Write your answer on a separate sheet of paper. (20 points)

1. The characters in these limericks are Ben, Dougal MacDougal, and an old man. Tell how these three characters are alike and how they are different.

2. Would a poem about something serious or sad be effective if it were written with the rhythm and rhyme patterns of a limerick? Explain your answer.

D. Linking Literature to Life. Answer the following question based on your own experience and knowledge. Write your answer on a separate sheet of paper. (18 points)

Think of something you could say about yourself that might be presented in a humorous way. Write a limerick describing something about yourself. You might want to start, "There once was a student named _____."

The Fun They Had (page 574)

Selection Test

A. Think about the setting of this story. In the chart below, write notes describing when and where the story takes place. Then compare the story setting with our world by naming one difference between the two and one similarity. (12 points each)

1. Setting	2. Comparison
When	**Difference**
Where	**Similarity**

B. Write the letter of the best answer. This exercise is continued on the next page.
(5 points each)

_____ 1. At the beginning of the story, Tommy has found an old book about
         a. school.
         b. computers.
         c. television.
         d. math.

_____ 2. What did the county inspector do at Margie's house?
         a. He read Tommy's book.
         b. He warned Margie to study more.
         c. He repaired the mechanical teacher.
         d. He gave Margie a geography lesson.

_____ 3. From reading this story, you can tell that Margie has never had
         a. classmates her own age.
         b. lessons about fractions.
         c. geography lessons.
         d. help with her homework.

_____ 4. What does Margie conclude about children who went to school
"in the old days"?
a. They were bored.
b. They studied useless subjects.
c. They worked very hard.
d. They enjoyed themselves.

C. Words to Know. Write the letter of the best answer. (4 points each)

_____ 1. A person who speaks <u>loftily</u> probably feels that he or she is
a. superior.   b. young.   c. popular.

_____ 2. If you <u>dispute</u> another person's ideas, you express
a. thanks.   b. amazement.   c. disagreement.

_____ 3. Which of these might be a <u>sector</u> in a town?
a. a mayor   b. a neighborhood   c. a sign

_____ 4. If you walk <u>nonchalantly</u>, you are probably feeling
a. relaxed.   b. unsure.   c. determined.

_____ 5. Someone who has a <u>scornful</u> expression is most likely to be
a. grinning.   b. yawning.   c. scowling.

D. Answer **one** of the following questions based on your understanding of the selection. Write your answer on a separate sheet of paper. (20 points)

1. Do you think Margie's feelings about school would be different if she had a person for a teacher? Why or why not?

2. In your opinion, what are the advantages and disadvantages to the type of school Margie attends?

E. Linking Literature to Life. Answer the following question based on your experience and knowledge. Write your answer on a separate sheet of paper. (16 points)

Do you think computers make our lives better or worse? Give reasons for your answer.

Name _____ Date _____

The Sand Castle (page 580)

Selection Test

A. How is the world in which Mrs. Pavloff grew up different from the world in which her grandchildren are growing up? Compare the two settings by listing three details from the story about each world. (24 points)

Mrs. Pavloff's World When She Was a Child	Her Grandchildren's World

B. Write the letter of the best answer. This exercise is continued on the next page. (5 points each)

_____ 1. In this story, the sun is a problem because
a. Earth has moved too close to the sun.
b. the sun is running out of energy.
c. much of Earth's ozone layer has been damaged.
d. days have become much longer than nights.

_____ 2. In the story, what have scientists concluded about the problem with the sun?
a. It is too late to fix the problem.
b. In the future, the situation will improve.
c. The problem is not as serious as people think.
d. The problem continues to get worse.

_____ 3. How had Mrs. Pavloff's grandchildren felt about the seashore on their previous trips there?
a. bored   c. afraid
b. happy   d. amazed

_____ 4. For Mrs. Pavloff, taking her grandchildren to the sea is a way for her to
   a. give them experiences she never had.
   b. teach them the dangers of the sun.
   c. show them how much the world has changed.
   d. relive her childhood memories with them.

C. Words to Know. Write the letter of the best answer. (4 points each)

_____ 1. A person wearing <u>cumbersome</u> clothing is most likely to feel
   a. fashionable.   b. warm.   c. uncomfortable.

_____ 2. <u>Ultraviolet</u> light is a kind of light that
   a. you can't see.   b. does not burn.   c. has no energy.

_____ 3. Which word describes a <u>hostile</u> environment?
   a. natural   b. dangerous   c. relaxing

_____ 4. When you do something <u>listlessly</u>, you have a lack of
   a. energy.   b. skill.   c. directions.

_____ 5. You would likely say a house looks <u>forlorn</u> if it is
   a. tidy.   b. large.   c. abandoned.

D. Answer **one** of the following questions based on your understanding of the selection. Write your answer on a separate sheet of paper. (20 points)

1. How does Mrs. Pavloff feel about the world in which her grandchildren are growing up? Use details from the story to support your answer.

2. Why do Mrs. Pavloff's memories of her childhood cause her to feel both happiness and sadness? Explain.

E. Linking Literature to Life. Answer the following question based on your own experience and knowledge. Write your answer on a separate sheet of paper. (16 points)

Suppose that you have traveled forward in time, and you now live in this future world where Mrs. Pavloff's grandchildren live. How do you think you would feel about it? What do you think you would miss most from the "old days"?

Name _____   Date _____

Unit Four: Wondrous Worlds
Part Two Open-Book Test

A. Write your answer to each question on the lines. (5 points each)

1. In *The Phantom Tollbooth*, why does Milo go in search of Rhyme and Reason?

_____

2. What is usually the author's purpose in writing limericks?

_____

3. Which selection in this part is a science fiction story about school?

_____

4. In "The Sand Castle," what part of the environment has become dangerous?

_____

B. In several selections in this part, characters change as a result of something they learn or experience for the first time. Choose characters you want to discuss from **two** selections. In the boxes below, write each character's name and what the character learns or experiences. Then tell how the character changes as a result. (20 points)

Character	Character
What the Character Learns or Experiences	**What the Character Learns or Experiences**
How the Character Changes as a Result	**How the Character Changes as a Result**

C. Answer **two** of the following essay questions based on your understanding of the selections. Write your answers on a separate sheet of paper. (20 points each)

1. Most of the selections in this part offer visions of other worlds or of this world in future times. Which selection offers the vision that seems most realistic? Give at least three reasons for your choice.

2. Imagine that you could give some advice to a character from one of the selections. Which character would you choose, and what would your advice be?

3. Several selections in this part concern the theme of good versus evil. Choose **one** selection and explain how it illustrates this theme.

4. If you could spend one day as a visitor to one of the places in these selections, which place would you visit? What would you hope to see and do while you were there?

D. In this part you have read about several "imaginary worlds." Which imaginary world seems most appealing to you, and which is least appealing? In the chart below, write the titles of the selections you want to discuss. Then write notes describing the main features of the worlds you choose and why you find each world appealing—or not. (20 points)

Most Appealing World	Least Appealing World
Selection	**Selection**
Main Features	**Main Features**
Why It Is Appealing	**Why It Is Not Appealing**

Name _____ Date _____

Words on a Page (page 614)

Selection Test

A. One theme of *Words on a Page* is presented below. Complete the chart by writing notes telling how the elements of character, setting, and plot in this teleplay provide support for this theme. (8 points each)

Theme: No matter where we go or what we do in life, home is always a part of us.	
1. Character	
2. Setting	
3. Plot	

B. Write the letter of the best answer. This exercise is continued on the next page. (5 points each)

_____ 1. At the beginning, Lenore tells her father that she has dreamed about
       a. a beaver with a skinny tail.
       b. fish swimming through black water.
       c. a canoe drifting downstream.
       d. a raven that hovers over her head.

_____ 2. How is Lenore like the girl in the story she has written?
       a. She longs to move to a city.
       b. She does not care about Native American ways.
       c. She feels a powerful connection to home.
       d. She wants to become famous.

_____ 3. Lenore refuses to read her story at Parents' Night because
   a. her father is not there.
   b. she suddenly becomes nervous.
   c. her mother tells her not to.
   d. she knows it is not her best work.

_____ 4. After hearing the end of Lenore's dream, Pete realizes that
   a. she will never return to the village.
   b. he should finally learn to read.
   c. she was meant to be a writer.
   d. he wishes he had a son.

C. Words to Know. Write the letter of the best answer. (4 points each)

_____ 1. If a decision you make is <u>tentative</u>, you are probably feeling
   a. bold.   b. unsure.   c. pleased.

_____ 2. Which of these has <u>foliage</u>?
   a. a tree   b. a beaver   c. a rock

_____ 3. Which of these can <u>hover</u>?
   a. a train   b. a motorcycle   c. a helicopter

_____ 4. When would you feel <u>anticipation</u> about an event?
   a. before it happens   b. while it happens   c. after it happens

_____ 5. You are making a <u>gesture</u> when you
   a. talk to a friend.   b. wave to a friend.   c. think of a friend.

D. Answer **one** of the following questions based on your understanding of the selection. Write your answer on a separate sheet of paper. (20 points)

1. Before the trip to Thunder Bay, how does Pete feel about Lenore's writing talent? Give at least **two** reasons for the way he feels.

2. Compare how Miss Walker and Connie react to Lenore's problem with Pete, and tell why they react in different ways.

E. Linking Literature to Life. Answer the following question based on your own experience and knowledge. Write your answer on a separate sheet of paper. (16 points)

How would you feel about leaving your home and family to pursue an exciting career? What do you think you would decide to do, and why?

from All I Really Need to Know I Learned in Kindergarten (page 636)

Selection Test

A. Think about the information and ideas expressed in Fulghum's personal essay. Then, in the boxes, write notes about each aspect of the essay. (8 points each)

1. Tell what makes this essay a work of **nonfiction.**	
2. Give an example of a **personal anecdote** from the essay.	
3. Give an example of an **opinion** expressed in the essay.	

B. Write the letter of the best answer. This exercise is continued on the next page. (5 points each)

_____ 1. The "credo" that Fulghum writes each spring is probably best described as a
a. code of behavior.
b. set of predictions.
c. list of problems.
d. collection of memories.

_____ 2. In recent years, Fulghum's credo has become
a. harder to write.
b. more serious.
c. shorter and simpler.
d. wiser and more sophisticated.

_____ 3. According to Fulghum, too much "high-content information" makes him feel like
  a. a child who needs a nap.
  b. an old car with deluxe gasoline.
  c. the roots of a plant.
  d. a hamster in a cage.

_____ 4. According to Fulghum, what is the biggest word of all?
  a. look
  b. share
  c. ecology
  d. politics

C. Words to Know. Write the letter of the best answer. (4 points each)

_____ 1. What does a <u>cynical</u> remark express?
  a. regret   b. scorn   c. approval

_____ 2. An audience is most likely to react to a <u>bland</u> speech by
  a. cheering.   b. booing.   c. yawning.

_____ 3. The purpose of good <u>sanitation</u> is to help people
  a. stay healthy.   b. work together.   c. feel important.

_____ 4. You might be called <u>naive</u> if you tend to
  a. waste time.   b. put yourself first. c. trust others easily.

_____ 5. Which word describes someone with a lot of <u>idealism</u>?
  a. selfish   b. hopeful   c. talented

D. Answer **one** of the following questions based on your understanding of the selection. Write your answer on a separate sheet of paper. (20 points)

1. How is the world we live in like a kindergarten class? Use at least **two** details from the selection to express your view.

2. In this essay, Fulghum says, "When you go out into the world, watch out for traffic, hold hands and stick together." Explain what this statement means in adult terms. Then give a specific example of how you might follow this rule in your life.

E. Linking Literature to Life. Answer the following question based on your own experience and knowledge. Write your answer on a separate sheet of paper. (16 points)

Of all the rules you try to live by, which one is most important to you? State the rule and explain its importance in your life by describing what it has helped you learn or be.

You Sing (Sonnet 52)/How to Paint the Portrait of a Bird (page 643)

Selection Test

A. Think about how these poems use sensory details. For each poem, jot down two sensory details and tell which sense(s) the details appeal to. (14 points each)

1. "You Sing (Sonnet 52)"	2. "How to Paint the Portrait of a Bird"
Detail	**Detail**
Appeals to the sense(s) of	Appeals to the sense(s) of
Detail	**Detail**
Appeals to the sense(s) of	Appeals to the sense(s) of

B. Write the letter of the best answer. This exercise is continued on the next page. (9 points each)

_____ 1. Which word from "You Sing (Sonnet 52)" is an example of onomatopoeia?
    a. fills
    b. drops
    c. jangle
    d. returns

_____ 2. The speaker of "You Sing (Sonnet 52)" compares the person's voice to
    a. a soaring arrow.
    b. a pine tree.
    c. a creaking wheel.
    d. the bottom of the sea.

_____ 3. According to the speaker of "How to Paint the Portrait of a Bird," what should be painted first?
      a. a tree's leaves and branches
      b. a cage with an open door
      c. something pretty for the bird
      d. dust in the sun

_____ 4. In "How to Paint the Portrait of a Bird," which of these is a sign that the picture is bad?
      a. The bird does not come for many years.
      b. The bird enters the cage.
      c. The bird is missing one feather.
      d. The bird does not sing.

C. Answer **one** of the following questions based on your understanding of the poems. Write your answer on a separate sheet of paper. (20 points)

1. Both poems include details about singing. Explain the significance of singing in each poem. Support your answer with details from the poems.

2. Do you think the speakers of the two poems express similar ideas about inspiration? Explain your answer.

D. Linking Literature to Life. Answer the following question based on your own experience and knowledge. Write your answer on a separate sheet of paper. (16 points)

Think of something you created all by yourself that you consider a success. Your creation might have been a poem, a costume, a recipe—anything at all. Explain what inspired your creation and why you consider it a success.

The Scribe (page 653)

Selection Test

A. What do you learn about James from his words and actions and from the words and actions of other characters? For each detail from the story listed below, write notes telling what it reveals about James's character. (8 points each)

Story Detail	What It Reveals About James
1. James sets up a card table on the sidewalk with a sign that says, "PUBLIC SCRIBE— ALL SERVICES FREE."	
2. A cop tells James it's against the law to operate a business without a license, so James leaves.	
3. As James leaves, a little old lady shakes her umbrella at the cop and hollers, "You big bully!"	
4. After learning that banks cash checks for free, James asks his father, "So why can't people see they lose money when they *pay* to have their checks cashed?"	

B. Write the letter of the best answer. This exercise is continued on the next page. (6 points each)

_____ 1. How do Mr. Silver and Mr. Dollar seem to feel toward their customers?
   a. appreciative
   b. trusting
   c. scornful
   d. fearful

_____ 2. What does Mom tell James about the scribes who lived in ancient times?
   a. They made all the laws.
   b. They were the only people who could write.
   c. They worked for free.
   d. They helped to educate other people.

_____ 3. The cop's main reason for talking to James about his scribe service is that
   a. he thinks James deserves to be paid for his work.
   b. James is committing a crime by not charging his customers.
   c. Mr. Silver and Mr. Dollar have complained.
   d. the crowd around the table is blocking the sidewalk.

_____ 4. James tells people about the bank mostly because he
   a. wants to help them save money.
   b. hopes to drive the Silver Dollar out of business.
   c. wants people to meet his friend, Mrs. Adams.
   d. likes to show that he knows more than adults.

_____ 5. After helping Mrs. Franklin open an account at the bank, James has the confidence to
   a. bring more people to the bank.
   b. think about applying for a license to be a scribe.
   c. set up his own bank account.
   d. cash checks at the Silver Dollar.

C. Answer **one** of the following questions based on your understanding of the story. Write your answer on a separate sheet of paper. (20 points)

1. If you could ask James why he decided to become a scribe, what reasons might he give? Use details from the story to support your answer.

2. What do you think is the theme, or message, of this story? How is this theme revealed or communicated in the story?

D. Linking Literature to Life. Answer the following question based on your own experience and knowledge. Write your answer on a separate sheet of paper. (18 points)

If you could design a community service project that would match both your abilities and the needs of your community, what would it be? Write a short description of the project, and explain why it is a good match for both you and your community.

Crow Call (page 668)

Selection Test

A. Think about the symbols in "Crow Call." For each symbol listed in the chart below, write notes telling what the symbol might represent and what it suggests about the relationship between the narrator and her father. (6 points each)

Symbol	What It Represents	What It Suggests
1. The hunting shirt		
2. The father's gun		
3. Cherry pie		
4. The crow call		

B. Write the letter of the best answer. This exercise is continued on the next page. (5 points each)

_____ 1. For the narrator and her father, the main purpose of their trip is to
   a. buy a shirt.
   b. have breakfast.
   c. hunt crows.
   d. enjoy time together.

_____ 2. The narrator thinks of her father as a "stranger" because
   a. they have never met before.
   b. he has been away fighting in the war.
   c. they have nothing in common.
   d. he is not her real father.

3. How did the narrator feel when she realized her father was not going to shoot any crows?
   a. grateful
   b. disappointed
   c. puzzled
   d. upset

4. Which sentence best expresses the sense of change in the relationship between the narrator and her father?
   a. "I felt totally surrounded by shirt."
   b. "The diner's menu . . . seemed not to include honey."
   c. "Dark roofs of houses lay scattered, separated by pastures."
   d. "My father came down the hill to meet me coming up."

C. Words to Know. Write the letter of the best answer. (4 points each)

1. You would be most likely to see a mannequin in a
   a. grocery store.   b. diner.   c. clothing store.

2. The top of a dining-room table would be marred by a
   a. scratch.   b. tablecloth.   c. salt shaker.

3. A person who acts arrogantly is most likely to be
   a. very patient.   b. overly proud.   c. not awake.

4. Which person is most likely to be described as poised?
   a. taxi driver   b. ballet dancer   c. dairy farmer

5. People who feel disgruntled are
   a. satisfied.   b. pleased.   c. upset.

D. Answer **one** of the following questions based on your understanding of the story. Write your answer on a separate sheet of paper. (20 points)

1. What are the narrator's concerns as she and her father go out hunting? Describe at least **three** things she is worried about.

2. In what ways are the narrator and her father like the crows? Use details from the story to support your answer.

E. Linking Literature to Life. Answer the following question based on your own experience and knowledge. Write your answer on a separate sheet of paper. (16 points)

If you met the narrator of this story, do you think that you and she could become close friends? Why or why not? Explain your answer.

from Looking Back (page 678)

Selection Test

A. Think of what Lois Lowry says about each item listed below. Write notes for each one describing how she felt or thought about it when she was little and what her voice reveals about how she felt as an adult when she wrote this selection. (6 points each)

Her Views When She Was Little	Her Views as an Adult
1. Modest Storewrecker	
2. Her little brother, Jon	
3. The vigil in *The Yearling*	
4. The football uniform	

B. Write the letter of the best answer. This exercise is continued on the next page. (5 points each)

_____ 1. You can tell from this selection that when Lowry was a little girl, she did not like most of the
a. books she read.
b. people she knew.
c. places she visited.
d. clothes she wore.

_____ 2. Which of these made the most positive impression on Lowry when she was young?
a. reading *The Yearling*
b. crossing the Pacific Ocean
c. wearing lederhosen from Switzerland
d. living in Japan

_____ 3. In the game that Lowry likes to play, she sees a scene and tries to
   a. write a detailed description of it.
   b. name the book it reminds her of.
   c. take a photograph of it.
   d. make up a story about it.

_____ 4. The tone of this selection suggests that Lowry recalls her childhood with a feeling of
   a. resentment.
   b. sadness.
   c. fondness.
   d. confusion.

C. Words to Know. Write the letter of the best answer. (4 points each)

_____ 1. A person would be most likely to <u>peer</u> through a
   a. telescope.   b. garden.   c. swimming pool.

_____ 2. During a <u>vigil</u>, it would be most important to
   a. make money.   b. stay alert.   c. play music.

_____ 3. A person who has a feeling of <u>mortification</u> feels
   a. embarrassed.   b. grateful.   c. respected.

_____ 4. A <u>modest</u> person would probably not ask for
   a. attention.   b. directions.   c. assistance.

_____ 5. <u>Obnoxious</u> children are most likely to be thought of as
   a. helpers.   b. pals.   c. brats.

D. Answer **one** of the following questions based on your understanding of the selection. Write your answer on a separate sheet of paper. (20 points)

1. From this selection, describe Lowry's most positive and most negative memories.

2. What kind of person was Lowry as a child? Use details from the selection to support your answer.

E. Linking Literature to Life. Answer the following question based on your own experience and knowledge. Write your answer on a separate sheet of paper. (16 points)

What part of this selection did you identify with most closely? Why?

Unit Five: Making Your Mark

Part One Open-Book Test

A. Write your answer to each question on the line provided. (5 points each)

1. Which selection in this part discusses writing personal credos?

   _____

2. In "How to Paint the Portrait of a Bird," how does the painter know if the painting is good?

   _____

3. What is the main conflict in *Words on a Page?*

   _____

4. In which selection does the author describe scenes from her childhood?

   _____

B. In several selections in this part, the goal that a person or character tries to achieve is closely linked to his or her education. Choose **two** selections you want to discuss. In the boxes below, write the name of each person and selection you choose. Then write notes about the person's goal and how his or her education affected the person's choice of this goal. (20 points)

Person/Selection	**Person/Selection**
What is the person's goal?	**What is the person's goal?**
How does the person's education influence the choice of this goal?	**How does the person's education influence the choice of this goal?**

C. Answer **two** of the following essay questions based on your understanding of the selections. Write your answers on a separate sheet of paper. (20 points each)

1. Several selections in this part focus on writers or artists, and each person puts his or her talent to a different use. Choose the **one** writer or artist you most admire and tell why you admire him or her. Give at least three reasons for your choice.

2. Sometimes inspiration comes from within, and sometimes it comes from others. Choose **one** selection and explain whether it deals with inspiration that comes from within, from others, or both. Use details from the selection to support your answer.

3. Of all the themes or messages presented in these selections, which one is most important to you? State the theme and explain why you think it is so important.

4. These selections suggest that children can learn from adults and that adults can also learn from children. Choose **two** selections you want to discuss. Tell what the children or adults learn and from whom.

D. The selections in this part demonstrate that "finding your voice" is a learning process. As people discover what they are capable of doing with their talents and beliefs, they gain new and important knowledge. Choose **one** of the selections. Write the name of the person or character who finds his or her voice. Then write notes describing the process the person goes through to find this voice and the new knowledge the person gains. (20 points)

Selection
Person
How does the person discover his or her voice?
What new knowledge does the person gain through this process?

The Dog of Pompeii (page 700)

Selection Test

A. Think about how this story weaves together actual history with imagined details. In the boxes on the left, write three historical facts or events that are incorporated into the story. In the boxes on the right, write three details that the writer imagined. (12 points each)

1. Historical Facts or Events	2. Details Imagined by the Writer

B. Write the letter of the best answer. This exercise is continued on the next page. (5 points each)

_____ 1. Bimbo leaves Tito three times a day to
   a. explore the forum.   c. play with other children.
   b. find food for Tito.   d. sleep under the wall.

_____ 2. The buildings of Pompeii have been rebuilt after the old ones were destroyed by
   a. an earthquake.   c. a fire.
   b. a flood.   d. a war.

_____ 3. How does the stranger with the thin voice feel about the smoke above Vesuvius?
   a. puzzled   c. amused
   b. alarmed   d. hopeful

_____ 4. What wakes Tito the morning after the celebration of Caesar's birthday?
  a. The ground beneath him is shaking.
  b. The hot, ashed-filled air is choking him.
  c. Bimbo is pulling him to his feet.
  d. People all around him are running and shouting.

C. Words to Know. Write the letter of the best answer. (4 points each)

_____ 1. If you plan to <u>restore</u> an old building, your goal is to make it
  a. larger.   b. like it used to be.   c. totally modern.

_____ 2. If you enter a <u>shrine</u>, you are most likely to see people
  a. eating.   b. shopping.   c. praying.

_____ 3. When some type of <u>eruption</u> occurs, it is usually
  a. sudden and loud.   b. small and neat.   c. useful and lovely.

_____ 4. Someone who is <u>dislodging</u> rocks along a roadside is
  a. marking them.   b. removing them.   c. counting them.

_____ 5. Which of these creates <u>vapor</u>?
  a. boiling water   b. bright lights   c. whispering voices

D. Answer **one** of the following questions based on your understanding of the story. Write your answer on a separate sheet of paper. (20 points)

 1. Why does Bimbo return to the city rather than join Tito at the sea gate? What does that tell you about Bimbo's character?

 2. Is Bimbo a hero? Why or why not? Support your answer with details from the story.

E. Linking Literature to Life. Answer the following question based on your own experience and knowledge. Write your answer on a separate sheet of paper. (16 points)

 Can an animal truly be a person's friend? Explain your opinion.

Tutankhamen (page 718)

Selection Test

A. Think about the factual information presented in this story. For each person or place listed below, write an important fact you learned about him or it by reading this selection. (6 points each)

Person/Place	What You Learned About the Person/Place
1. Howard Carter	
2. Lord Carnarvon	
3. Valley of the Tombs of the Kings	
4. King Tutankhamen's tomb	

B. Write the letter of the best answer. This exercise is continued on the next page. (5 points each)

_____ 1. What convinced Carter and Carnarvon that the tomb of Tutankhamen was in the center of the Valley of the Kings?
   a. a hunch or strong feeling
   b. the opinions expressed by other experts
   c. the appearance of the valley
   d. clues found in the center of the valley

_____ 2. Carter and Carnarvon felt uneasy as they stood before the first door to the tomb because they realized that
   a. the door carried the seal of Tutankhamen.
   b. breaking down the door would destroy a valuable object.
   c. the door showed signs of having been broken down.
   d. opening the door would be disrespectful to the dead.

_____ 3. Which objects discovered by Carter and Carnarvon led them to believe that Tutankhamen's body lay just beyond the third sealed door?
   a. boxes of food offerings
   b. two statues of a king
   c. gilt couches carved in animal forms
   d. caskets

_____ 4. What did Carter and Carnarvon plan to do with the treasure they discovered?
   a. cover it up again   c. destroy it
   b. sell it   d. study it

C. Words to Know. Write the letter of the best answer. (4 points each)

_____ 1. When you do a <u>tedious</u> chore, you would usually feel
   a. bored.   b. rushed.   c. amused.

_____ 2. To <u>dissuade</u> a person who is planning something, you would most likely
   a. offer your help.   b. criticize the plan.   c. say nothing.

_____ 3. One who always does things <u>systematically</u> could best be described as
   a. organized.   b. lazy.   c. generous.

_____ 4. Which object would probably be <u>intact</u> after being dropped?
   a. a teacup   b. an egg   c. a baseball

_____ 5. A <u>sentinel</u> is expected to be
   a. friendly.   b. watchful.   c. creative.

D. Answer **one** of the following questions based on your understanding of the selection. Write your answer on a separate sheet of paper. (20 points)

1. What **two** factors would you say were most responsible for the discovery of the tomb of Tutankhamen? Explain why these factors were so important.

2. Informative nonfiction often provides more than factual information. What insights, inspirations, or other enjoyment did you get out of reading this selection? Explain.

E. Linking Literature to Life. Answer the following question based on your own experience and knowledge. Write your answer on a separate sheet of paper. (16 points)

   If you could explore any place or subject in the world, what would you explore, and why? What is it about the place or subject that appeals to you? How would you go about exploring it?

Name _____ Date _____

The First Emperor (page 728)

Selection Test

A. In this selection, the author's subject is expressed through his ideas and the details he chooses to include. Read each excerpt on the left and decide what the main idea is. Next to each excerpt, write down the main idea and/or important details of the excerpt. (8 points each)

The Author's Words	Main Idea and Important Details
1. "There is what may turn out to be the greatest archaeological find of modern times, one that may ultimately outshine even the discovery of the tomb of Tutankhamen."	
2. "Shih Huang Ti searched constantly for the secret of immortality. He became prey to a host of phony magicians and other fakers who promised much but could deliver nothing."	
3. "It was also said that loaded crossbows were set up all around the inside of the tomb and that anyone who did manage to penetrate the inner chambers would be shot full of arrows."	

B. Write the letter of the best answer. This exercise is continued on the next page. (5 points each)

_____ 1. Shih Huang Ti was able to overcome rival kings to become emperor over all of China because he
    a. was a strong warrior.
    b. had noble ancestors.
    c. ruled with great wisdom.
    d. was popular and respected.

_____ 2. While he was emperor, Shih Huang Ti was most concerned about
    a. international trade.
    b. enlarging the size of China.
    c. his personal safety.
    d. improving the lives of his people.

_____ 3. What item from Shih Huang Ti's tomb was discovered by a peasant near Mount Li?
   a. a map of the empire
   b. a statue of a warrior
   c. a crossbow
   d. a reproduction of his palace

_____ 4. The Chinese government has moved slowly in carrying out the excavation of the tomb because government leaders
   a. are uneasy about disturbing an emperor's burial place.
   b. believe the tomb was probably robbed long ago.
   c. regard the excavation as wasteful and unimportant.
   d. want to be sure the excavation is done carefully and well.

C. Words to Know. Write the letter of the best answer. (4 points each)

_____ 1. If you surpass a friend in height, you are
   a. taller.   b. the same height.   c. shorter.

_____ 2. What does the preservation of an object involve?
   a. replacing it   b. protecting it   c. creating it

_____ 3. People who thought a man was insignificant would probably
   a. praise him.   b. fear him.   c. ignore him.

_____ 4. Which behavior is associated with a tyrant?
   a. laziness   b. cruelty   c. cowardice

_____ 5. A person who wishes for immortality wants to
   a. live forever.   b. be a leader.   c. have great wealth.

D. Answer **one** of the following questions based on your understanding of the selection. Write your answer on a separate sheet of paper. (20 points)

1. What are some reasons that Shih Huang Ti is more popular among the people of China today than he seems to have been while he was alive?

2. What do you think was the author's main purpose in writing "The First Emperor"— to entertain, to inform, to express an opinion, or to persuade? Support your answer.

E. Linking Literature to Life. Answer the following question based on your own experience and knowledge. Write your answer on a separate sheet of paper. (16 points)

   Imagine that, a hundred years from now, someone reads about you in an encyclopedia. What would you like it to say about you and your life?

Barbara Frietchie (page 737)

Selection Test

A. Think about what the Union flag means to Barbara Frietchie and what it means to Stonewall Jackson. Then, in the boxes below, write notes to answer the questions. (15 points each)

1. Why do you think Barbara Frietchie raises the flag?	
2. Why do you think Stonewall Jackson allows the flag to fly?	

B. Write the letter of the best answer. This exercise is continued on the next page. (6 points each)

_____ 1. Lines 1 and 2 of this poem are a couplet because they
   a. have the same number of syllables.
   b. form a pair of rhymed lines.
   c. are the first two lines of the poem.
   d. form a complete stanza.

_____ 2. To the approaching Confederate soldiers, Frederick looks
   a. abandoned.   c. inviting.
   b. strange.   d. dangerous.

_____ 3. Which of the following is suggested in lines 13–16?
   a. The people of Frederick had displayed 40 Union flags, but the flags had been taken down.
   b. The soldiers march through Frederick waving 40 Confederate flags.
   c. The people of Frederick raise 40 Confederate flags and the soldiers bring 40 more.
   d. The soldiers waited until noon to raise 40 Confederate flags.

4. When Barbara Frietchie raises the Union flag, she knows that
   a. her action will make her famous.
   b. she might provoke an angry reaction.
   c. the townspeople will follow her lead.
   d. Stonewall Jackson will protect her.

5. Just after the soldiers fire on the flag, Barbara Frietchie
   a. waves the shredded flag.
   b. covers her head and hides.
   c. begs Stonewall Jackson to help her.
   d. threatens to fire back.

6. Stonewall Jackson's attitude toward Barbara Frietchie is best described as
   a. scornful.
   b. amused.
   c. respectful.
   d. impatient.

C. Answer **one** of the following questions based on your understanding of the poem. Write your answer on a separate sheet of paper. (20 points)

1. Do you think Barbara Frietchie's action is worth the risk she takes? Give at least **two** reasons for your opinion.

2. What do you think is the main message of this poem? Explain.

D. Linking Literature to Life. Answer the following question based on your own experience and knowledge. Write your answer on a separate sheet of paper. (14 points)

What does the American flag mean to you, and why?

Unit Five: Making Your Mark

Part Two Open-Book Test

A. Write the letter of the best answer to each question. (5 points each)

_____ 1. Which selection is an example of historical fiction?
    a. "The Dog of Pompeii"   c. "The First Emperor"
    b. "Tutankhamen"   d. "Barbara Frietchie"

_____ 2. In "Barbara Frietchie," the old woman is best described as
    a. foolish.   c. cowardly.
    b. defiant.   d. generous.

_____ 3. Which selection focuses on the discovery made by a British archaeologist
    and his financial supporter?
    a. "Barbara Frietchie"   c. "The First Emperor"
    b. "The Dog of Pompeii"   d. "Tutankhamen"

_____ 4. According to "The First Emperor," Shih Huang Ti was obsessed with
    a. preventing his own death.
    b. earning his people's respect.
    c. increasing his personal wealth.
    d. choosing a proper heir.

B. In this part, three selections portray archaeologists at work and suggest traits, or personal qualities, that this profession requires. Choose **one** of the selections. Then, in the boxes below, write notes describing two traits the selection suggests and how the archaeologists in the selection demonstrate those traits. (20 points)

Selection _____

Trait of an Archaeologist	How These Archaeologists Demonstrate Each Trait
1.	
2.	

C. Answer **two** of the following essay questions based on your understanding of the selections. Write your answers on a separate sheet of paper. (20 points each)

1. Several people or characters in this part rise above their own interests to "do the right thing." Choose **one** of these people or characters and describe his or her action, what it reveals about him or her, and what happens as a result.

2. If you could visit or explore one of the places described in this part, which place would you choose? What would you hope to see and do during your visit? Give reasons for your answer.

3. Selections in this part suggest different attitudes toward death. Choose **two** of the selections and discuss the attitude toward death reflected in each one.

4. Choose the **one** character from these selections for whom you feel the most sympathy. Give at least three reasons for your choice.

D. The people in these selections lived long ago, but they had many of the same needs and problems that people do today. Choose **two** selections. In the boxes below, write the name of a person from each selection and describe his or her problem or need. Then give an example from today's world that illustrates the same need or problem. (20 points)

Person/Selection	Person/Selection
What need or problem did the person face?	**What need or problem did the person face?**
What example from today's world illustrates this need or problem?	**What example from today's world illustrates this need or problem?**

Links to Unit One: Tests of Courage (page 772)

Selection Test

A. Think about the challenges faced by the characters in these selections, how they respond to those challenges, and what the consequences, or results, of their responses are. Then, in the boxes below, write notes about one challenge faced by each of the characters. (8 points each)

1. Daedalus in "The Boy Who Flew"

What is one challenge that he faces?	How does he respond?	What are the consequences?

2. Arachne in "Arachne"

What is one challenge that she faces?	How does she respond?	What are the consequences?

3. Ceres in "The Story of Ceres and Proserpina"

What is one challenge that she faces?	How does she respond?	What are the consequences?

B. Write the letter of the best answer. This exercise is continued on the next page. (5 points each)

_____ 1. In "The Boy Who Flew," Daedalus helps kill the Minotaur because he wants to
a. save young people from being sacrificed.
b. get revenge against King Minos.
c. keep the Minotaur from escaping.
d. punish Queen Pasiphae.

_____ 2. To whom does Arachne give credit for her skills?
  a. Athena   c. spiders
  b. her father   d. herself

_____ 3. In "The Story of Ceres and Proserpina," Proserpina is kidnapped by
  a. Pluto.   c. a prince.
  b. Jupiter.   d. Ceres.

_____ 4. Pluto tricks Proserpina by persuading her to
  a. admit that she loves him.
  b. become queen of the underworld.
  c. eat a pomegranate seed.
  d. return to her mother.

C. Words to Know. Write the letter of the best answer. (4 points each)

_____ 1. A barren field is most likely to be
  a. fruitful.   b. overgrown.   c. bare.

_____ 2. A man's face is most likely to become distorted when he is
  a. very angry.   b. sleepy.   c. proud of himself.

_____ 3. A creature that is immortal is one that
  a. can fly.   b. never dies.   c. has horns.

_____ 4. Which animal is known for being obstinate?
  a. a mule   b. a chicken   c. a peacock

_____ 5. Which person is most likely to feel isolated?
  a. a dancer   b. a teacher   c. a prisoner

D. Answer **one** of the following questions based on your understanding of the selections. Write your answer on a separate sheet of paper. (20 points)

1. What do you think is the message of "Arachne"? Is it still an important message today? Explain your opinion.

2. Do you think the main characters in these stories deserve what happens to them? Explain why they deserve the punishments they get or why they do not.

E. Linking Literature to Life. Answer the following question based on your own experience and knowledge. Write your answer on a separate sheet of paper. (16 points)

What is a lesson about life that you think is difficult for people your age to learn? Why is it so difficult?

Links to Unit Two: Growth and Change (page 788)

Selection Test

A. Think about how the main character in each story grows and changes. In the chart below, write notes describing what each character is like at the beginning, what event or events bring about a change, and how the character changes. (12 points each)

	1. The boy in "The Disobedient Child"	2. The narrator of "The Bamboo Beads"
What the Character Is Like at the Beginning		
What Event Brings About a Change		
How the Character Changes		

B. Write the letter of the best answer. This exercise is continued on the next page. (5 points each)

_____ 1. In "The Disobedient Child," the boy gets into trouble because he
    a. refuses to cook dinner.
    b. ignores the old man's warnings.
    c. cannot count to 13.
    d. takes the old man's yellow cape.

_____ 2. In "The Disobedient Child," the boy's misbehavior is shown to be
    a. incurable.
    b. harmless.
    c. rewarding.
    d. forgivable.

3. In "The Bamboo Beads," Tantie first gives the old man bread because she
   a. is afraid of him.
   b. feels sorry for him.
   c. thinks he will pay for it later.
   d. wants him to give her a necklace.

4. Which of the following is rewarded in "The Bamboo Beads"?
   a. beauty
   b. wisdom
   c. bravery
   d. kindness

C. Words to Know. Write the letter of the best answer. (5 points each)

1. When noise subsides, it
   a. builds up.   b. fades away.   c. stops suddenly.

2. Which is designed to emit water?
   a. a faucet   b. a bathtub   c. a drain stopper

3. If you tolerate something, you
   a. bear it.   b. share it.   c. prepare it.

4. Signs that forbid entry to someone else's property would likely make you feel
   a. neighborly.   b. welcome.   c. excluded.

D. Answer **one** of the following questions based on your understanding of the selections. Write your answer on a separate sheet of paper. (20 points)

1. What is one lesson taught by the folktale "The Bamboo Beads"? Do you think that this is a good lesson to learn? Explain.

2. Do you think the boy in "The Disobedient Child" is behaving wrongly when he disobeys the old man? Explain your opinion.

E. Linking Literature to Life. Answer the following question based on your own experience and knowledge. Write your answer on a separate sheet of paper. (16 points)

What do you think are the main rewards of being kind and respectful? Support your ideas with real examples or examples from literature.

Links to Unit Three: A Sense of Fairness (page 800)

Selection Test

A. The saying, "What goes around, comes around," means that a person will be treated in the same way he or she treats others. In each box below, write notes explaining how the saying relates to "In the Land of Small Dragon" and to "King Thrushbeard." (12 points each)

1. "In the Land of Small Dragon"	2. "King Thrushbeard"

B. Write the letter of the best answer. This exercise is continued on the next page. (5 points each)

_____ 1. In "In the Land of Small Dragon," physical beauty is shown to be a sign of
  a. suffering.
  b. goodness.
  c. great wisdom.
  d. unimportance.

_____ 2. How do Cám and Number Two Wife feel toward T'âm?
  a. generous
  b. affectionate
  c. respectful
  d. jealous

_____ 3. In "King Thrushbeard," the king becomes upset with his daughter because she
  a. breaks all the clay pots.
  b. cannot weave or spin.
  c. makes fun of all the suitors.
  d. vows never to get married.

_____ 4. After King Thrushbeard is rejected by the princess, he decides to
  a. teach her a lesson.
  b. make her a beggar.
  c. marry someone else.
  d. move to a faraway land.

C. Words to Know. Write the letter of the best answer. (4 points each)

_____ 1. An <u>indolent</u> worker is most likely to get
  a. tired.   b. fired.   c. hired.

_____ 2. People are most likely to think that a person who speaks <u>curtly</u> is
  a. sad.   b. impolite.   c. well educated.

_____ 3. Which of these is most likely to be described as <u>succulent</u>?
  a. a new coat   b. a fairy tale   c. roast beef

_____ 4. Which fairy tale character could best be described as <u>ravishing</u>?
  a. Snow White   b. Big Bad Wolf   c. the wicked stepmother

_____ 5. An <u>insolent</u> person is best described as
  a. smart.   b. lazy.   c. rude.

D. Answer **one** of the following questions based on your understanding of the selections. Write your answer on a separate sheet of paper. (20 points)

1. Discuss how the following proverb from "In the Land of Small Dragon" relates to T'âm, the elder daughter: "A jewel box of gold and jade / Holds only jewels of great price."

2. Do you think that the princess in "King Thrushbeard" deserves the treatment she receives? Explain your answer.

E. Linking Literature to Life. Answer the following question based on your own experience and knowledge. Write your answer on a separate sheet of paper. (16 points)

Give at least two reasons why you agree or disagree with this proverb from "In the Land of Small Dragon": "In truth, beauty seeks goodness: / What is beautiful is good."

Links to Unit Four: Wondrous Worlds (page 816)

Selection Test

A. Think about the human traits shown by characters in these stories. For each story, write notes describing one human trait that is portrayed as a weakness and one that is portrayed as a strength. Explain who exhibits each trait and in what situation. (8 points each)

Story	Trait/Weakness	Trait/Strength
1. "Why Monkeys Live in Trees"		
2. "The Legend of the Hummingbird"		
3. "The Living Kuan-yin"		

B. Write the letter of the best answer. This exercise is continued on the next page. (5 points each)

_____ 1. In "Why Monkeys Live in Trees," what trait does Monkey show that the other animals do not as they compete in the contest?
   a. courage
   b. cleverness
   c. confidence
   d. stubbornness

_____ 2. "The Legend of the Hummingbird" explains why hummingbirds
   a. fly fast.
   b. have colorful feathers.
   c. have slender bills.
   d. are attracted to red flowers.

_____ 3. What is the main reason Chin Po-wan doesn't ask Kuan-yin his question?
   a. It would force him to break a promise.
   b. His question has already been answered.
   c. He knows that it is unnecessary to ask the question.
   d. He decides that it would be better to find the answer on his own.

_____ 4. In order to get what they want, both the snake and the rich man must
   a. be lucky.   c. pass a test.
   b. risk danger.   d. give up something.

C. Words to Know. Write the letter of the best answer. (4 points each)

_____ 1. An amiable person is
   a. good-natured.   b. selfish.   c. very shy.

_____ 2. A person who shows compassion is
   a. unfeeling.   b. fun-loving.   c. kindhearted.

_____ 3. A person who dresses extravagantly is most likely to be seen as a
   a. showoff.   b. bully.   c. beggar.

_____ 4. Destitute people could best be described as
   a. angry.   b. needy.   c. jealous.

_____ 5. If you do something inadvertently, you are most likely to say
   a. "Ha!"   b. "Wow!"   c. "Oops!"

D. Answer **one** of the following questions based on your understanding of the selections. Write your answer on a separate sheet of paper. (20 points)

1. Do you think that King Gorilla should be angry with the monkeys in "Why Monkeys Live in Trees"? Support your opinion with details from the story and your own ideas about competing.

2. How is the folktale "The Living Kuan-yin" different from other familiar tales in which people get three wishes?

E. Linking Literature to Life. Answer the following question based on your own experience and knowledge. Write your answer on a separate sheet of paper. (16 points)

Do you think promises should always be kept? Are there times when promises should be broken? If so, what might the consequences be? Explain.

Links to Unit Five: Making Your Mark (page 830)

Selection Test

A. Think about how the main character in each story pursues a goal, faces a difficult obstacle, and "makes a mark" in the end. In the chart below, write notes describing how the character in each story accomplishes these things. (12 points each)

	1. Frog	**2. Buffalo Calf Road Woman**
Character's Goal		
Obstacle He or She Faces		
How the Character Makes His or Her Mark		

B. Write the letter of the best answer. This exercise is continued on the next page. (5 points each)

_____ 1. Frog is not allowed to sing at first because
a. he is green and has warts.
b. his parents refuse to give him permission.
c. he has no money to pay Fox.
d. only the birds are allowed to sing.

_____ 2. When Frog tries to begin his act at the Friday night concert, the other animals react by
a. applauding loudly.
b. throwing fruit at him.
c. leaving the building.
d. sitting in silence.

_____ 3. The title of the story "Where the Girl Rescued Her Brother" refers to a
   a. battle.   c. road.
   b. small town.   d. campsite.

_____ 4. Buffalo Calf Road Woman became famous for
   a. killing a grizzly.   c. saving Comes-in-Sight.
   b. making beautiful quilts.   d. marrying Black Coyote.

C. Words to Know. Write the letter of the best answer. (4 points each)

_____ 1. A person would be most likely to <u>vault</u> onto a
   a. horse.   b. barn.   c. computer.

_____ 2. A country that works with another is an
   a. enemy.   b. ally.   c. invader.

_____ 3. A person's <u>ambition</u> is most like a
   a. weakness.   b. reputation.   c. goal.

_____ 4. A <u>hypnotic</u> speaker is most likely to be
   a. boring.   b. long-winded.   c. fascinating.

_____ 5. People who are <u>contemplating</u> an issue are
   a. arguing about it. b. thinking about it.   c. publicizing it.

D. Answer **one** of the following questions based on your understanding of the selections. Write your answer on a separate sheet of paper. (20 points)

1. What lessons about human behavior are taught in these two stories? Use details from the stories to support your answer.

2. What cultural values and customs are described or implied in each of these stories? Support your answer.

E. Linking Literature to Life. Answer the following question based on your own experience and knowledge. Write your answer on a separate sheet of paper. (16 points)

Think about an experience you have had that was like Frog's experience. What did you do, and how did people react? Explain.

Unit Six: The Oral Tradition

Open-Book Test

A. Write your answer to each question on the lines. (5 points each)

1. In which selection is the main character rewarded for keeping his promises?

   _____

2. In which selection is a girl turned into a flower?

   _____

3. What does King Thrushbeard do to teach the princess a lesson?

   _____

4. In "The Disobedient Child," who is the old man?

   _____

B. In many of these selections, characters learn lessons about life. Choose **two** characters from the list below that you wish to discuss and write your choices on the blank lines in the boxes. In each box, write notes describing the lesson that the character learns. (20 points)

Daedalus in "The Boy Who Flew"   the boy in "The Disobedient Child"
the narrator in "The Bamboo Beads"   the princess in "King Thrushbeard"
the wealthy host in "The Living Kuan-yin"

_____ learns that . . .	_____ learns that . . .

C. Answer **two** of the following essay questions based on your understanding of the selections. Write your answers on a separate sheet of paper. (20 points each)

1. Choose **one** selection from this unit that is a "why story"—that is, one that offers an explanation for things in nature. What does the story explain? Do you think the explanation is a good one? Elaborate.

2. Choose **two** characters from this unit, one who you think is treated fairly in the selection and one who is treated unfairly. Support your choices with details from the selections and your own ideas.

3. Choose **one** selection from this unit that reveals the values of the society from which the story comes. Tell what values are revealed by the story and how you can tell from the story that these were, or are, the society's values.

4. Think about what occurs in these selections as a result of the characters' strengths and weaknesses. Choose **two** characters you wish to discuss. Note a personality trait of each character and describe what happens as a result of the personality trait.

D. In many of these selections, the characters struggle against something or someone. Circle the letter of **one** character you wish to discuss, and write notes in the boxes to answer the questions about that character's conflict. (20 points)

  a. T'âm in "In the Land of Small Dragon"
  b. Frog in "The Frog Who Wanted to Be a Singer"
  c. Arachne
  d. Taroo in "The Legend of the Hummingbird"

What does the character struggle against?	Why does the character win or lose this struggle?

End-of-Year Test

Directions: Read the selection below. Then answer the questions that follow.

How to Bring Up a Lion

Rudyard Kipling

Now this is a really-truly tale. It all truthfully happened, and I saw it and heard it.

Once there was a mother lion that lived in a cage halfway up a mountain in Africa, behind the house where I was living, and she had two little baby lions. She bit one of them so hard that it died. But the keeper in charge of the cages pulled out the other little lion just in time and carried him down the hill. He put him in an egg box, along with a brindled bulldog puppy, called Budge, to keep him warm.

When I went to look at the little thing, the keeper said, "This baby lion is going to die. Would you like to bring up this baby lion?" And I said, "Yes," and the keeper said, "Then I will send him to your house at once, because he is certainly going to die here, and you can bring him up by hand."

Then I went home and found Daniel and Una, who were little children, playing. I said, "We are going to bring up a baby lion by hand!" and both children said, "Hurrah! He can sleep in our nursery and not go away for ever and ever."

Then Daniel and Una's mother said to me, "What do you know about bringing up lions?" And I said, "Nothing whatever." And she said, "I thought so," and went into the house to give orders.

Soon the keeper came, carrying the egg box with the baby lion and Budge, the brindled bulldog pup, asleep inside. Behind the keeper walked a man with iron bars and a roll of wire netting and some picks and shovels. The men built a den for the baby lion in the backyard, and they put the box inside and said, "Now you can bring the lion up by hand. He is quite, quite certain to die."

The children's mother came out of the house with a bottle, the kind that you feed very small babies from, and she filled it with milk and warm water. She said, "I am going to bring up this baby lion, and he is not going to die."

She pulled out the baby lion (his eyes were all blue and watery and he couldn't see), and she turned him on his back and tilted the bottle into his little mouth. He moved all his four little paws like windmills, but he never let go of the bottle, not once, until it was quite empty and he was quite full.

The children's mother said, "Weigh him on the meat scales," and we did. He weighed four pounds, three ounces. She said, "He will be weighed once every week, and he will be fed every three hours on warm milk and water—two parts milk and one part water. The bottle will be cleaned after each meal with boiling water."

I said, "What do you know about bringing up lions by hand?" and she said, "Nothing whatever, except that this lion is not going to die. You must find out how to bring up lions."

So I said, "The first thing to do is to stop Daniel and Una from hugging and dancing around him because if they hug him too hard or step on him he will surely die."

For ten days the baby lion ate and slept. He didn't say anything; he hardly opened his eyes. We made him a bed of wood shavings (they are better than straw), and we built him a real little house with a thick roof to keep the sun off. And whenever he looked at all hungry, it was time for him to be fed out of the bottle.

Budge tried to make him play, but the little lion wouldn't. When Budge chewed his ears too hard, he would stretch himself all over the puppy and Budge would crawl from under him, half choked.

We said, "It is an easy thing to bring up a lion," and then visitors began to call and give advice.

One man said, "Young lions all die of paralysis[1] of the hindquarters." And another man said, "They perish of rickets,[2] a condition that comes on just as they are cutting their first teeth."

We looked at the baby lion, and his hind legs were very weak indeed. He rolled over when he tried to walk, and his front paws doubled up under him. His eyes were dull and blind.

I went off to find someone who knew about animals' insides. "You must give him broth," I was told. "Milk isn't enough for him. Give him mutton broth at eight in the morning and four in the afternoon. You must also buy a dandy brush, same as they brush horses with, and brush him every day to make up for his own mother not being able to lick him with her tongue."

So we bought a dandy brush (a good hard one) and mutton for broth, and we gave him the broth from the bottle. In two days he was a different lion. His hind legs grew stronger, and his eyes grew lighter, and his furry, woolly skin grew cleaner.

1. **paralysis:** a loss of the ability to move a body part.
2. **rickets:** a disease in which bones fail to grow normally, caused by a lack of vitamin D.

We all said, "Now we must give him a real name of his own." We inquired into his family history and found that his parents were both Matabele[3] lions from the far north and that the Matabele word for lion was "umlibaan." But we called him Sullivan for short, and that very day he knocked a bit of skin off his nose trying to climb the wire fence.

He began to play with Daniel and Una—especially with Una, who walked all around the garden, hugging him till he squeaked.

One day, Una went out as usual and put her hand in Sullivan's house to drag him out, just as usual, and Sullivan flattened his little black-tipped ears back to his thick woolly head and opened his mouth and said "Ough! Ough! Ough!" like a monkey.

Una pulled her hand back and said, "I think Sullivan has teeth. Come and look." And we saw that he had six or eight very pretty little teeth about a quarter of an inch long, so we said, "Why should we give up our time to feeding this monarch of the jungle every few hours with a bottle? Let him feed himself."

He weighed eight pounds, eight ounces, and he could run and jump and growl and scratch, but he did not like to feed himself.

For two days and two nights, he wouldn't feed himself at all. He sang for his supper, like little Tommy Tucker, and he sang for his breakfast and his dinner, making noises deep in his chest, high noises and low noises and coughing noises. Una ran about saying, "Please let my lion have his bottle!"

Daniel, who didn't speak very plainly, would go off to the lion's den, where poor Sullivan sat looking at a plate of cold broth. He would say, "Tullibun, Tullibun, eat up all your dinner or you'll be hungry."

At last Sullivan made up his mind that bottles would never come again and he put down his little nose and ate for dear life. I was told that the children's mother had been out in the early morning and dipped her finger in mutton broth and coaxed Sullivan to lick it off. She discovered that his tongue was as raspy as a file. Then we were sure he ought to feed himself.

So we weaned Sullivan, and he weighed ten pounds, two ounces, and the truly happy times of his life began. Every morning, Una and Daniel would let him out of the den. He was perfectly polite so long as no one put a hand into his house. He would come out at a steady, rocking-horse canter that looked slow but was quicker even than Una's run.

---

3. **Matabele:** having to do with people of southwestern Zimbabwe (a country in the southern part of Africa).

He would be brushed, first on his yellow tummy and then on his yellow back, and then under his yellow chin where he dribbled mutton broth, and then on his dark yellow mane. The mane hair of a baby lion is a little thicker than the rest of his hair, and Sullivan's was tinged with black.

After his brushing, he would go out into the garden to watch Daniel and Una swing. Or he would hoist himself up on the porch to watch their mother sew or he would go into my room and lie under the couch. If I wished to get rid of him I had to call Una, for at her voice he would solemnly trundle out with his head lifted and help her chase butterflies among the hydrangeas. He never took any notice of me.

One of the many queer things about him was the way he matched his backgrounds. He would lie down on the bare tiled porch in the full glare of the sun, and you could step on him before you saw him. He would sit in the shadow of a wall or slide into a garden border, and, till he moved, you could not tell that he was there. That made him difficult to photograph.

Sudden noises, like banging doors, always annoyed him. He would go straight backward almost as fast as he ran forward, till he got his back up against a wall or a shrub. There he would lift one little broad paw and look wicked until he heard Una or Daniel call him.

If he smelled anything in the wind, he would stop quite still and lift his head high into the air, very slowly, until he had quite made up his mind. Then he would slowly steal upwind with his tail twitching a trifle at the very end.

The first time he played with a ball he struck it just as his grandfather must have struck at the big Matabele oxen in the far north—one paw above and one paw below, with a wrench and a twist—and the ball bounced over his shoulder.

He could use his paws as easily as a man can use his arms, and much more quickly. He always turned his back on you when he was examining anything. That was a signal that you were not to interfere with him.

We used to believe that little lions were only big cats, as the books say. But Sullivan taught us that lions are always lions. He would play in his own way at his own games, but he never chased his tail or patted a cork or a string or did any foolish, kitten tricks. He never forgot that he was a lion, not a dog or a cat, but a lion.

When he lay down, he would cross his paws and look like the big carved lions in Trafalgar Square.[4] When he rose and sniffed, he looked like a bronze lion, and when he

4. **Trafalgar Square:** a plaza in London, England, that is the site of a famous monument (Nelson's Column) surrounded by four large statues of lions.

lifted one paw and opened his mouth and wrinkled up his nose to be angry (as he did when we washed him all over with carbolic and water because of fleas), he looked like the lions the old Assyrians[5] drew on stone.

He never did anything funny. He was never silly or amusing (not even when he had been dipped in carbolic and water), and he never behaved as though he were trying to show off. Kittens do.

He kept to himself more and more as he grew older. One day I shall never forget, he began to see out of his eyes—really see. Up till then his eyes had been dull and stupid, just like a young baby's eyes. But that day—I saw them first under the couch—they were grown-up lion's eyes, soft and blazing at the same time, without a wink in them, eyes that seemed to look right through you and out over all Africa.

Though he had been born in captivity, as were his parents, and though the only home he had ever known was on the slopes of the big Table Mountain where Africa ended, we never saw him once look up the hill when he lay down to do his solemn, serious thinking. He always faced squarely to the north, to the great open plains and the ragged, jagged mountains beyond them—looking up and into the big, sunny, dry Africa that had once belonged to his people.

That was curious. He would think and he would sigh, exactly like a man. He was full of curious, half-human noises, grunts and groans and mutters and rumbles.

He grew to weigh more than fifteen pounds when we had to leave him. We were very proud of this, and triumphed over the keeper and the other people who had said we could never bring him up by hand.

"You've certainly won the game," they said. "You can have this lion if you like and take him home and give him to the Zoological Gardens in London."

But we said, "No, Sullivan is one of the family, and if he were taken to a cold, wet, foggy zoo, he'd die. Let him stay here."

5. **Assyrians:** a people of southwestern Asia whose powerful empire lasted from the ninth to the seventh century B.C.

A. The following items test your understanding of the selection. Circle the letter of the response that best completes the sentence or answers the question.

1. This essay describes an event that took place in
   a. England.
   b. India.
   c. Africa.
   d. Assyria.

2. What is the main topic of this essay?
   a. raising a lion
   b. how Kipling became a writer
   c. hunting in Africa
   d. where Kipling found the lion

3. You can tell from this essay that carbolic is
   a. a kind of food.
   b. something used for farming.
   c. a kind of animal.
   d. something used for cleaning.

4. The keeper took the lion cub out of its cage because
   a. the bulldog puppy tried to bite it.
   b. the mother lion would have killed it.
   c. the lion cub was sick.
   d. the mother lion died while giving birth.

5. Who was the only person the lion cub obeyed?
   a. the narrator
   b. Una
   c. Daniel and Una's mother
   d. the keeper

6. When the narrator and his family had to leave Africa, they
   a. took the lion cub with them.
   b. had the lion cub put to sleep.
   c. left the lion cub behind.
   d. sent the lion cub back to its mother.

B. The following items check your understanding of literary elements in the selection. Circle the letter of the response that best completes the sentence or answers the question.

7. The tone of this essay can best be described as
   a. humorous.
   b. sarcastic.
   c. resentful.
   d. matter-of-fact.

8. When the lion reached a weight of 15 pounds, the narrator and his family felt
   a. disappointed that he was so small.
   b. proud of themselves for saving him.
   c. afraid that he would attack them.
   d. relieved to set him free.

9. Which word best describes the attitude of Daniel and Una's mother when the lion cub first arrived?
   a. determined
   b. irritated
   c. nervous
   d. delighted

10. Which sentence best expresses the main theme of this essay?
   a. "He is quite, quite certain to die."
   b. "Budge tried to make him play but the little lion wouldn't."
   c. "He always turned his back on you when he was examining anything."
   d. "Sullivan taught us that lions are always lions."

C. The following items check your understanding of the way in which the selection is written. Write your response after each item.

11. Write a brief explanation of the author's purpose or purposes in this essay.

_____

_____

_____

_____

12. What pattern of organization does Kipling use in this essay to present his ideas?

_____

_____

_____

_____

13. How does the writer's point of view in this essay influence how the reader feels about the events he describes?

_____

_____

_____

_____

D. The following items check your ability to analyze and evaluate the selection. Circle the letter of the response that best completes the sentence or answers the question.

14. In this selection, Daniel and Una's mother's main goal was to
    a. make sure Sullivan did not die.
    b. teach the children to be responsible.
    c. set the lion free in the wild.
    d. provide a pet for the children.

15. The narrator believed that the lion acted just like a man when he
    a. matched his background.
    b. sniffed the wind.
    c. thought and sighed.
    d. crossed his paws.

16. Which sentence states an opinion?
   a. "Then I went home and found Daniel and Una, who were little children, playing."
   b. "When he rose and sniffed, he looked like a bronze lion."
   c. "He weighed four pounds, three ounces."
   d. "His hind legs grew stronger, and his eyes grew lighter."

17. What did the narrator think was most curious about the lion?
   a. He rolled on his back when he first got a bottle.
   b. He did not like to play with Budge.
   c. He had to be cleaned and brushed every day.
   d. He always looked to the north when he lay down.

E. The following items check your ability to analyze and evaluate the selection. Write your response after each item.

18. According to the narrator, how was Sullivan different from a kitten?

_____

_____

_____

_____

19. Do you think it really was "an easy thing to bring up a lion"? Explain why or why not.

_____

_____

_____

_____

_____

20. What did the narrator realize when he noted that the lion suddenly had grown-up eyes "that seemed to look right through you and out over all Africa"?

_____

_____

_____

_____

_____

Writing Exercise The following activity is designed to assess your writing ability. The prompt asks you to describe a process. Think of your audience as being any reader other than yourself.

When scorers evaluate your writing, they will look for evidence that you can

- respond directly to the prompt.

- make your writing thoughtful and interesting.

- organize your ideas so that they are clear and easy to follow.

- develop your ideas thoroughly by using appropriate details and precise language.

- stay focused on your purpose for writing by making sure that each sentence you write contributes to your composition as a whole.

- communicate effectively by using correct spelling, capitalization, punctuation, grammar, usage, and sentence structure.

Prompt: Kipling's essay describes how he and his neighbors took care of a baby lion. Write a short essay that describes the process of raising a lion cub, or think of something else you know how to do. It might be taking care of another kind of animal, building something, or creating artwork.

Use the bottom of the page to organize your ideas. Then write your essay on a separate sheet of paper.

_____

_____

_____

_____

_____

_____

_____

_____

_____

_____

_____

_____

Revising/Editing The purpose of the following exercise is to check your ability to proofread and revise a piece of writing in order to improve its readability and presentation of ideas. Read the following paragraph. Then, for each underlined section, circle the letter of the revision below that most improves the writing. Or, if the section is best left as it is, circle the letter *d*.

Joseph Rudyard Kipling was born in India in 1865. <u>Spent most</u> of his
                                                          1.
childhood in England. In the 1880s, he <u>returned to India worked</u> as a
                                                    2.
journalist. Kipling <u>became famous</u> as a writer of stories, novels, and poems.
                          3.
Some of his most popular <u>works was</u> children's books such as *The Jungle*
                                4.
Book, Just So Stories, and *Captains Courageous.* All three of these books

were written while Kipling was living <u>at Vermont of the United States</u>.
                                                    5.
Kipling won the Nobel Prize for literature <u>in 1907, he died in 1936.</u>
                                                          6.

1. a. Then spent most
   b. He spent most
   c. Spending most
   d. correct as is

2. a. returned to India and worked
   b. returning to India worked
   c. returned to India working
   d. correct as is

3. a. became famously
   b. become famous
   c. becoming famous
   d. correct as is

4. a. works is
   b. works being
   c. works were
   d. correct as is

5. a. at Vermont in the United States
   b. in Vermont of the United States
   c. in Vermont in the United States
   d. correct as is

6. a. in 1907; he died in 1936.
   b. in 1907, then he died in 1936.
   c. in 1907—died in 1936.
   d. correct as is

Additional Test Generator Questions

Contents

To the Teacher

The following pages contain additional selection questions, which you may wish to use to construct tests that are customized to better meet the needs of your students. Correct responses to questions on these pages are marked with an asterisk. Read the questions and determine if any of them are appropriate for your students. Then use the Test Generator software to call up the questions and add them to your customized tests. Directions for using the Test Generator software are included in the *Test Generator User's Guide,* which accompanies the software.

UNIT ONE

Part One
Eleven
Test Generator

1. The day when this story takes place is special to Rachel because
   a. she gets a new sweater.
   *b. it is her eleventh birthday.
   c. her father is coming home.
   d. she leaves school early.

2. Who first claims that the red sweater belongs to Rachel?
   *a. Sylvia Saldívar
   b. Phyllis
   c. Mrs. Price
   d. Rachel

3. As she tells this story, Rachel is mainly concerned about her
   a. rights.
   b. education.
   c. birthday party.
   *d. feelings.

4. When Mrs. Price tells Rachel to put the sweater on, Rachel
   a. starts crying.
   b. refuses to put it on.
   *c. puts it on even though it is not hers.
   d. begins to wonder if the sweater is really hers.

5. Which of the following could Rachel know and tell the reader?
   a. why Phyllis thinks the sweater is hers
   b. how Mrs. Price feels about being older than Rachel
   c. how Phyllis feels when she remembers the sweater is hers
   *d. how she feels when Mrs. Price puts the sweater on her desk

President Cleveland, Where Are You?
Test Generator

1. Jerry and the other boys resented Rollie Tremaine because Rollie
   a. was bigger than they were.
   *b. had more money.
   c. was a better athlete.
   d. had a job.

2. Armand asked Jerry for money to buy
   a. flowers for Sally.
   b. a new pair of shoes for himself.
   c. cowboy cards.
   *d. a birthday gift for their father.

3. Jerry, Roger, and Rollie were collecting president cards because they wanted to
   *a. win a baseball glove.
   b. impress Sister Angela.
   c. learn about presidents.
   d. trade them for cowboy cards.

4. The climax of the story occurs when
   a. Jerry finds Armand's letter to Sally.
   b. Rollie wins the baseball glove.
   *c. Jerry gets a Grover Cleveland card.
   d. Roger slips through the fence.

5. Jerry seems to think that love is
   a. a wonderful thing.
   *b. a waste of time.
   c. something fine and noble.
   d. very expensive.

6. Jerry sold the Grover Cleveland card so he could
   *a. give the money to Armand.
   b. buy a new pair of shoes.
   c. become friends with Rollie.
   d. get a new baseball glove.

Scout's Honor
Test Generator

1. The narrator of the story planned to meet the requirements of "Scout Craft" by
   a. taking a trip on the subway.
   *b. going camping in the country.
   c. lighting a fire.
   d. making a lean-to.

2. Where did the boys go to camp?
   a. the narrator's backyard
   b. Ebbets Field
   c. George Washington Bridge
   *d. the Palisades

3. Two of the boys leaped off the train at the last minute because
   a. Max started crying.
   b. the narrator got scared.
   *c. Horse forgot his mattress.
   d. their compass did not work.

4. The boys crossed the George Washington Bridge because they
   *a. would not admit they were afraid.
   b. had no other way to get home.
   c. took the wrong train.
   d. did not know how to read a compass.

5. At the end of the story, the boys agreed that they would
   a. try to go camping again soon.
   b. claim they had completed the overnight hike.
   c. quit the Boy Scouts.
   *d. not tell Mr. Brenkman about their trip.

Nadia the Willful
Test Generator

1. Nadia is known as "the Willful" because of her
   a. positive attitude.
   b. sense of humor.
   *c. stubborn temper.
   d. kind-hearted nature.

2. Hamed's death appears to have been the result of
   a. a murder.
   *b. an accident.
   c. an act of war.
   d. old age.

3. After losing Hamed, the sheik's attitude toward his people becomes
   *a. harder.
   b. weaker.
   c. more fearful.
   d. more understanding.

4. How does not talking about Hamed make Nadia feel?
   *a. sad
   b. guilty
   c. proud
   d. mature

5. What is the key to bringing Hamed back to life?
   a. forgiving Hamed
   b. accepting things as they are
   c. respecting the authority of the law
   *d. remembering and talking about Hamed

Part Two
Matthew Henson at the Top of the World
Test Generator

1. The selection suggests that the death of Henson's parents led him to
   a. become determined to be famous.
   b. take many unnecessary risks.
   *c. become independent at a young age.
   d. withdraw from other people.

2. Captain Childs treated Henson as if Henson were his
   *a. son.
   b. business partner.
   c. rival.
   d. best friend.

3. Henson quit his job on the *Katie Hines* when
   a. he went to live with his uncle.
   *b. Captain Childs died.
   c. he took a job in a restaurant.
   d. Peary asked him to join his expedition.

4. Henson first traveled with Peary to
   a. Greenland.
   b. China.
   c. Russia.
   *d. Nicaragua.

5. What was Henson's first impression of Peary?
  *a. Henson thought that he and Peary were very much alike.
  b. Henson thought Peary was too bossy and demanding.
  c. Henson thought that he had more skills and experience than Peary.
  d. Henson thought that Peary was too proud and self-centered.

6. What did Peary do when the expedition reached the North Pole?
  a. He claimed that he reached the North Pole without Henson.
  b. He did some scientific experiments.
  *c. He took measurements to prove he had reached the North Pole.
  d. He thanked Henson for his help.

7. The author of this selection suggests that Henson was someone who
  *a. kept going when things went wrong.
  b. always tried to help others.
  c. mostly cared about having fun.
  d. blamed others for his problems.

Summer of Fire
Test Generator

1. Before the summer of 1988, what did many people assume about wilderness fires in Yellowstone Park?
  *a. They could burn safely until a rainstorm extinguished them.
  b. They could be prevented by closing the park to visitors.
  c. They were harmful to the plants and animals that were native to the park.
  d. They should be extinguished immediately by fire fighters.

2. Fire spread especially quickly in Yellowstone during the summer of 1988 because
  a. there was little water for fighting fires.
  b. the forest areas were so large.
  c. few fire fighters were available.
  *d. the forests were dry and burned easily.

3. The policy in Yellowstone Park was to put out a fire only if it
  a. burned more than 100 acres.
  b. was started by a lightning strike.
  *c. endangered lives or property.
  d. might destroy scenic views.

4. By mid-July, officials at Yellowstone Park decided that
  a. animals should be moved.
  b. dead trees should be cut down.
  *c. all fires should be put out.
  d. the park should be closed.

5. Which of these prevented the Old Faithful Inn from being destroyed by fire?
  a. Fire fighters extinguished the fire with water.
  *b. The wind shifted and changed the fire's direction.
  c. The fire went out when a heavy rain fell.
  d. Chemicals dropped from helicopters put out the fire.

6. What was the result of the fires of 1988 in Yellowstone Park?
  a. Most of the geysers and steam vents were destroyed.
  b. Many park communities were badly damaged.
  *c. About one-third of the park was burned.
  d. Rare species of plant life were wiped out.

Ghost of the Lagoon
Test Generator

1. The people of Bora Bora most likely leave presents for Tupa to
  a. keep him nearby.
  *b. make sure he is never hungry.
  c. show him respect and honor.
  d. make him dependent on them.

2. Mako values Afa mainly because Afa
  a. keeps Mako out of danger.
  *b. is a constant companion to him.
  c. helps him find food.
  d. was once his father's dog.

3. Mako imagined that the coral reef he passed
   on his way to the island was
   a. a canoe.
   b. fruit to be harvested.
   *c. Tupa.
   d. a school of fish.

4. At the instant Mako attacked Tupa, he drew his
   strength and courage mostly from his desire to
   a. take revenge for his father's death.
   b. collect the king's reward.
   *c. save Afa's life.
   d. prove himself to his mother.

5. The main conflict in this story is between
   a. Tupa and Afa.
   b. Tupa and Mako's father.
   c. Mako and Afa.
   *d. Mako and Tupa.

6. Which would be the best title for the song that
   Mako's grandfather sings at the end of the story?
   a. "Hard Times"
   b. "A Boy and His Dog"
   c. "Tupa the Man Eater"
   *d. "Mako the Ghost Slayer"

from The Fun of It
Test Generator

1. For most of the flight described in this selection,
   where was Earhart flying?
   a. over the countryside of Ireland
   b. along the coast of the United States
   *c. across the Atlantic Ocean
   d. from New York to Newfoundland

2. Earhart had to reduce her altitude several
   times because
   a. she was low on fuel.
   b. her altimeter wasn't working.
   c. the clouds were very dense.
   *d. her plane iced up.

3. What did Earhart do when she saw that her
   exhaust system had a broken weld?
   a. She made a temporary repair.
   *b. She ignored the problem.
   c. She switched off the engine and glided.
   d. She made an emergency landing.

4. Where did Earhart land her plane?
   a. on a beach
   b. in a landing field
   *c. in a meadow
   d. on a road

5. According to Earhart, which instrument enabled
   her to fly successfully through thick fog?
   *a. the gyro compass
   b. the altimeter
   c. the tachometer
   d. the fuel gauge

6. Which statement best describes Earhart during
   the flight?
   a. She was reckless and pushed hard to set
      a new record with the flight.
   b. She was frightened and in danger for most
      of the flight.
   *c. She made calm and confident judgments
      throughout the flight.
   d. She mostly relaxed and enjoyed all she
      could see during the flight. 7.   Earhart's
      comments in this account are mostly about
   *a. the flying conditions she encounters.
   b. her growing fame as a pilot.
   c. the need for better airplanes.
   d. her love of flying.

Older Run
Test Generator

1. Why was Paulsen making the run he describes
   in this selection?
   a. He was delivering supplies.
   b. He was on a trapping expedition.
   *c. He was training Cookie's pups.
   d. He was racing against another team.

2. Paulsen knew that it was risky to make the run
   *a. with so many dogs.
   b. at night.
   c. without a partner.
   d. along the railroad grades.

3. As the run began, Paulsen was feeling
   a. nervous and uncertain.
   *b. confident and relaxed.
   c. weary and depressed.
   d. surprised and grateful.

4. What had snowmobilers done to the railroad trestles to make the trestles passable?
   a. attached rails to the sides
   b. paved them with tar
   c. pulled off the railroad ties
   *d. covered them with plywood boards

5. Where did Paulsen land when the sled stopped?
   a. in the river
   *b. in a snow bank
   c. on the dogs' backs
   d. in the woods

6. Paulsen could not turn the sled around on the trestle because
   a. the sled runners were broken.
   b. the pups were fighting.
   c. Cookie was frozen with fear.
   *d. the trestle was too narrow.

7. When Cookie ran off, Paulsen felt
   a. relieved.
   *b. betrayed.
   c. amused.
   d. frightened.

8. What made Paulsen think Cookie had brought the dogs back to him?
   a. They returned together.
   *b. They all had been bitten on their ears.
   c. They returned immediately.
   d. They seemed upset and tired.

from Woodsong

Test Generator

1. The bears that came to Paulsen's home were most often a threat to
   *a. the dogs.
   b. the goats.
   c. the chickens.
   d. Paulsen and his wife.

2. Paulsen would say his trouble with Scarhead happened mostly because he
   a. fed his dogs food that attracted bears.
   b. burned trash when bears could smell it.
   *c. became too relaxed about having bears around.
   d. kept yard animals that were afraid of bears.

3. Paulsen became angry when he saw that Scarhead had
   a. found the dogs' food.
   b. frightened the goats.
   *c. ripped apart the burn enclosure.
   d. eaten tomatoes from the garden.

4. Paulsen suggests that Scarhead did not attack him because Paulsen was
   a. a good source of food.
   *b. not worth the trouble.
   c. sorry for what he had done.
   d. a dangerous enemy.

5. Paulsen almost shot Scarhead because he wanted to
   a. save his own life.
   b. warn other bears to stay away from his home.
   c. protect his yard animals.
   *d. get even with Scarhead for threatening him.

6. What feeling toward Scarhead does Paulsen express at the end of the selection?
   a. fear
   b. resentment
   c. love
   *d. respect

UNIT TWO

Part One
I'm Nobody! Who Are You?
It Seems I Test People
Growing Pains
Test Generator

1. In "I'm Nobody! Who Are You?" the speaker compares being a well-known person to being
   a. a nobody.
   *b. a frog.
   c. a bog.
   d. an advertisement.

2. How does the speaker in "I'm Nobody! Who Are You?" feel about being a "nobody"?
   a. determined to be famous someday
   b. sad but accepting
   *c. completely contented
   d. ashamed

3. In "It Seems I Test People," the speaker seems to feel that he is
   a. just like everyone else.
   *b. bigger and louder than most people.
   c. meaner and more dangerous than others.
   d. kinder and gentler than other people.

4. The speaker in "It Seems I Test People" suggests that he makes people feel
   a. happy.
   b. bored.
   *c. uncomfortable.
   d. frightened.

5. In "It Seems I Test People," what do other people do when the speaker appears?
   a. They laugh.
   b. They argue.
   c. They applaud.
   *d. They leave.

6. When the speaker in "Growing Pains" says "I'm just a kid," she most likely means
   *a. "I'm not ready to deal with this."
   b. "I'm immature for my age."
   c. "I'll do the best I can, but kids can't do much."
   d. "I'm tired of being treated like a kid."

7. In "Growing Pains," the speaker finds it unusual to need to
   a. hide from her mother.
   b. talk with her mother.
   c. fight with her mother.
   *d. comfort her mother.

Three Haiku
Test Generator

1. In the haiku by Patterson, what is really on Grandmother's knees?
   *a. sunlight
   b. a shadow
   c. a yellow quilt
   d. yellow clothing

2. In which of the following do the lines follow a five–seven–five syllable pattern?
   a. the haiku by Bashō
   b. the haiku by Issa
   c. the haiku by Patterson
   *d. none of the three haiku

3. Using these haiku as examples, a reader can tell that a haiku communicates
   a. a story.
   *b. an image and a feeling.
   c. a problem and a solution.
   d. a question and an answer.

4. Which word best describes the mood of the poem by Bashō?
   *a. questioning
   b. grateful
   c. ashamed
   d. grief stricken

5. The mood of Patterson's poem is
   a. worried and scared.
   b. cool and unemotional.
   *c. tender and loving.
   d. teasing and naughty.

6. What is Issa's poem about?
   a. a beautiful scene in nature that makes the viewer feel sad and empty
   b. a rare and strange event in nature
   *c. a common scene viewed in an unusual way
   d. a beautiful woman hiding behind a paper screen

All Summer in a Day
Test Generator

1. What kind of mood are the children in at the beginning of the story?
   a. sad because they cannot remember the sun
   b. bored because they are tired of hearing about the sun
   c. afraid because they are going to see the sun
   *d. excited because they have been prepared to see the sun

2. In the poem she writes, Margot compares the sun to
   *a. a flower.
   b. a jungle.
   c. an old photograph.
   d. a bead necklace.

3. What is the children's main impression when the rain first stops?
   a. the color of the sky
   b. the warmth of the sun
   c. the freshness of the air
   *d. the silence of the world

4. The people in this future world are unable to
   a. travel to other planets.
   b. build underground cities.
   c. create artificial sunshine.
   *d. control the weather.

5. How do Margot's classmates feel at the end of the story?
   a. angry and cruel
   b. joyous and forgetful
   *c. sad and ashamed
   d. calm and peaceful

Chinatown *from* The Lost Garden
Test Generator

1. In the Chinatown that Yep remembers, greenery was
   a. plentiful and carefully maintained.
   b. plentiful but out of control.
   c. not appreciated.
   *d. hard to find.

2. In his youth, what was Yep's experience of Chinatown?
   a. He both lived and went to school there.
   b. He neither lived nor went to school there.
   c. He lived there but went to school in a wealthy, white neighborhood.
   *d. He went to school in Chinatown, but he lived outside it.

3. Yep tells about the time he went with his friend Harold to deliver newspapers to a Nob Hill hotel in order to
   a. show that Chinese Americans felt free and relaxed when they entered the white world.
   b. show how rare it was for Chinese Americans to be allowed to work outside Chinatown.
   *c. contrast the different worlds that existed in San Francisco.
   d. demonstrate that life was basically the same for Chinese Americans and white Americans living in San Francisco.

4. What made Yep feel different from his school friends?
   a. He was Chinese, but most of them were not.
   *b. Most of them spoke Chinese, but he did not.
   c. He had to work after school, but most of them did not.
   d. He loved music and singing, but most of them did not.

5. Yep's difficulties in sports were caused by people who
   a. thought he had no skills.
   b. would not give him a chance to try.
   *c. expected him to do better than he could do.
   d. resented the fact that he was a better athlete than they were.

6. Yep's main concern as a child had to do with confusion about
   a. what he wanted to do with his life.
   b. why he had so much trouble with his schoolwork.
   *c. who he was and where he fit in.
   d. where his family had come from.

Part Two
Aaron's Gift
Test Generator

1. Aaron's grandmother crumbles up her breakfast rolls because she
   a. doesn't like them.
   b. is too worried about Aaron to eat.
   c. is having bad memories of her childhood.
   *d. wants to share them with the birds.

2. Why does Aaron's mother want him to stay away from the boys in the club?
   *a. She doesn't like the boys.
   b. She is punishing Aaron for coming home late.
   c. She is worried about Pidge.
   d. She thinks Aaron should spend his free time caring for his grandmother.

3. The Cossacks didn't kill anyone in Aaron's grandmother's family because the Cossacks
   a. felt sorry for the children in the family.
   *b. didn't know the family was there.
   c. only killed animals, such as the family's goat.
   d. were frightened away by the men in the family.

4. Aaron wants to join Carl's gang because he wants to
   a. get into trouble.
   b. rescue wild animals.
   *c. have the feeling of belonging.
   d. make the gang members better people.

5. The boys in the club want to use Pidge as a
   a. mascot.
   b. message carrier.
   c. pet.
   *d. sacrifice.

6. How does the grandmother feel at the end of the story?
   *a. proud of Aaron for standing up to the gang
   b. distressed because the pigeon is lost
   c. disappointed in Aaron for sneaking out
   d. scared because she is reminded of the Cossacks

The Circuit
Test Generator

1. What is the mood at the beginning of the story, as work in the strawberry fields comes to an end?
   a. joyous
   b. despairing
   c. angry
   *d. weary

2. What does Papa's attitude toward his car show about him?
   a. He is easygoing and irresponsible.
   b. He knows nothing about automobiles.
   *c. He is extremely careful with what little money he has.
   d. He is ashamed of having such an old car.

3. Why is it Mama instead of Papa who talks to the owner of the labor camp in Fresno?
   *a. She speaks English.
   b. She is braver than Papa.
   c. She is in charge of the family.
   d. She thinks Papa's rude manners will anger the owner.

4. The narrator's parents do not send him to school during grape-picking season because they
   a. are greedy.
   b. do not realize that school has started.
   c. think school is a waste of time for Panchito.
   *d. need the money their son can bring in.

5. Why doesn't Roberto go to school when Panchito does?
   a. He has already graduated from high school.
   b. He doesn't care about getting an education.
   *c. His family needs the money he can earn from picking cotton.
   d. His school doesn't start till later in the year.

6. The attention he gets from Mr. Lema makes the narrator feel
   a. embarrassed.
   *b. happy.
   c. suspicious.
   d. resentful.

7. Because the narrator's family is moving away from Fresno, he won't be able to learn to
   a. speak English.
   b. read.
   *c. play the trumpet.
   d. write stories.

8. The attitude of Panchito's parents to their life seems to be
   a. joyous and energetic.
   b. angry and rebellious.
   *c. tired but accepting.
   d. calm but ambitious for change.

Oh Broom, Get to Work
Test Generator

1. When Yoshiko comes home with the dead bird and finds her mother with a visitor, she feels
   a. delighted.
   b. confused.
   c. embarrassed.
   *d. frustrated.

2. Why does Yoshiko want her mother to help her bury the bird?
   a. She is afraid of dead creatures.
   b. She isn't strong enough to dig a grave by herself.
   *c. Her mother could make up a better prayer.
   d. Her mother could make a cross for the grave.

3. Yoshiko thinks that Reverend Kimura and his songs are
   *a. entertaining.
   b. foolish.
   c. dull.
   d. pompous.

4. When young men come to the house as guests, Yoshiko's father likes to
   a. introduce them to Yoshiko.
   *b. give them advice.
   c. give them vitamins and herbs.
   d. lend them money.

5. Yoshiko thinks that most of the visitors are
   a. fascinating.
   *b. boring.
   c. filthy.
   d. amusing.

6. What do their parents seem to expect from Yoshiko and Keiko when guests arrive?
   *a. They are expected to help out with guests but are not expected to be perfectly behaved.
   b. They are expected to be friendly to the guests and are punished if they giggle or leave the room.
   c. They are required to excuse themselves whenever guests arrive.
   d. They are required to sit with guests but are forbidden from talking.

7. At Yoshiko's, meals with guests are often times of
   *a. fun.
   b. silence.
   c. fighting.
   d. homesickness and sadness.

Western Wagons
Night Journey
Test Generator

1. In "Western Wagons," what do the writers seem to feel toward the Western pioneers?
   *a. admiration
   b. pity
   c. dislike
   d. irritation

2. How are the pioneers pictured in "Western Wagons"?
   a. They have never traveled before, but now they are getting ready to leave home.
   b. They have traveled before but failed to tame the land they reached.
   *c. They have settled land once but are still hungry for a new frontier.
   d. They have had the experience of being pioneers in the past and now are content to stay where they are.

3. What is the attitude of the pioneers in "Western Wagons" toward the dangers of the trail?
   a. They don't believe there will be any dangers.
   b. They fear the dangers and don't want to make the trip because of them.
   c. They are completely confident that they will survive any dangers.
   *d. They know the dangers are real but choose to go and face them.

4. In the line from "Western Wagons," "With <u>banjo</u> <u>and with frying</u> pan—Susanna, don't you cry," which underlined syllable is stressed?

   *a. ban
   b. jo
   c. and
   d. ing

5. What is true of the rhyme pattern in "Night Journey"?

   a. Each pair of lines rhymes.
   b. In each set of five lines, the first and fifth lines rhyme and the second and fourth lines rhyme.
   c. In each set of four lines, the second and fourth lines rhyme.
   *d. Many of the lines rhyme, but there is no regular rhyming pattern.

6. What does the poet mean when he writes, "My muscles move with steel"?

   a. The speaker is very strong.
   b. The berth is hard and hurts the speaker's muscles.
   *c. The speaker feels his body move with the train.
   d. The speaker is moving his home.

UNIT THREE

Part One
Damon and Pythias
Test Generator

1. The king of Sicily was a
   a. weak leader.
   b. just lawmaker.
   c. loyal friend.
   *d. cruel tyrant.

2. How were Damon and Pythias different from the other people of Sicily?
   *a. They dared to speak out against the king.
   b. They thought the laws of the country were unfair.
   c. They used violence to try to change the government.
   d. They believed that the king was a great ruler.

3. Pythias wanted to leave prison to
   a. seek help from other citizens.
   *b. settle things for his mother and sister.
   c. make money to leave to Damon.
   d. try to escape the country.

4. Damon asked the king to
   a. set Pythias free forever.
   b. support Pythias's family.
   *c. let him take Pythias's place in prison for a while.
   d. let him stay in prison with his friend.

5. When the robbers tied him up, Pythias was
   *a. desperate to return to Damon.
   b. relieved that he might be saved from execution.
   c. terrified that the robbers would kill him.
   d. worried that the king would punish him.

6. Just before Damon's execution was to be carried out, he felt
   a. terrified.
   b. bitter.
   c. defiant.
   *d. willing.

7. At the end of the play, the king realized that the most important thing in the world was
   a. power.
   b. gold.
   c. cleverness.
   *d. loyalty.

Cricket in the Road
Test Generator

1. "Cricket in the Road" is told through the eyes of
   *a. Selo.
   b. Vern.
   c. Amy.
   d. Vern and Amy's mother.

2. At the beginning of the story when Vern yells, "Selo! Selo! First bat!" he means
   a. "You bat first!"
   *b. "I get to bat first!"
   c. "Let's decide who gets to bat first."
   d. "First get the bat so we can play!"

3. Whenever there is a thunderstorm, Selo
   a. tries to drink the falling rain.
   b. plays in the mud.
   c. sings a song.
   *d. hides under his bed.

4. What does Selo do with the old cricket bat and ball?
   a. He throws them at Vern and Amy.
   b. He replaces them with new equipment.
   *c. He throws them into some bushes.
   d. He keeps them in his room.

5. The most likely reason that Selo's heart thumps violently when he sees Vern and Amy again is that he
   a. is still angry with them.
   b. didn't realize they were still around.
   c. thinks they will hit him with the new bat.
   *d. wants so badly to be friends again.

6. What will most likely happen after Selo stops crying at the end of the story?
   *a. The three friends will play cricket.
   b. Amy will seize the bat and run away.
   c. Rain will suddenly begin to fall.
   d. Vern will laugh at Selo for being such a baby.

The Quarrel
Fable
Test Generator

1. The climax of the plot in "The Quarrel" occurs when
   a. the brother and the speaker argue.
   b. the afternoon turns black.
   *c. the brother apologizes.
   d. the speaker takes the blame.

2. What does the speaker of "The Quarrel" mean when she says, "The afternoon turned black"?
   *a. The brother and the speaker felt miserable all afternoon.
   b. The sky turned dark during the afternoon.
   c. The afternoon quickly turned into night.
   d. No one could remember what happened that afternoon.

3. In "The Quarrel," the brother thumped the speaker on the back as a way to
   a. hurt the speaker.
   b. wake the speaker from sleep.
   *c. show affection.
   d. get attention.

4. In "Fable," the squirrel seems to think that he or she is
   a. weak and disgraced.
   *b. small but skilled.
   c. pretty and wise.
   d. a "Little Prig."

5. Which proverb best sums up the theme of "Fable"?
   a. He who laughs last, laughs best.
   *b. It takes all kinds to make a world.
   c. Beauty is skin deep.
   d. Look before you leap.

6. How does the squirrel show his or her sense of fairness to the mountain?
   *a. by acknowledging the mountain's good points
   b. by refusing to quarrel with the mountain
   c. by saying that the mountain is better because it is bigger
   d. by offering to teach the mountain new skills

Part Two
Abd al-Rahman Ibrahima
Test Generator

1. What did Ibrahima's people expect him to be when he came of age?
   a. a teacher
   b. a farmer
   *c. a political leader
   d. a physician

2. The selection suggests that the Fula helped Dr. Cox because they
   *a. felt sorry for him.
   b. were afraid of him.
   c. wanted him to take them back to his country.
   d. thought he had riches they could steal.

3. When the slave ships landed in America, the slaves were given clothing and medical treatment so that
   a. they would be more comfortable.
   b. no one would guess that they had been mistreated.
   c. they would not try to run away.
   *d. they would bring a higher price.

4. The story suggests that Thomas Foster called Ibrahima "Prince" in order to
   a. show Ibrahima respect.
   b. show Ibrahima affection.
   c. impress other slave owners.
   *d. mock Ibrahima.

5. At first Ibrahima reacted to slavery by
   a. accepting his condition humbly.
   *b. refusing to work.
   c. leading a revolt.
   d. trying to locate Dr. Cox.

6. What was it about Ibrahima that made him interesting to Andrew Marschalk and others to whom Cox told Ibrahima's story?
   a. his education
   b. his intelligence
   *c. his royal background
   d. his appearance

7. The story suggests that Foster at first refused the government's request to release Ibrahima because Foster did not want to
   *a. think of Africans as civilized people.
   b. help the U.S. government.
   c. lose a good worker.
   d. be unfair to his other slaves.

from The Story of My Life
Test Generator

1. From Helen Keller's perspective, Anne Sullivan's greatest gift to her was
   a. an understanding of language.
   b. a doll.
   *c. love.
   d. travel.

2. Why did Helen break the doll that Miss Sullivan had brought?
   a. She was angry that it had been made by blind children.
   b. She confused it with her big rag doll.
   c. She was upset that she couldn't tell what it looked like.
   *d. She was frustrated by a lesson Miss Sullivan was trying to teach.

3. This selection suggests that if a person has no language, the person cannot
   a. move well.
   *b. have clear thoughts.
   c. feel strong emotions.
   d. sense change.

4. What happened when Helen felt the well water on her hand?
   *a. She realized that the word "w-a-t-e-r" stood for water.
   b. She got thirsty.
   c. She thought that Miss Sullivan was trying to punish her for the doll.
   d. She realized that water was for bathing as well as drinking.

5. What filled Helen with energy and hope at the end of the selection?
   a. the realization that Miss Sullivan was staying
   *b. the understanding of language
   c. the realization that the doll could be repaired
   d. the belief that she would soon regain her sight

Street Corner Flight
Words Like Freedom
Test Generator

1. At the beginning of "Street Corner Flight," how are the two boys like the pigeons?
   a. They are fat.
   b. They move like the wind.
   c. They are free.
   *d. They are trapped.

2. In "Street Corner Flight," what happens to the pigeons?
   a. They escape.
   *b. They are let go.
   c. They die.
   d. Their wings are damaged.

3. "Street Corner Flight" suggests that the neighborhood where the boys live is
   a. poor but cozy and friendly.
   b. an area where there are few people.
   *c. full of sadness and limitations.
   d. full of excitement and possibility.

4. In "Words Like Freedom," what does the speaker mean by the phrase, "On my heartstrings freedom sings"?
   a. I am someone who sings songs about freedom.
   b. I care more about matters of the heart than about freedom.
   c. I think that a lack of freedom has damaged my health.
   *d. I care deeply about freedom.

5. The speaker in "Words Like Freedom" implies that he or she is different from the reader in that he or she is
   a. smarter.
   *b. more appreciative.
   c. happier.
   d. more easygoing.

The School Play
Test Generator

1. Belinda is best known among the other students for being
   a. funny.
   *b. tough.
   c. smart.
   d. polite.

2. Mrs. Bunnin gave speaking roles to those who scored well on a spelling test because she wanted to cast actors who
   a. spoke loudly and clearly.
   *b. would remember their lines.
   c. would take their roles seriously.
   d. could take time away from their studies.

3. On the day before the play, Robert feels
   a. terrified.
   b. bored.
   c. nervous.
   *d. confident.

4. Before going on stage, Belinda tries to make sure Robert does well by
   *a. scaring him.
   b. teasing him.
   c. encouraging him.
   d. going over his lines with him.

5. During the play, Belinda's behavior shows that her attitude toward performing is
   *a. serious.
   b. careless.
   c. silly.
   d. shy.

6. When the performance is over, Mrs. Bunnin feels
   a. numb.
   b. embarrassed.
   c. furious.
   *d. satisfied.

Ode to My Library
Test Generator

1. The speaker's attitude toward the library is one of
   a. dislike.
   b. shy awe.
   c. lack of interest.
   *d. pride.

2. The library is described as very
   *a. small.
   b. dusty.
   c. noisy.
   d. fancy.

3. What does the speaker dream of doing?
   a. visiting his grandparents' ranch
   b. taking his grandparents to Mexico
   *c. bringing his grandparents to the library
   d. painting a mural of his grandparents

4. What does the speaker admire about the Aztec warrior?
   a. his kindness
   *b. his power
   c. his intelligence
   d. his gentleness

5. The speaker is most likely
   a. rich.
   b. naughty and rebellious.
   *c. a good student.
   d. sophisticated.

The Jacket

Test Generator

1. According to the narrator, boys in fifth and sixth grades wanted most to be
   a. feared by others.
   *b. popular with the girls.
   c. skilled in sports.
   d. admired for being smart.

2. What kind of jacket did Soto ask for?
   a. a vinyl jacket
   *b. a leather jacket
   c. a down jacket
   d. a wool jacket

3. What is the most likely reason why Soto wore the green jacket?
   a. He secretly liked it.
   b. His mother was a mean person who would punish him severely if he complained about the jacket.
   c. He wanted to look ugly so girls would leave him alone.
   *d. He knew his family was too poor to afford a new jacket, no matter how he felt about it.

4. Which of the following conclusions is most likely false?
   *a. All Soto's problems were caused by the jacket.
   b. Some people thought Soto's jacket was ugly.
   c. Soto's mother was trying to do her best.
   d. There were families poorer than Soto's family.

5. Which word best describes the narrator of "The Jacket"?
   a. confident
   b. naughty
   *c. lonely
   d. successful

UNIT FOUR

Part One
Lob's Girl
Test Generator

1. Why did Lob jump through the Pengellys' window?
   a. He smelled Mrs. Pengelly's puddings.
   *b. He was looking for Sandy.
   c. He was chasing a stick Sandy threw.
   d. He was trying to find Mr. Dodsworth.

2. Sandy went to the train station to
   *a. see Lob once more before he left.
   b. say good-bye to Mr. Dodsworth.
   c. ask Mr. Dodsworth to give up Lob.
   d. invite Lob and Mr. Dodsworth to visit soon.

3. Each time Lob returned to Sandy, her main reaction was a feeling of
   a. annoyance.
   b. embarrassment.
   c. fear.
   *d. joy.

4. Mr. Dodsworth gave Lob to the Pengellys because he
   a. was too old to take care of a dog.
   *b. knew Lob would be happy only with Sandy.
   c. realized he did not like Lob.
   d. did not have enough money to feed Lob.

5. Who first found Sandy after she was hit by the truck?
   a. Lob
   b. her brother Don
   c. Aunt Becky
   *d. Dr. Travers and his wife

6. Just after the accident, Sandy's brother discovered that Lob was
   a. looking for Sandy at the beach.
   b. waiting for Sandy at home.
   *c. killed by the truck.
   d. taken to the hospital.

7. What question is left unanswered at the end of the story?
   a. How did the accident happen?
   b. What became of the driver of the truck?
   c. Where did Don go on the night of the accident?
   *d. Was it really Lob that appeared at the hospital?

My First Dive with the Dolphins
Test Generator

1. Before taking the job at Marine World, the writer has been trained to
   *a. be a scuba diver.
   b. communicate with dolphins.
   c. be a marine scientist.
   d. clean algae from tanks.

2. How is the writer feeling as he gets ready for his first dive?
   a. scared and worried
   *b. awkward and uncertain
   c. confident and relaxed
   d. excited and happy

3. To avoid being harmed by a charging dolphin, the writer
   a. waves the dolphin away.
   b. offers food to the dolphin.
   *c. freezes where he is.
   d. swims to another part of the tank.

4. The writer would probably describe Ernestine, the smallest dolphin, as
   *a. playful.
   b. shy.
   c. fearful.
   d. aggressive.

5. The writer understands that it is important to show Lucky, "the king bull," that the writer
   a. is afraid of Lucky's strength.
   b. wants to be Lucky's friend.
   c. is as intelligent as Lucky.
   *d. respects Lucky's territory.

6. The dolphin probably makes the "klonking" sound for which purpose?
   *a. as a warning
   b. to express happiness
   c. as a friendly greeting
   d. to ask for food

7. For the writer, what part of the experience he describes is "magic"?
   a. staying underwater for hours at a time
   b. cleaning algae off the tank floor
   c. learning the dolphin's names
   *d. coming face to face with the dolphins

8. The writer's main purpose for writing this essay is to
   a. give scientific information about dolphins.
   b. persuade others to take an interest in dolphins.
   *c. describe his personal experiences with dolphins.
   d. compare dolphins with other animals.

Something Told the Wild Geese
Questioning Faces
Test Generator

1. In "Something Told the Wild Geese," the geese will fly because they want to
   *a. find a warm winter home.
   b. escape from people.
   c. find a place to die.
   d. warn other geese of trouble.

2. In "Something Told the Wild Geese," the word "something" refers to
   a. other animals.
   b. human voices.
   *c. the geese's instincts.
   d. ancient beliefs.

3. In "Something Told the Wild Geese," the orchards are sagging because
   a. the geese are there.
   *b. the branches are loaded with fruit.
   c. the trees are old and weak.
   d. snow has bent the branches.

4. In "Questioning Faces," the owl was probably flying
   a. over a pond.
   b. in a forest.
   c. over a mountain.
   *d. near a house.

5. In "Questioning Faces," the owl's movements are best described as
   a. small and careful.
   b. slow and graceful.
   *c. sudden and sharp.
   d. weak and unsteady.

Zlateh the Goat
Test Generator

1. Aaron's father decided to sell Zlateh to a
   a. farmer.
   *b. butcher.
   c. furrier.
   d. shopkeeper.

2. Aaron agreed to take Zlateh to the town mostly because he
   *a. felt he must obey his father.
   b. was anxious to buy Hanukkah supplies.
   c. was glad to get rid of Zlateh.
   d. hoped to have an adventurous journey.

3. Aaron and Zlateh were forced to take shelter in a
   a. cave.
   b. barn.
   *c. haystack.
   d. cottage.

4. What happens to Aaron during the time he and Zlateh spend in the shelter?
   a. He grows resentful of Zlateh for the trouble she has caused him.
   b. He feels frightened and completely alone.
   c. He thinks only of his family.
   *d. He comes to love Zlateh more deeply than before.

5. Throughout the story, Zlateh's behavior is best described as
   a. frightened and suspicious.
   b. frisky and high-spirited.
   c. slow and stubborn.
   *d. patient and trusting.

6. The climax of the story occurs when
   a. Aaron starts out for the town with Zlateh.
   b. snow begins falling on Aaron and Zlateh.
   *c. Aaron decides never to part with Zlateh.
   d. Aaron's family includes Zlateh in their Hanukkah celebration.

7. What lesson does Aaron learn in this story?
   a. Depend only on yourself.
   *b. Love will provide.
   c. Trust in the wisdom of adults.
   d. Fear is the strongest emotion.

Part Two
The Phantom Tollbooth
Test Generator

1. What is inside the package that Milo opens at the beginning of the play?
   a. a toy car
   b. a talking clock
   *c. a turnpike tollbooth
   d. a package of letters

2. To get out of the Doldrums, Milo has to
   a. rest.
   *b. think.
   c. make noise.
   d. eat.

3. In Dictionopolis, Milo meets
   *a. King Azaz.
   b. the Lethargarians.
   c. the Whether Man.
   d. Rhyme and Reason.

4. What does Azaz give to Milo for protection on his journey?
   a. the sounds of laughter
   b. some sparkling numbers
   c. a pencil
   *d. a bag of letters

5. According to Dischord, what is the most valuable thing in the world?
   a. reason
   b. words
   *c. noise
   d. time

6. What is unusual about the stew that Mathemagician serves to Milo, Tock, and Humbug?
   *a. The more stew they eat, the hungrier they feel.
   b. The stew is delicious, but they cannot make themselves eat it.
   c. A tiny amount of stew is more than enough for everyone.
   d. They eat and eat, but they never empty their bowls.

7. Milo rescues Rhyme and Reason by
   a. drawing a door with his magic staff.
   b. climbing through an open window.
   c. knocking down the castle wall.
   *d. spelling E-N-T-R-A-N-C-E to make a door.

8. By the end of the play, Milo
   a. knows all there is to know.
   *b. has become enthusiastic about learning.
   c. has gotten sick of numbers and words.
   d. is too old to go to school.

The Walrus and the Carpenter
Fairy Lullaby
Test Generator

1. In "The Walrus and the Carpenter," when the moon sees that the sun is shining at night, the moon is
   a. frightened.
   *b. annoyed.
   c. grateful.
   d. amazed.

2. What do the Walrus and the Carpenter dislike about the beach?
   *a. the sand
   b. the sun
   c. the fish
   d. the birds

3. What happens to the Oysters at the end of the poem?
   a. They run away from the Walrus and the Carpenter.
   b. They return to the sea.
   *c. They are eaten by the Walrus and the Carpenter.
   d. They play in the sand.

4. Why is it odd for the Walrus to be crying in the next-to-last stanza?
   a. The Walrus has not shown any emotion before.
   b. It is the Carpenter, not the Walrus, that should cry.
   *c. The Walrus has caused the problem that makes him sad.
   d. The poem describes only joyful events.

5. The fairies in "Fairy Lullaby" can best be described as
   a. evil.
   *b. protective.
   c. afraid.
   d. carefree.

6. "Fairy Lullaby" is sung by
   a. a queen.
   b. spiders.
   c. a newt.
   *d. fairies.

Three Limericks
Test Generator

1. In the limerick by Prelutsky, what happens after Ben swallows his watch?
   a. He eats his plate.
   b. He ticks.
   *c. He coughs up the date.
   d. He chimes.

2. In Prelutsky's limerick, Ben's actions seem
   a. brave.
   *b. ridiculous.
   c. clever.
   d. dull.

3. According to Nash's limerick, which of these is most important to Dougal MacDougal?
   *a. saving money
   b. becoming a great musician
   c. owning a fine bugle
   d. inventing new things

4. In Nash's limerick, what does Dougal MacDougal do?
   a. He sings.
   b. He hums.
   c. He snores.
   *d. He sneezes.

5. What happens to the old man in Lear's limerick?
   a. He sings to birds.
   *b. He finds birds in his beard.
   c. He gets stuck in a nest.
   d. He shaves off his beard.

The Fun They Had
Test Generator

1. What makes "The Fun They Had" a work of science fiction?
   a. It has an imaginary setting.
   *b. It tells how technology might be used in the future.
   c. It has characters that are made up.
   d. It describes events that actually happened.

2. Which of these was a new experience for Margie?
   *a. reading a book on paper
   b. using a computer
   c. doing schoolwork
   d. writing in a diary

3. Margie was doing worse and worse in geography because
   a. she refused to study.
   *b. the lessons were too advanced.
   c. she was not very bright.
   d. the lessons were boring.

4. When the county inspector repaired the mechanical teacher, Margie was
   a. relieved.
   b. impressed.
   c. surprised.
   *d. disappointed.

5. Margie finds it hard to believe that
   a. math lessons could be difficult.
   b. a computer could break down.
   *c. a man could be a teacher.
   d. children did homework in the old days.

6. Margie decides that school was fun for children in the old days mostly because the children
   a. read lots of books.
   b. studied different subjects.
   c. never had tests.
   *d. learned with other children.

The Sand Castle
Test Generator

1. In this story, the children wear special clothing and gloves to protect themselves from
   a. the sand.
   *b. the sun's burning rays.
   c. freezing temperatures.
   d. ozone in the air.

2. When Mrs. Pavloff was a girl, how did she feel about the sea?
   *a She loved it.
   b. She thought it was a sad, lonesome place.
   c. She thought it was pretty but boring.
   d. She feared it.

3. For Mrs. Pavloff, taking her grandchildren to the sea is a way for her to
   *a. relive her childhood memories with them.
   b. remind them of the dangers of the sun.
   c. show them how much the world has changed.
   d. give them experiences she never had.

4. When Mrs. Pavloff and her grandchildren get to the sea, they
   a. collect seashells.
   b. watch the seagulls.
   c. swim in the ocean.
   *d. build a sand castle.

5. From reading this story, you can tell that Mrs. Pavloff's grandchildren have probably never
   a. ridden on a bus.
   b. been outside during the day.
   c. heard about the sun problem.
   *d. been on a picnic.

6. In this story, the sand castle is a symbol of
   a. destruction.
   b. protection.
   *c. hope.
   d. science.

UNIT FIVE

Part One
Words on a Page
Test Generator

1. At the beginning of the story, Pete probably thinks it is most important for Lenore to
   a. choose a career she loves.
   b. make good friends at school.
   *c. learn about Native American ways.
   d. prepare to attend university.

2. At first, what is Pete's attitude toward Lenore's writing talent?
   *a. disapproval
   b. pride
   c. envy
   d. encouragement

3. Lenore's mother probably reminds her about the story of the Sun and the Wind in order to
   a. give Lenore an idea for a new story.
   b. prove that Ojibway stories are the best.
   c. demonstrate the importance of winning contests.
   *d. suggest a way for Lenore to deal with her father.

4. Lenore wants her father to go to Parents' Night mainly to
   a. talk to her teachers.
   *b. hear her story.
   c. see her artwork and tests.
   d. meet the principal.

5. What does Miss Walker do when she goes to Lenore's house for dinner?
   a. She praises Pete for raising a fine daughter.
   b. She interests Pete in teaching an Ojibway Studies course.
   *c. She argues with Pete about Lenore's future.
   d. She reads Lenore's story to Pete.

6. Pete reveals that he has not read Lenore's story because he
   a. is afraid the story will make him sad.
   b. thinks writing is a useless skill.
   c. refuses to cooperate with Miss Walker.
   *d. never learned how to read.

7. In Lenore's dream, the birds represent
   a. native children.
   *b. letters of words.
   c. teachers at the university.
   d. people in an audience.

from All I Really Need to Know I Learned in Kindergarten
Test Generator

1. This selection is an example of
   a. a biography.
   *b. a personal essay.
   c. informative nonfiction.
   d. a short story.

2. Fulghum's personal statement in this essay is best described as a list of
   *a. rules he tries to live by.
   b. tasks he will complete.
   c. mistakes he has made.
   d. goals he has achieved.

3. According to Fulghum, he used to write long personal statements when he was young because he
   a. loved the process of writing.
   *b. didn't want to leave anything out.
   c. had so much energy.
   d. remembered everything he had ever learned.

4. How does "too much high-content information" make Fulghum feel?
   a. rich
   *b. confused
   c. youthful
   d. intelligent

5. Fulghum says, "When you go out into the world, watch out for traffic, hold hands and stick together." In adult terms, what does this statement mean?
   a. Never go out alone.
   b. Expect danger at every turn.
   c. Learn the rules of traffic and follow them.
   *d. Take care of one another.

6. Which sentence best expresses what the title of this essay means?
   a. We should treasure the happiness and innocence of young children.
   b. Childhood is the time when we must learn to follow rules.
   *c. We can lead a good life by following a few basic principles.
   d. The lessons we learn as children are the ones we remember best.

You Sing (Sonnet 52)
How to Paint the Portrait of a Bird
Test Generator

1. Which word from "You Sing (Sonnet 52)" is an example of onomatopoeia?
   a. sing
   b. sky
   *c. creak
   d. rain

2. The speaker of "You Sing (Sonnet 52)" suggests that the voice is
   a. terrifying.
   b. hushed.
   c. shrill.
   *d. powerful.

3. The instructions in "How to Paint the Portrait of a Bird" emphasize the importance of being
   *a. patient.
   b. strong.
   c. clever.
   d. young.

4. In "How to Paint the Portrait of a Bird," the painter paints everything except the
   a. cage.
   b. branches.
   *c. bird.
   d. leaves.

5. In "How to Paint the Portrait of a Bird," what does the bird's singing mean?
   a. The bird must be freed.
   *b. The painting is good.
   c. More birds will come.
   d. The painter should speak.

6. The main subject of both poems is
   *a. inspiration.
   b. nature.
   c. courage.
   d. failure.

The Scribe
Test Generator

1. James gets mad at the people who run the Silver Dollar mostly because they
   *a. are disrespectful to their customers.
   b. have a dreary-looking office.
   c. are putting the bank out of business.
   d. pretend to be well educated.

2. James thinks the photographs taken of customers who cash checks at the Silver Dollar are
   a. overpriced.
   *b. insulting.
   c. necessary.
   d. flattering.

3. Why does James decide to offer scribe services for free?
   a. He knows his work contains some errors.
   *b. He wants to help people.
   c. He knows he will be arrested if he takes money without a license.
   d. He doesn't want to bother Mr. Silver and Mr. Dollar.

4. The cop puts an end to the work James is doing for free because the cop
   a. wants to keep the sidewalk clear.
   b. realizes neighbors are taking advantage of James.
   c. thinks James is too young to be in business.
   *d. is looking out for the interests of Mr. Silver and Mr. Dollar.

5. For James, what is the most important reason his neighbors should cash checks at the bank instead of the Silver Dollar?
   a. They can get to know Mrs. Adams.
   b. They can do business in a fancy building.
   *c. They can save money.
   d. They can get to know other parts of the city.

6. Why does the old man refuse to go to the bank with James?
   *a. He is afraid.
   b. He wants to spend his money, not save it.
   c. He doesn't have time.
   d. He likes doing business at the Silver Dollar.

7. Which character inspires James to think about applying for a license to be a scribe?
   a. James's mother
   b. the cop
   *c. Mrs. Franklin
   d. Mr. Silver

Crow Call
Test Generator

1. On the hunting trip with her father, the narrator's job is to
   *a. call the crows.
   b. load the gun.
   c. carry supplies.
   d. shoot the crows.

2. The narrator feels nervous about hunting because she
   a. does not trust her father.
   b. has never seen crows before.
   *c. does not know what to do.
   d. thinks she might get shot.

3. What does the narrator have for breakfast?
   a. coffee
   b. honey and milk
   c. cereal
   *d. cherry pie

4. The narrator admits to her father that she is afraid of
   a. him.
   *b. his gun.
   c. the dark.
   d. the crows.

5. The father probably does not shoot any crows that day because
   *a. he does not want to upset his daughter.
   b. the narrator is afraid of loud noises.
   c. he cannot get a clear shot at them.
   d. the narrator keeps getting in the way.

from Looking Back
Test Generator

1. In this selection, Lois Lowry gently criticizes her mother for her
   a. desire to travel.
   *b. taste in clothes.
   c. lack of education.
   d. interest in reading.

2. Lowry jokes that she has never completely forgiven her brother for
   a. being a bully.
   b. wearing glasses.
   c. looking like her.
   *d. breaking her doll.

3. As a child, Lowry felt humiliated when she
   *a. had to wear boys' lederhosen.
   b. put on a football uniform.
   c. was caught pretending to be Jody.
   d. found out what a "vigil" was.

4. When she was eight, Lowry frightened her little brother by
   a. setting off fireworks.
   b. pushing him into the water.
   *c. wearing a football uniform.
   d. hiding in his closet.

5. You can tell from this selection that all her life Lowry has enjoyed
   *a. reading good stories.
   b. traveling to Europe.
   c. living in Japan.
   d. shopping for new clothes.

Part Two
The Dog of Pompeii
Test Generator

1. Why is Tito "not exactly a merry" boy?
   a. He does not like living in Pompeii.
   b. He is always worried about earthquakes.
   c. He has to work hard to take care of his dog.
   *d. He is blind and has no parents.

2. What is Tito's main method of getting food each day?
   a. He begs strangers for food.
   b. Friends give him food.
   c. He steals food from merchants.
   *d. Bimbo brings food to him.

3. Tito does his best to make up for his blindness mainly by
   a. asking other people to help him.
   *b. relying on his other senses.
   c. staying in one place and avoiding risks.
   d. pretending that he can see.

4. After hearing the stranger's comments about Mt. Vesuvius, his listeners feel
   a. embarrassed.
   b. relieved.
   *c. confused.
   d. terrified.

5. What is the first sign of the eruption that affects Tito?
   *a. a thick cloud of dust in the air
   b. the ground shaking
   c. the sky lit up with flames
   d. a loud, rumbling sound

6. During the eruption of Mt. Vesuvius, Bimbo's main goal is to
   a. hide from the confusion.
   *b. protect Tito.
   c. get someone to rescue him.
   d. help the stranger with the thin voice.

7. Bimbo bites Tito because Bimbo is
   a. hungry.
   b. angry.
   *c. desperate.
   d. resentful.

Tutankhamen
Test Generator

1. At first Carter and Carnarvon did not dig in the area near the tomb of Rameses VI because they
   - *a. did not want to block visitors' access to the tomb.
   - b. were superstitious about bothering the spirit of Rameses VI.
   - c. were refused permission by authorities to work there.
   - d. felt sure that Tutankhamen's remains were not there.

2. Other archaeologists thought Carter and Carnarvon would not find Tutankhamen's tomb because these archaeologists believed that
   - a. the tomb was too well hidden.
   - b. Tutankhamen's remains were never placed in a tomb.
   - *c. the tomb had already been discovered.
   - d. Carter and Carnarvon were looking in the wrong place.

3. Why did Carter wait for Carnarvon's arrival before exploring the tomb?
   - a. Carter was afraid to enter the tomb alone.
   - *b. Carter wanted to share the experience with Carnarvon since they were partners.
   - c. Carnarvon was a better archaeologist, and Carter needed his help.
   - d. Carnarvon would withdraw his financial support if Carter proceeded without him.

4. How did Carter and Carnarvon react when they noticed the patched-up part on the first door?
   - *a. They worried that what was once behind the doors had been stolen.
   - b. They grew doubtful that they had discovered Tutankhamen's tomb.
   - c. They felt regret that the door's beauty had been spoiled.
   - d. They were amazed that an ancient tomb could have such minor damage.

5. From the information in this selection, you can conclude that both Carter and Carnarvon were
   - a. greedy.
   - *b. determined.
   - c. impatient.
   - d. courageous.

The First Emperor
Test Generator

1. According to the selection, why is Shih Huang Ti's tomb a more impressive archaeological discovery than Tutankhamen's tomb?
   - a. Shih Huang Ti lived longer ago than Tutankhamen.
   - b. Shih Huang Ti's tomb was much harder to locate than Tutankhamen's tomb.
   - c. Shih Huang Ti's tomb held more treasures than Tutankhamen's tomb.
   - *d. Shih Huang Ti was a more important historical figure than Tutankhamen.

2. Unlike other kings of states in ancient China, Shih Huang Ti managed to
   - *a. unite China under his rule.
   - b. avoid violence.
   - c. gain the people's trust.
   - d. enjoy public life.

3. According to the selection, Shih Huang Ti became obsessed with
   - a. collecting beautiful sculpture.
   - b. increasing his wealth.
   - *c. finding a way to live forever.
   - d. naming an heir to his throne.

4. What is the main reason the author thinks the location of Shih Huang Ti's tomb was known in ancient times?
   - a. The men who carried the emperor's remains into the tomb were sealed inside.
   - *b. The tomb took years to build, and it was surrounded by walls that enclosed 500 acres.
   - c. The tomb was meant to be the emperor's "spirit city."
   - d. A map of the entire empire was said to be placed in the tomb.

5. What opinion does the author express about the Chinese who are excavating the tomb?
   - a. They do not appreciate the importance of the tomb's treasures.
   - *b. They are working slowly but carefully.
   - c. They have been too secretive about what they are uncovering.
   - d. They are rushing the job in hopes of making themselves rich.

Barbara Frietchie

Test Generator

1. In this poem, the town of Frederick is compared to
   *a. the Garden of Eden.
   b. a soldier's coffin.
   c. a starry night.
   d. a tattered flag.

2. In the poem, Barbara Frietchie's raising of the flag is presented as
   a. hopeless.
   b. shameful.
   *c. noble.
   d. wise.

3. What does the poem indicate about Barbara Frietchie?
   *a. She is an old woman.
   b. She often acts without thinking.
   c. She is loved by the townspeople.
   d. She is afraid to die.

4. When Stonewall Jackson hears Barbara Frietchie's words, he feels
   a. relieved.
   b. angry.
   c. amused.
   *d. ashamed.

5. Stonewall Jackson orders the soldiers to
   a. take down the flag.
   b. capture Barbara Frietchie.
   c. raise a Confederate flag in Frederick.
   *d. leave Barbara Frietchie and the flag alone.

6. For the speaker of the poem, the Union flag is a symbol of
   a. shame.
   *b. freedom.
   c. power.
   d. rebellion.

UNIT SIX

Links to Unit One: Tests of Courage

Test Generator

1. In "The Boy Who Flew," Daedalus is put into prison because he
   a. knows the secret of the maze.
   b. puts the Minotaur into a maze.
   *c. helps to kill the Minotaur.
   d. tries to leave the island.

2. Daedalus and his son escape from prison by
   *a. making wings.
   b. building a maze.
   c. turning into seagulls.
   d. making a deal with King Minos.

3. In "Arachne," Arachne is punished mainly for having too much
   a. skill.
   b. curiosity.
   c. greed.
   *d. pride.

4. In her contest with Athena, Arachne makes a weaving that shows
   a. people who defied the gods.
   b. Athena fighting Poseidon.
   *c. the gods doing unfair things.
   d. Athena becoming a spider.

5. In "The Story of Ceres and Proserpina," what happens to Proserpina?
   a. She runs away with a true love.
   b. She is punished by Hecate.
   c. She marries Helios.
   *d. She is kidnapped by Pluto.

6. "The Story of Ceres and Proserpina" is a myth that explains
   a. why the underworld is gloomy.
   *b. how the seasons came to be.
   c. why the sun sets each day.
   d. how pomegranates were created.

Links to Unit Two: Growth and Change
Test Generator

1. In "The Disobedient Child," the boy often makes his parents feel
   a. appreciated.
   b. pleased.
   *c. disappointed.
   d. foolish.

2. The boy gets into trouble at the old man's house because he
   a. does not cook enough beans.
   b. steals food from the old man.
   c. runs away from the old man.
   *d. disobeys the old man's instructions.

3. At the end, the boy discovers that the old man is
   *a. a rain god.
   b. his grandfather.
   c. an evil spirit.
   d. his father.

4. In "The Bamboo Beads," Tantie's mother stops worrying about what Papa Bois is counting for Tantie when she realizes that
   *a. Tantie has been kind to him.
   b. Tantie already knows what it is.
   c. Papa Bois is not dangerous to anyone.
   d. Papa Bois is the one who has been leaving the beads.

5. The beads that Papa Bois gives Tantie are for counting
   a. her sins.
   b. the stars in the sky.
   c. the days she has left.
   *d. the children she will have.

6. What happens to the narrator at the end of "The Bamboo Beads"?
   a. Papa Bois punishes her.
   *b. Tantie gives the beads to her.
   c. Papa Bois returns the bread to her.
   d. Tantie tells her to sell their bread.

Links to Unit Three: A Sense of Fairness
Test Generator

1. In "In the Land of Small Dragon," who does the following proverb best describe—"An evil heart keeps records / On the face of its owner"?
   a. Father
   b. the Emperor
   c. T'âm, the elder daughter
   *d. Cám, the younger daughter

2. Cám becomes the Number One Daughter mainly through
   a. luck.
   *b. trickery.
   c. hard work.
   d. social customs.

3. Which of the following best restates what is meant by this proverb: "A man's worth is what he does, / Not what he says he can do"?
   a. Silence is golden.
   *b. Actions speak louder than words.
   c. One picture is worth a thousand words.
   d. Children should speak only when spoken to.

4. The proverb "What is to be must happen / As day follows after night" suggests that the marriage of the Prince and T'âm
   a. is doomed.
   b. is purely accidental.
   c. wasn't meant to happen.
   *d. couldn't have been prevented.

5. In "King Thrushbeard," the princess's main weakness is her
   *a. pride.
   b. greed.
   c. lack of skill.
   d. stubbornness.

6. Being the wife of a minstrel fills the princess with
   a. pride.
   *b. regret.
   c. happiness.
   d. a sense of purpose.

7. Which of the following is rewarded in "King Thrushbeard"?
   a. pride
   *b. humility
   c. generosity
   d. physical strength

8. Of the following characters, whose personality changes the most?
   a. T'âm's
   b. Cám's
   *c. the princess's
   d. King Thrushbeard's

Links to Unit Four: Wondrous Worlds
Test Generator

1. In "Why Monkeys Live in Trees," which is the only animal that does not brag about its chances of winning the contest?
   a. Lion
   *b. Monkey
   c. Leopard
   d. Hippopotamus

2. During the contest, Monkey goes into the tall grass after a bite to
   a. rest.
   b. spit out the pepper.
   c. wash out his mouth and throat.
   *d. allow a different monkey to take his place.

3. In "The Legend of the Hummingbird," which of the following leads Alida to turn to her god?
   a. fear
   b. anger
   c. shame
   *d. sorrow

4. When the god changes Alida into a flower and Taroo into a hummingbird, the god means to
   *a. help them.
   b. punish them.
   c. save their lives.
   d. teach them a lesson.

5. In "The Living Kuan-yin," which of the following is the greatest help to Chin Po-wan as he tries to find the answer to his problem?
   a. his wealth
   b. his reputation
   *c. his generosity
   d. his cleverness

6. Chin Po-wan is well rewarded in the end mainly because he
   a. demonstrates his love for the innkeeper's daughter.
   b. makes friends with a dragon.
   *c. does not ask his own question of Kuan-yin.
   d. gives away all his money.

Links to Unit Five: Making Your Mark
Test Generator

1. In "The Frog Who Wanted to Be a Singer," the only support Frog gets at first comes from
   *a. his parents.
   b. the birds.
   c. Fox.
   d. other frogs.

2. "The Frog Who Wanted to Be a Singer" explains the creation of
   a. poetry.
   *b. rhythm and blues.
   c. public concerts.
   d. microphones.

3. Which is a theme of this story?
   a. Only the strong survive.
   b. Beauty is only skin-deep.
   c. We are all living on the same planet.
   *d. Don't be afraid to follow your dream.

4. In "Where the Girl Rescued Her Brother," Buffalo Calf Road Woman is best described as
   *a. courageous.
   b. pretty.
   c. respectful.
   d. friendly.

5. The white people are called "spider people"
   because they
   a. build large webs.
   b. travel in groups.
   *c. are beautiful but dangerous.
   d. kill more buffalo than they need.

6. A battle is named for Buffalo Calf Road Woman
   because she
   a. dies during the battle.
   *b. saves her brother's life.
   c. kills a grizzly bear.
   d. kills General Crook.

Writing Assessment

Contents

To the Teacher

This section provides several different tools to help you conduct holistic evaluations of your students' writing. Holistic evaluation is a quick, guided method for evaluating writing. An evaluator reads the piece through, considers certain important features, and immediately assigns a grade. The grade may be a single rating for the entire piece of writing or a set of ratings for the different features being considered.

- **Holistic Scoring Guide** (177–178) Helps you rate papers objectively and consistently. This guide can be used to assign an overall rating after you have analyzed a paper using the General Rubric or a mode-specific rubric. To adapt to a three-point rating system, focus on the level designations (strong, average, weak).

- **General Rubric** (179) Demonstrates a multi-rating type of holistic evaluation, based on a list of major attributes of content and form that characterizes most types of writing. This rubric is useful for almost any type of writing.

- **Writing Prompts** (180–184) Available to help your students prepare for essay tests.

For guidance in evaluating your students' writing, you can refer to the scored student models and rubrics that appear in the Unit Resource Books.

Holistic Scoring Guide

The following 6-point scale shows the features that tend to appear in a range of student papers representing various levels of accomplishment. The aim of the scale is to guide teachers in the evaluation of student papers according to a set of standards that are similar to those used in large-scale evaluations of student writing all across the country. A single student's paper may not include all the characteristics identified with any one score point, but it can be assigned a score by looking for the description that most nearly matches its features or its dominant impression. Some allowance should be made for minor errors in style, usage, mechanics, and spelling on the unit assessment, since that test does not provide time for revision.

Level: Strong

Exceptional 6 points	Commendable 5 points
A paper at score point 6 • Has a clear and consistent focus • Has a logical organization • Uses transitions to connects ideas • Supports ideas with details, quotations, examples, and/or other evidence • Exhibits well-formed sentences varying in structure • Exhibits a rich vocabulary, including precise language that is appropriate for the purpose and audience of the paper • Contains almost no errors in usage, mechanics, and spelling	A paper at score point 5 has the same general features of organization and effective elaboration as a 6-point paper, but it represents a somewhat less accomplished performance. It may, for example, • Have an organization that is predictable or unnecessarily mechanical • Lack the depth and logical precision of a 6-point paper in presenting its argument and supporting evidence • Exhibit appropriate sentence variety and vocabulary but without the control and richness of a 6-point paper • Contain a few errors in usage, mechanics, and spelling

Level: Average

Proficient 4 points	Basic 3 points

A paper at score point 4

- Has a fairly clear focus that may occasionally become obscured
- Shows an organizational pattern, but relationships between ideas may sometimes be difficult to understand
- Contains supporting evidence that may lack effect and so only superficially develops ideas
- Has complete and varied sentences most of the time
- Contains some errors in usage, mechanics, and spelling but which do not confuse meaning

A paper at score point 3

- Has a vague focus and so may contain irrelevant details or digressions
- Shows an attempt at organization, but connections between ideas are difficult to understand
- Lacks important supporting evidence, or the evidence cited does not sufficiently develop ideas
- Shows little sentence variety
- Contains several serious errors in usage, mechanics, and spelling which causes distraction and some confusion about meaning

Level: Weak

Limited 2 points	Minimal 1 point

A paper at score point 2

- Has a topic but does not include any elaboration
- Lacks plausible support for ideas
- Shows limited word choice
- Contains serious and numerous errors in usage, mechanics, and spelling which leads to confusion about meaning

A paper at score point 1

- Only minimally addresses the topic and lacks a discernible idea
- Has only a few simple sentences
- Shows minimal word choice
- May be incoherent and/or have serious errors in almost every sentence

A paper is unable to be scored if it is
- illegible
- unrelated to the topic
- only a rewording of the prompt
- written in a foreign language
- not written at all

General Rubric

Ideas and Content	Weak	Average	Strong
1. Contains an engaging introduction that identifies the topic			
2. Develops a writing topic appropriate to the assignment			
3. Fulfills the writer's general purpose and specific goals			
4. States ideas clearly and elaborates on them with specific supporting details and examples			
5. Uses vivid, precise language that is appropriate to the audience and the writing type			
6. Includes an effective conclusion			

Structure and Form			
7. Includes a well-developed introduction, body, and conclusion			
8. Demonstrates proper and effective paragraphing			
9. Uses a logical, effective organizational strategy consistent with the writing type			
10. Includes transitional words and phrases to show relationships among ideas and maintain coherence within and between paragraphs			
11. Uses a variety of sentence structures			

Grammar, Usage, and Mechanics			
12. Contains no more than two or three minor errors in grammar and usage			
13. Contains no more than two or three minor errors in spelling, capitalization, and punctuation			

Additional Comments

_____

_____

Prompts for Personal and Expressive Writing

If you could do something really impressive, what would it be? Would you write a hit song? Invent a pollution-free car? Try to break a world record? Write a short essay about someone who has done something really special—you.

Is there someone you want to be like when you grow up? When you think of role models, who comes to your mind? Identify a personal role model. Then write a journal entry. Explore why you admire this person and what he or she means to you.

Is there someone you haven't seen in a while? Someone you miss and have been meaning to contact? Write that person a friendly letter. Focus your letter on a single topic. For example, you might share something you've recently accomplished, a scary experience you've had, or something that's troubling you. Make sure to format your letter correctly.

A friend who is a songwriter has written a melody that has a happy feeling. Now she needs your help with the lyrics. Make a list of things that make you happy. Your list might include blue skies, crisp fall days, time spent with a good friend, deep-dish pizza, or fresh linens on your bed. Then share your list in a letter to the songwriter.

Prompts for Observation and Description

What's your favorite place in your town? If tourists came to visit, where would you suggest they visit? A pizza parlor? A video arcade? A park? Write a description of this place for a travel brochure. Use lots of sensory details, concrete nouns, and action verbs to bring the place to life.

Your favorite magazine is running a special feature on holiday celebrations around the world. The editors have already collected recipes for special occasions. Now they need well-written descriptions of the customs practiced on these holidays. Think of a holiday you enjoy. Then describe a custom you or your family members practice on this special day.

Think of a person—a friend, a teacher, a coach—whom you'd like someone else to meet. Then write a description of that person. Show how the person looks, sounds, and acts, so your reader can get to know the individual almost as well as you do.

You are writing a children's story based on the tale "The Ugly Duckling." Write a description of your main character just after he or she has been transformed in some way. Your character may have become beautiful, smart, strong, kind, or changed in some other way. Whenever you can, show, rather than tell.

Prompts for Narrative and Literary Writing

Imagine that you could have any pet you like—for example, a tiger, a unicorn, an elephant, an eagle, a dinosaur. For your school literary magazine, write a brief narrative that tells the story of an adventure you've had with your pet.

A close friend or relative is having a birthday. Write a poem to give to this person on his or her special day.

Your class has decided to put on a show called "A Wonderful Thing Happened to Me. . . ." In the show, each class member will read a personal narrative that he or she has written. Parents, teachers, and students will be in the audience. Write your personal narrative for the show. Keep in mind that it should be about something wonderful that has happened to you.

Your school literary magazine needs stories for an issue on "Things They Don't Teach at School." Write a story for the magazine about something you've learned outside the classroom. You could write about an experience that taught you the importance of being patient with a younger child—or the value of taking time to talk with an older relative. Conclude your story by sharing what you learned from the experience.

Prompts for Informative Writing

Explaining How

Everybody is an expert at doing something. What is your specialty? Drawing cats? Throwing curve balls? Making hero sandwiches? Choose something you know how to do well, and write a simple step-by-step explanation of how to do it. Make your directions simple and clear enough for anyone to follow—even someone who has never attempted the activity before.

What would a new student at your school need to know? Jot down a few of the important ins and outs that you wish someone had taken the time to explain to you. Your list might include how to get along with older students, how to study for tests, or how to try out for the soccer team. Then, for a handbook for new students, write an explanation of how to do one of these things.

Your school is putting together material to include in a time capsule to be opened in 200 years. Your job is to explain some simple, everyday task to the people of the future. Choose an ordinary task that you perform all the time, such as tying your shoe, making a peanut butter sandwich, or walking the dog. Be sure to name any equipment you need, and write clear, step-by-step directions. Include drawings if you wish.

Your pen pal in another country wants to know more about the games you and your friends enjoy playing. Pick one of your favorite games. Then write an explanation of how to play it. Make sure your directions are clear and complete enough for your pen pal to follow, and mention any special materials your pen pal may need.

Prompts for Persuasion

Imagine that the editor of a local entertainment magazine has asked you to find out which radio station your friends like best and why. You have polled your friends for their opinions and reasons. Now think about what your friends would say. Then write a brief magazine article in which you share the results of your survey.

You and a friend have had a disagreement about which of you is a better musician. In fact, every time you try to settle the issue, you wind up arguing. Write your friend a letter in which you express your opinion on this matter. Support your opinion with facts, examples, reasons, and other details.

You are going to be interviewed for an article about teenagers. The reporter will want to know your opinions on everything from parents and teachers to what's happening in the world around you. Begin preparing for this interview by writing your opinion about one of these topics.

Your town is going to build a teen community center. The town leaders wish to know what services and activities you and your friends would want at such a place. Would you like to have tutors there to help you with homework? Would you like a video game room? Prepare a short speech to give at the next town meeting. In your speech, tell what you think teens would welcome at a community center. Whenever possible, support your opinions with reasons and quotations.

Standardized Test Practice

Contents

To the Teacher

This section provides opportunities for your students to develop strategies for typically performing well on standardized tests. Practice items are included for areas found on standardized tests: analogies, sentence completion, error identification, error correction, revisions in context passages, and critical reading passages.

Each set of practice items explains the purpose of that particular test, provides an example, and describes specific strategies students can use to be successful. The To the Student form on the facing page provides general test-taking strategies. You may wish to duplicate this form, distribute it to your students, and discuss the strategies.

To the Student

During the next few years you will be taking many standardized tests that evaluate your understanding of English. No matter what type of test you are facing, there are steps you can take beforehand to maximize your performance. As you work on the sample test questions in this booklet, you will begin to develop strategies that will help you perform well. You might also want to try using the following general strategies, which work for many people.

Physical and Emotional Preparation

- Before the test get at least eight hours of sleep and eat a good breakfast and/or lunch.

- Wear comfortable clothes.

- Try to relax and maintain a positive attitude.

Taking the Test

- When you receive the test, glance over it, noting the types of questions and the number of points to be awarded for each.

- Read and listen to direction carefully.

- Budget your time, making sure that you do not spend too much time on any single question.

- Read each question and all answer choices before answering. Many items include choices that may seem right at first glance but are actually wrong.

- Complete the questions that you can answer easily. Then go back to the more difficult items.

- Do not make wild guesses. Since points are deducted for incorrect answers on many standardized tests, random guessing can harm your score. If you can eliminate one or two of the answer choices, however, your chance of choosing the correct answer is increased.

Spelling

Spelling items test your ability to recognize the correct spelling of a word. On some tests you will be asked to identify the misspelled word in a list of words. On other tests you will be asked to choose the correct spelling of a particular word in the context of a sentence. Here are two sample questions.

A (A) difficult
(B) equalize
(C) Wenesday
(D) humble
(E) No mistakes

B Our trip to Walt Disney World was really _____.
(A) enjoyible
(B) enjoible
(C) enjoyuble
(D) enjoyable

The following strategies can help you answer these types of questions:

Example A

- Read all the answer choices carefully, looking for misspellings.

- Then choose the word that is misspelled. Mark *E* if all the words in the list are spelled correctly.

- In the example, *Wednesday* is misspelled, so the correct answer is *C*.

Example B

- Read the entire sentence first.

- Then read each answer choice and pick the one that completes the sentence and is spelled correctly.

- In the example, *enjoyable* is the correct spelling of the missing word, so the correct answer is *D*.

Part A

Choose the misspelled word in each list. If all the words are spelled correctly, mark *E*.

1. (A) experience
   (B) apreciate
   (C) inhabitant
   (D) although
   (E) No mistakes

2. (A) easyer
   (B) permanent
   (C) zipper
   (D) reality
   (E) No mistakes

3. (A) explain
   (B) dismiss
   (C) totaly
   (D) statement
   (E) No mistakes

4. (A) genius
   (B) policy
   (C) mileage
   (D) seperate
   (E) No mistakes

5. (A) numerous
   (B) centimeter
   (C) university
   (D) pursue
   (E) No mistakes

6. (A) beautify
   (B) receive
   (C) fatige
   (D) variable
   (E) No mistakes

7. (A) grammer
   (B) exceed
   (C) vacuum
   (D) innocent
   (E) No mistakes

8. (A) complicate
   (B) distress
   (C) attitude
   (D) fisical
   (E) No mistakes

9. (A) equator
   (B) autum
   (C) freight
   (D) muscle
   (E) No mistakes

10. (A) thermometer
    (B) acquaint
    (C) physician
    (D) exterior
    (E) No mistakes

11. (A) purchase
    (B) sufficient
    (C) astronaut
    (D) Febuary
    (E) No mistakes

12. (A) hitchhike
    (B) oppose
    (C) alblum
    (D) illegal
    (E) No mistakes

13. (A) analisys
    (B) intelligence
    (C) specialize
    (D) economics
    (E) No mistakes

14. (A) itself
    (B) possible
    (C) quite
    (D) linear
    (E) No mistakes

15. (A) except
    (B) arcitect
    (C) expect
    (D) ballet
    (E) No mistakes

16. (A) cemetery
    (B) existence
    (C) thurough
    (D) route
    (E) No mistakes

17. (A) courteous
    (B) perspire
    (C) aquariam
    (D) oxygen
    (E) No mistakes

18. (A) effortless
    (B) possessed
    (C) ultimate
    (D) witch
    (E) No mistakes

19. (A) ought
    (B) efficient
    (C) publicity
    (D) noticable
    (E) No mistakes

20. (A) colapse
    (B) occurrence
    (C) amateur
    (D) annually
    (E) No mistakes

Part B
Choose the correct spelling of the missing word in each sentence.

21. Fire regulations require that an _____ be left between the seats.
    - (A) aile
    - (B) isle
    - (C) aisle
    - (D) I'll

22. The team was in _____ after losing the championship.
    - (A) dispare
    - (B) despair
    - (C) disapear
    - (D) despare

23. It's not the heat but the _____ that makes people uncomfortable.
    - (A) humility
    - (B) humidity
    - (C) hyumidity
    - (D) humitidy

24. When the fire alarm sounds, _____ immediately to the nearest fire exit.
    - (A) proceed
    - (B) preceed
    - (C) precede
    - (D) procede

25. My sister plays the drums and other _____ instruments.
    - (A) purcussion
    - (B) purrcushen
    - (C) pecusion
    - (D) percussion

26. Zachary gets very upset at any disruption in his _____.
    - (A) rutene
    - (B) ruotine
    - (C) routine
    - (D) ruetine

27. The doctors could not agree on a _____ of my disease.
    - (A) diagnosus
    - (B) diagnoses
    - (C) diagnosis
    - (D) diugnosis

28. Since Sasha began studying _____, he thinks he understands everyone's behavior.
    - (A) psychology
    - (B) physcology
    - (C) sychology
    - (D) pyschology

29. Learning any new skill requires _____ and discipline.
    - (A) pacience
    - (B) payshens
    - (C) pascience
    - (D) patience

30. Before you make a _____, be sure you understand what you are being asked to do.
    - (A) comitment
    - (B) commitment
    - (C) committee
    - (D) comittment

31. On our vacation we visited the state _____.
    - (A) caputil
    - (B) capital
    - (C) capatul
    - (D) capitle

32. Ants are very _____ insects.
    - (A) industrious
    - (B) industryus
    - (C) industreaous
    - (D) industrius

33. My parents just celebrated their twentieth wedding _____.
    - (A) aniversery
    - (B) anniversary
    - (C) anaversery
    - (D) annuversary

34. _____ is the cause of many accidents.
    - (A) Negligance
    - (B) Neglagence
    - (C) Negligence
    - (D) Negligens

35. I _____ with you but don't know what I can do to help.
(A) simpathize
(B) sympathise
(C) sympatize
(D) sympathize

36. I know it's strange, but I don't like _____ at all.
(A) choclate
(B) chaklut
(C) chocolate
(D) chokulate

37. Lionel said that it _____ will rain tomorrow, since he is planning to wash his family's car.
(A) probly
(B) probably
(C) probubbly
(D) probable

38. Alicia's uncle is a _____ at the local city hospital.
(A) surgeon
(B) serjean
(C) sirgion
(D) surgen

39. If two lines are _____, they will never meet, no matter how far they are extended.
(A) parrallell
(B) paralell
(C) parrallel
(D) parallel

40. It is _____ to watch babies as they learn to understand the world around them.
(A) facinating
(B) fascinateing
(C) fasinating
(D) fascinating

Vocabulary

Tests include many types of questions that assess your knowledge of the meanings of words, or **vocabulary.** In one type of question, you are given a sentence in which a word is underlined. You are then asked to choose another sentence in which that word has the same meaning. Here is a typical question:

I will **review** both the material in my textbook and my homework assignments in preparation for the test.
(A) The critic wrote a very bad review of the new movie.
(B) Review the recipe carefully before beginning to cook.
(C) The general will review the troops at 1:00.
(D) Many actors never read the reviews of their performance.

The following strategies can help you answer these types of questions:

- Read the numbered sentence carefully, noting the meaning of the underlined word.

- Then read each of the answer choices. Pay special attention to the way the underlined word is used and to the part of speech it is. In the sample question, for example, *review* is used in the sentence as a verb that means "to examine or study again." That is also the way in which the word is used in sentence B. In contrast, *review* is used as a noun that means "a critical evaluation" in sentences A and D and as a verb that means "to inspect" in sentence C. The correct answer, therefore, is *B*.

Choose the sentence in which the underlined word is used in most nearly the same way as it is in the example sentence.

1. Everyone has a **stake** in the world economy; if it doesn't thrive, neither do we.
   (A) Being hurt by someone you love can be like having a stake driven into your heart.
   (B) Before deciding how much cement you need to cover your driveway, stake out the area carefully.
   (C) Eric's parents had a large stake in his success at the Olympics, since they had invested a tremendous amount of time and money in his training program.
   (D) Be sure to pound the tent stakes into the ground firmly, or the tent may collapse.

2. Alice's decision to stop taking piano lessons is **sheer** foolishness, since she has so much talent.
   (A) After hiking in the mountains all day, we collapsed from sheer exhaustion.
   (B) The cliff was so sheer that not even the most experienced climber would attempt to scale it.
   (C) Sheer curtains look pretty but don't offer any privacy.
   (D) It is easy for a sailor to sheer off course if he doesn't react quickly to changes in the wind.

3. I **appreciate** your frustration with the public transportation system, but there's no other way for you to get to school.
   - (A) In a year the value of our house will appreciate by 10 percent or more.
   - (B) I appreciate your attention and concern.
   - (C) A person should appreciate the thought behind a gift even if he or she doesn't like the gift itself.
   - (D) Even though we don't agree, can you appreciate my point of view?

4. Detectives didn't find a **trace** of the missing body.
   - (A) Trace the dress pattern onto the material with chalk before cutting out the pieces.
   - (B) All four freshly baked loaves of bread vanished without a trace.
   - (C) Please trace the steps you followed in solving the problem so that everyone can understand your thinking.
   - (D) Some animals can trace the path of their prey for many miles by scent alone.

5. Fun-house mirrors produce a distorted **image** of reality.
   - (A) Enrique is the image of his mother's brother.
   - (B) My image of construction workers changed when I met my friend's sister Beatrice.
   - (C) The image in the photograph doesn't match the scene I saw through the camera lens.
   - (D) After talking to the doctor on the telephone, I had the image of a middle-aged woman in my mind; so I was very surprised to learn that she was only twenty-eight years old.

6. The **subject** of today's lesson is words with multiple meanings.
   - (A) Carmi's mother is subject to fainting spells.
   - (B) In Kenya, high school students take thirteen subjects at a time.
   - (C) If you disobey traffic laws, you may be subject to arrest.
   - (D) Feel free to change the subject of your report if you have trouble finding information on the topic you chose.

7. The **depth** of the water is not great enough to allow diving.
   - (A) To find the volume of a rectangular box, calculate the product of its depth, its width, and its height.
   - (B) We will never run out of water because the depth of our well is so great.
   - (C) Isaac Asimov's science fiction books show great depth of thought, although they are not difficult to understand.
   - (D) Earthquakes originate in the depths of the earth.

8. I **assume** that you will finish your homework before you watch television.
   - (A) We can't always assume that people will act logically.
   - (B) If the plane is about to crash, assume a position with your head between your knees.
   - (C) If the President dies, the Vice-President will assume the presidency.
   - (D) An important part of growing up is learning to assume responsibility for your own behavior.

9. The sign at the entrance to the park said Public **Property,** Please Enjoy.
   (A) The physical <u>properties</u> of water change when it is frozen.
   (B) My parents were surprised to learn that the <u>property</u> next to the lake was listed for sale.
   (C) Our neighbors lost all of their <u>property</u> in the flood.
   (D) An important <u>property</u> of diamonds is their hardness.

10. So many fans came to the rock concert that a television **monitor** had to be set up for those who couldn't get into the auditorium.
   (A) Tests are a good way to <u>monitor</u> your progress in your classes.
   (B) The security guard watched the <u>monitor</u> carefully to make sure that there were no disturbances anywhere in the building.
   (C) To determine which food my brother was allergic to, the doctor told him to carefully <u>monitor</u> everything he ate for a week and record how he felt.
   (D) Since Rodolfo was the class <u>monitor</u> he was responsible for passing out and collecting the test papers.

Sentence Completion

A **sentence completion** question tests not only your vocabulary but also your understanding of the relationships among the words in a sentence. In such a question, you are given a sentence with a word missing and are asked to choose the word that best completes the sentence. Here is a typical question:

> Although the students had been late for class, the teacher dismissed them _____ at 3:00.
> (A) randomly   (B) individually   (C) promptly   (D) distinctly   (E) anxious

The following strategies can help you answer these types of questions:

- Read the entire sentence first. Look for clues indicating what part of speech the missing word must be—noun, pronoun, verb, adverb, or adjective. In the sample question, for example, the missing word must be an adverb modifying the verb *dismissed.*

- Try each answer choice in the sentence. Eliminate those that do not fit grammatically or do not make sense. In the sample question, you can eliminate *E, anxious* because it is an adjective, not an adverb.

- Pay special attention to words that show relationships such as difference *(although, but, however)* and similarity *(and, also, another, likewise)*. The word *although* in the sample question is a clue that the correct word will indicate a contrast with the students' being late for class. The correct answer is *C, promptly.*

Choose the word that best completes each sentence.

1. With more people moving into the area every year, experts expect the suburbs of Phoenix to _____.
   (A) disappear   (B) rapidly   (C) control   (D) expand   (E) move

2. Exotic fruits and flowers grow in _____ on the lush tropical island.
   (A) aquarium   (B) abundance   (C) cages   (D) secret   (E) leisure

3. The elements sodium and chlorine _____ to form table salt.
   (A) neatly   (B) repel   (C) forget   (D) tasty   (E) combine

4. All students are required to _____ an assembly this afternoon.
   (A) attend   (B) planning   (C) reluctantly   (D) discipline   (E) gather

5. The rock star's performance was fast paced and _____.
   (A) relaxing   (B) energetic   (C) disappointing   (D) boring   (E) depressing

6. Too much _____ to the sun can cause serious damage to the skin.
   (A) revolving   (B) bathing   (C) exposure   (D) respect   (E) rays

7. I know you like that new recording, but don't you find it _____ to listen to it for hours at a time?
   (A) nervous   (B) comfortable   (C) boring   (D) forgotten   (E) mysteriously

8. The people of the city have _____ their first mayor by naming a street for her.
   (A) disgusted   (B) restored   (C) eliminated   (D) remembering   (E) honored

9. After the referee's bad call, the fans angrily shouted their _____.
   (A) agreement   (B) forgiveness   (C) supporting   (D) disapproval   (E) purpose

10. Because of its large vocabulary and the many exceptions to its rules, English is often called the most most _____ language to learn.
    (A) difficult   (B) entertaining   (C) understandably   (D) hardest   (E) musical

11. At the trial the witness was asked to _____ about what had happened on the day of the crime.
    (A) guess   (B) testify   (C) forget   (D) explaining   (E) accuse

12. During the half-time show, the band members formed a(n) _____ that looked like a rocket taking off.
    (A) noise   (B) pattern   (C) mistake   (D) operation   (E) riot

13. Please don't grade this composition because it's only a first _____.
    (A) ideal   (B) trying   (C) page   (D) draft   (E) estimated

14. One of many _____ is that breaking a mirror will bring seven years of bad luck.
    (A) suspicion   (B) mystery   (C) superstitions   (D) tragedies   (E) amusing

15. When I called my cousin in Africa, the _____ was so good that he sounded as if he were in the next room.
    (A) connection   (B) feelings   (C) interesting   (D) depressed   (E) handicapped

16. Our local stadium has special ramps and doorways so that _____ persons can attend sporting events.
    (A) less   (B) foreign   (C) interesting   (D) depressed   (E) handicapped

17. No one who wants to get off at any of the first three stations should take the _____ express train.
    (A) slow   (B) finally   (C) electrical   (D) comfortable   (E) express

18. The lack of _____ value in Carmen's lunches was alarming.
    (A) color   (B) nutritional   (C) tasteful   (D) vegetable   (E) weight

19. Before taking an exam, be sure to get _____ rest and eat a good breakfast.
    (A) most   (B) less   (C) sufficient   (D) simply   (E) earlier

20. The shortest distance between two points is a(n) _____ line.
    (A) dotted   (B) straight   (C) curving   (D) invisible   (E) perfectly

Capitalization and Punctuation

Capitalization and punctuation questions test your ability to recognize mistakes in the mechanics of English sentences. Capitalization and punctuation skills may be tested in many ways. In one of the most common formats, you are given one or more sentences divided into three lines. You are asked to choose the line that includes a mistake in capitalization or punctuation or to mark *D, No mistakes* if there are no errors. Here is a typical question:

> (A) It was on July 20 1969,
> (B) that Neil Armstrong became
> (C) the first human to step on the moon.
> (D) (No mistakes)

The following strategies can help you answer these types of questions:

- Read lines *A, B,* and *C* of the question as you would read a complete sentence or paragraph.

- Then reread each line, looking for errors in capitalization or punctuation.

- Mark the letter of the line that includes an error. If there are no mistakes, mark *D, No mistakes.* In the sample question, there should be a comma between the date and the year—July 20, 1969—in the first line. Therefore, the answer is *A.*

Choose the letter of the line that includes a mistake in capitalization or punctuation. If there are no errors, mark *D, No mistakes.*

Part A—Capitalization

1. (A) "The sky looks as if
   (B) it were made of blue silk,"
   (C) said my Dad.
   (D) (No mistakes)

2. (A) When you travel
   (B) to the far East, be sure
   (C) to take a good camera.
   (D) (No mistakes)

3. (A) Hurry up! the
   (B) school bus is
   (C) ready to leave.
   (D) (No mistakes)

4. (A) Luke's dog,
   (B) Diogi, is an
   (C) Irish wolfhound.
   (D) (No mistakes)

5. (A) The new office
   (B) Building has special
   (C) ramps for handicapped persons.
   (D) (No mistakes)

6. (A) *Cry, the Beloved Country* is a novel
   (B) about race relations by the South African
   (C) Author Alan Paton.
   (D) (No mistakes)

7. (A) The word complex
   (B) comes from a latin word
   (C) meaning "to weave."
   (D) (No mistakes)

8. (A) The Japanese tourists
   (B) visited thirty-four States
   (C) on their tour of America
   (D) (No mistakes)

9. (A) Janus asked, "when will
   (B) the chocolate chip cookies
   (C) be ready?"
   (D) (No mistakes)

10. (A) Many people say that
    (B) Apple computers are the
    (C) best personal computers.
    (D) (No mistakes)

11. (A) My favorite animated
    (B) character is the dancing
    (C) Hippopotamus in Walt Disney's Fantasia.
    (D) (No mistakes)

12. (A) The Principal of our school
    (B) wants to be addressed as
    (C) Dr. Rodríguez, not Mrs. Rodríguez.
    (D) (No mistakes)

13. (A) Thousands of Canada geese
    (B) stop at Horicon Marsh in
    (C) Wisconsin as they head South for the winter.
    (D) (No mistakes)

14. (A) The Ten Commandments appear
    (B) in two books of the Bible—
    (C) Exodus and Deuteronomy.
    (D) (No mistakes)

15. (A) The large oil company Exxon
    (B) used to be known as standard
    (C) Oil of New Jersey.
    (D) (No mistakes)

Part B—Punctuation

16. (A) Are you a pizza
    (B) lover If so, don't miss
    (C) our new specialty called Pie in the Sky.
    (D) (No mistakes)

17. (A) The toppings you can choose
    (B) include mushrooms olives,
    (C) pineapple, and ground beef.
    (D) (No mistakes)

18. (A) Its no fun having to practice
    (B) the piano when all your friends
    (C) are playing outside.
    (D) (No mistakes)

19. (A) My dentist asked, "Do
    (B) you floss your teeth
    (C) every night, Ted?"
    (D) (No mistakes)

20. (A) Mario woke up at
    (B) 4.00 this morning
    (C) and couldn't get back to sleep.
    (D) (No mistakes)

21. (A) Fewer than one third
    (B) of the calories you eat in a day
    (C) should be from fats.
    (D) (No mistakes)

22. (A) The meeting this afternoon
    (B) is for Math Club
    (C) members' only.
    (D) (No mistakes)

23. (A) Be prepared to
    (B) laugh the new show
    (C) promises to be hilarious.
    (D) (No mistakes)

24. (A) Did the principal
    (B) say, "All afternoon
    (C) classes are canceled?"
    (D) (No mistakes)

25 (A) Arlo said that "he had
    (B) shaken the President's
    (C) hand at the parade today.
    (D) (No mistakes)

26. (A) I did so poorly
    (B) on the exam that
    (C) Ill have to take it again.
    (D) (No mistakes)

27. (A) The first bicycle
    (B) race was held on
    (C) May 31, 1868.
    (D) (No mistakes)

28. (A) That spiral notebook
    (B) isn't mine; it's
    (C) Charles'.
    (D) (No mistakes)

29. (A) "Nobody knows,"
    (B) says the popular song,
    (C) "the trouble I've seen."
    (D) (No mistakes)

30. (A) Wow! What an
    (B) incredible catch
    (C) I'm amazed!
    (D) (No mistakes)

Analogies

Analogies involve pairs of related words. In many analogy questions, you are given two words and are asked to find another pair of words that are related in the same way. Here is a typical question:

> SHOE : FOOT :: (A) head : hat (B) glove : hand (C) toe : sock
> (D) brush : teeth (E) toothpaste : brush

The analogy can be expressed this way: "A *shoe* is to a *foot* as a ___?___ is to a ___?___." Try the following approaches in answering analogy questions:

- Think about the relationship between the original pair of words. Then state that relationship in a sentence. For example, you might state the relationship expressed in the sample analogy like this:

"A *shoe* is covering worn on the *foot.*"

- Find another pair of words that shows the same relationship. In the sample analogy, the answer is *B, glove : hand.* Test the pair of words you have chosen by substituting them in your sentence:

"A *glove* is a covering worn on the *hand.*"

Here are some relationships that are often used in analogies:

Type of Analogy	Example
cause to effect	lightening : thunder :: cloud : rain
part to whole	knee : leg :: elbow : arm
object to characteristic	fire : heat :: ice : cold
object to function	pencil : write :: scissors : cut
word to synonym	far : distant :: close : near
word to antonym	start : end :: right : wrong
word to variation	drive : driver :: conduct : conductor

Choose the pair of words that best completes each analogy.

1. GO : WENT :: (A) walk : tiptoe (B) jog : run (C) lose : losing
   (D) drink : drank (E) give : take

2. CHEF : MEAL :: (A) tailor : suit (B) doctor : hospital (C) ship : harbor
   (D) soldier : war (E) food : kitchen

3. ZEBRA : MAMMAL :: (A) human : woman (B) grasshopper : insect
   (C) kitten : puppy (D) rose : thorn (E) caterpillar : butterfly

4. HAMMER : NAIL :: (A) ax : chop (B) pen : ink (C) screwdriver : screw
   (D) staple : stapler (E) mop : pail

5. GROW : INCREASE :: (A) less : more (B) large : small (C) big : bigger
   (D) rise : risen (E) shrink : decrease

6. TUESDAY : WEDNESDAY:: (A) Monday : Friday (B) today : tomorrow
   (C) yesterday : tomorrow (D) day : week (E) weekday : holiday

7. STOP : START :: (A) complete : finish (B) wait : waiting (C) end : begin
   (D) speak : sing (E) orange : red

8. ICE : SLIPPERY :: (A) snow : snowflake (B) blue : sky (C) glue : sticky
   (D) ski : mountain (E) chicken : egg

9. DOVE : PEACE :: (A) skull and crossbones : poison (B) army : war
   (C) crow : scarecrow (D) egg : omelet (E) airplane : bird

10. MONEY : BANKER :: (A) waiter : tray (B) doctor : medicine (C) library : books
    (D) bread : baker (E) ocean : water

11. THERMOMETER : TEMPERATURE :: (A) degree : measurement (B) Fahrenheit :
    Celsius (C) freezing : boiling (D) calendar : time (E) lightning : thunder

12. EYE : VISION :: (A) food : taste (B) ear : hearing (C) odor : nose
    (D) speech : words (E) mouth : teeth

13. EVOLVE : DEVELOP :: (A) add : subtract (B) bite : chew (C) speak : listen
    (D) reply : reject (E) bewilder : confuse

14. COURAGEOUS : SOLDIER :: (A) persuasive : salesperson (B) teacher : strict
    (C) artist : sculptor (D) clumsy : trapeze artist (E) books : librarian

15. FOLLOW : PRECEDE :: (A) leave : escape (B) predict : remember
    (C) advance : retreat (D) astonish : amaze (E) gone : went

16. STATE : RESTATE :: (A) do : done (B) renew : knew (C) view : review
    (D) lying : rely (E) accept : refuse

17. PLUM : FRUIT :: (A) applesauce : apple (B) coconut : palm (C) cat : kitten
    (D) oak : tree (E) ocean : lake

18. AMPLIFY : VOLUME :: (A) add : multiplication (B) magnify : size
    (C) mumble : voice (D) conduct : music (E) exercise : muscles

19. READING : BOOK :: (A) driving : automobile (B) spending : store
    (C) cooking : menu (D) sleeping : night (E) skiing : winter

20. WIND : SAILBOAT :: (A) bike : pedal (B) heat : air conditioner
    (C) gasoline : automobile (D) music : instrument (E) astronaut : space shuttle

21. PARENT : PARENTHOOD :: (A) brotherhood : brother (B) parka : hood
    (C) baby : childhood (D) daughter : mother (E) father : fatherhood

22. THREE : SIX :: (A) one : three (B) two : four (C) four : five (D) five : seven
    (E) zero : nine

23. NOVEL : WORDS :: (A) videotape : camera (B) recipe : directions (C) water : fish
    (D) yarn : knitting (E) symphony : notes

24. BREAKFAST : LUNCH :: (A) coffee : tea (B) night : evening (C) snack : feast
    (D) morning : noon (E) day : night

25. LENGTH : WEIGHT :: (A) short : tall (B) inches : pounds (C) area : volume
    (D) foot : feet (E) weigh : measure

Error Identification

In **error identification** questions, you are asked to find mistakes in English usage. In each sentence certain words or phrases are underlined and marked with letters. You are asked to choose the underlined part that contains an error or to mark *E* if the sentence is correct. Here is a typical question:

> The courses in <u>your</u> school <u>sounds</u> <u>more interesting</u> than the courses
>   A   B   C
>
> in <u>mine</u>. <u>No error</u>
>   D   E

The following strategies can help you answer error identification questions:

- Read the whole sentence carefully.

- Reread the sentence, paying attention to each underlined part. Check for lack of agreement, errors in capitalization and punctuation, and mistakes in sentence construction and in choice and form of words. In the sample question, the subject of the sentence, *courses,* is plural and therefore requires a plural verb. Since the verb *sounds,* is singular, the answer is *B.*

Choose the letter of the underlined part that contains an error. If the sentence is correct, mark *E.*

1. <u>No one</u> <u>is</u> <u>real sure</u> whether the kite <u>was invented</u> in Greece or in China.
   A   B   C   D

   <u>No error</u>
    E

2. <u>Many of the stories</u> about King Arthur <u>is</u> legendary, but <u>they are</u> based on
        A   B   C

   an actual person who lived around the year <u>A.D. 500</u>. <u>No error</u>
                                    D   E

3. We <u>can't</u> possibly divide all this wonderful <u>Italian food</u> <u>between</u> just
   A   B   C

   <u>you and I</u>. <u>No error</u>
    D   E

4. Although milk from <u>cows'</u> <u>is</u> popular in the United States, people in other
                 A   B

   parts of the <u>world</u> <u>drink</u> milk from goats, camels, and reindeer. <u>No error</u>
          C   D   E

5. "Please bring this package to <u>Louis's</u> <u>house</u>," said <u>my mother</u> to a friend
                                 A   B   C

   of <u>hers</u>. <u>No error</u>
       D   E

6. The <u>people</u> who live in <u>Milan,</u> Italy, <u>are knowed</u> as <u>Milanese</u>. <u>No error</u>
      A   B   C   D   E

7. The <u>members</u> of the marching band <u>look</u> <u>most happiest</u> when <u>they're</u>
      A   B   C   D

   performing. <u>No error</u>
              E

8. According to the <u>encyclopedia</u>, the <u>state of Kansas</u> <u>lays</u> midway <u>between</u>
                       A   B   C   D

   the Atlantic Ocean and the Pacific Ocean. <u>No error</u>
                                      E

9. In the <u>Middle Ages</u>, life in Europe was <u>extreme</u> hard, and people <u>lived</u>
        A   B   C

   an average of only <u>thirty years</u>. <u>No error</u>
                 D   E

10. <u>Its</u> time <u>to leave</u> for the <u>airport</u> now, so make sure <u>you're</u> ready to go.
    A   B   C   D

   <u>No error</u>
     E

11. Before <u>you speak,</u> <u>thought</u> about the effect <u>your</u> words <u>will have</u>
            A   B   C   D

   on other people. <u>No error</u>
                  E

12. The farmer <u>estimated</u> that the next <u>town, Beechwood,</u> <u>was</u> <u>approximately</u>
               A   B   C   D

   fifteen miles away. <u>No error</u>
                  E

13. <u>As</u> the storm <u>approach,</u> the wind grew <u>so violent</u> that the windows rattled
    A   B   C

   and the <u>house shook</u>. <u>No error</u>
            D   E

14. You can either stay home and watch a video and go to the movies.
   A   B   C   D

   No error
   E

15. People who are inactive lose about a quart of water in perspiration
            A   B

   a day, active men and women can give off as much as twenty quarts
        C   D

   in a day. No error
              E

16. Because of their razor-sharp teeth and their eagerness to attack
                     A

   anything that moves, the piranhas of South America are the more ferocious
        B   C   D

   of all fish. No error
                 E

17. Before the curtain rised, the auidence was already applauding
                     A   B   C

   enthusiastically. No error
        D   E

18. "Don't never run out into the street without looking again," my mother
        A   B   C

   yelled at my little sister. No error
    D   E

19. My teacher told me that I had done good on my English test and that she
                       A   B   C

   was proud of my hard word. No error
    D   E

20. On March 30, 1842, Dr. C. W. Long became the first doctor to use general
        A   B

   anesthesia for surgery when he taken a growth from a patient's neck.
                              C   D

   No error
   E

Error Correction

Error correction questions test your ability to identify and correct mistakes in grammar, usage, and the way sentences are put together.

Part A

In one type of error correction question, you are given a sentence with a part underlined, followed by four ways of rewriting that part. You are asked to choose the answer that best replaces the underlined words without changing the meaning of the sentence. Answer choice *A* is always the same as the original. Here is a sample question:

Hundreds of Native American languages were once spoken in North America, only a few have survived, however.
(A) America, only a few have survived, however.
(B) America only a few have survived however.
(C) America; of which only a few have survived, however.
(D) America. Only a few have survived, however.

The following strategies can help you answer this type of test question:

- Read the entire sentence first.

- Read each answer choice and substitute it in the sentence. Think about standard English usage and proper sentence construction. Then choose the most effective revision. If the original sentence is correct, mark *A*. In the sample question, *D* correctly revises the run-on sentence, creating two complete sentences.

Choose the answer that best corrects each sentence without changing its meaning. If the original sentence is correct, mark *A*.

1. More than 16 million newcomers to the United States passed through Ellis Island, where immigrants were processed there from 1892 to 1943.
   (A) Island, where immigrants were processed there from 1892 to 1943.
   (B) Island, where immigrants were processed from 1892 to 1943.
   (C) Island, processing immigrants there fom 1892 to 1943.
   (D) Island, on account of immigrants were processed there from 1892 to 1943.

2. The painters finished painting that there room in only two hours.
   (A) painting that there room
   (B) painted that there room
   (C) painting that room
   (D) their painting that room

3. Bartlett <u>pears being</u> the most popular pears in this country.
   (A) pears being
   (B) pears, which are
   (C) pears, having been
   (D) pears are

4. The ancient Egyptians greased the axles of their chariots with <u>petroleum that they found seeping from the ground.</u>
   (A) petroleum that they found seeping from the ground.
   (B) petroleum of which they found seeping from the ground.
   (C) petroleum, which, seeping from the ground, they found.
   (D) petroleum which was found by them seeping from the ground.

5. All the skiers in the group started out together, but <u>the end of the trail was not reached by everyone.</u>
   (A) the end of the trail was not reached by everyone.
   (B) everyone was not reached by the end of the trail.
   (C) not everyone reached the end of the trail.
   (D) no one didn't reach the end of the trail.

6. The city of <u>Kenosha lying</u> about thirty-five miles south of Milwaukee, Wisconsin.
   (A) Kenosha lying
   (B) Kenosha laid
   (C) Kenosha lies
   (D) Kenosha lain

7. Apologizing can sometimes be <u>the harder thing a person must do.</u>
   (A) the harder thing a person must do.
   (B) the hardest thing a person must do.
   (C) the most harder thing a person must do.
   (D) of the things a person must do, the harder to be done.

8. Inez <u>doesn't never like to watch</u> horror films.
   (A) doesn't never like to watch
   (B) does ever like to watch
   (C) ever like to watch
   (D) doesn't like to watch

9. <u>You and I</u> may never agree about baseball, but we can still be friends.
   (A) You and I
   (B) You and me
   (C) Me and you
   (D) The two of we

10. Another of those dangerous tropical storms are brewing far out in the Atlantic Ocean.
    - (A) Another of those dangerous tropical storms are brewing far out in the Atlantic Ocean.
    - (B) The Atlantic Ocean is brewing another of those far out, dangerous tropical storms.
    - (C) Another of those dangerous tropical storms is brewing far out in the Atlantic Ocean.
    - (D) Far out in the Atlantic Ocean another of those dangerous storms is tropically brewing.

11. Roentgen was a German physicist. Who discovered X-rays.
    - (A) physicist. Who discovered X-rays.
    - (B) physicist who discovered X-rays.
    - (C) physicist that was discovered by X-rays.
    - (D) physicist; until he discovered X-rays.

12. Those kind of animal may soon be added to endangered list.
    - (A) Those kind of animal
    - (B) That kind of animal
    - (C) These kind animals
    - (D) Them kinds of animal

13. Maureen enjoyed the crafts exhibit very much, and she didn't want to go back next year.
    - (A) very much, and she didn't want to go back next year.
    - (B) very much, because she doesn't want to go back next year.
    - (C) very much; for that reason, she didn't want to go back next year.
    - (D) very much, although she doesn't want to go back next year.

14. The farmers' market offers a wide variety of fresh fruits and vegetables, homemade baked goods, and items such as dried flowers and candles.
    - (A) a wide variety of fresh fruits and vegetables, homemade baked goods, and items such as dried flowers and candles.
    - (B) a variety of wide and fresh fruits and vegetables and homemade and baked goods. Also items such as dried flowers and candles.
    - (C) a wide variety of fresh and homemade and dried fruits, vegetables, baked goods, flowers, candles, and such other items.
    - (D) fresh fruits, vegetables; homemade baked goods; dried flowers, candles; and other items in such a wide variety.

15. By 1795 Vermont and Kentucky had become states, and two stars are added to the United States flag.
    - (A) and two stars are added
    - (B) along with two stars having added
    - (C) and two stars were added
    - (D) before which two stars added

Part B

In another type of error correction question, you are given a passage with certain words underlined and numbered. You must choose the best version of each numbered word or phrase from four choices listed at the right. If the original is correct, mark *A* or *F.* Here is a sample passage:

The dinosaur is usually pictured in movies as a	1. A. No change
	B. with any
huge, aggressive creature <u>with hardly no</u>	C. with hardly any
<div align="center">1</div>	D. hardly without no
intelligence. Current research on dinosaurs,	2. F. No change
	G. suggest
however, <u>suggests</u> that this image is not correct.	H. suggested
<div align="center">2</div>	J. were suggesting

The following strategies can help you answer these questions:

- Read the entire passage carefully.

- Then reread each sentence. Pay special attention to the underlined parts.

- Decide whether the underlined part contains an error. If it does, decide which rewording at the right corrects the error. In question 1 of the example, *with hardly no* is incorrect, since it includes a double negative. The correct rewording is *C, with hardly any.*

- If the underlined part is correct, select the first choice. In question 2 of the example, the underlined part is correct, so the answer is *F, No change.*

For centuries, infections from bacteria <u>was</u> a leading cause of death.
16

In fact, as recently as fifty years ago, a sore throat, <u>a wound; or</u> even a
17

small scratch could easily turn into a life-threatening illness. The reason

that infections used to be much <u>seriouser</u> than they are today <u>are</u> that
18   19

there were no drugs that could fight bacteria successfully. Few people

believed that antibiotics, <u>them modern</u> miracle drugs, would be possible.
20

Most doctors thought that if a medicine was strong enough to kill

<u>bacteria, then</u> it would probably kill the patient too. Therefore, they relied
21

on time, rest, nourishment, and the <u>bodys' own</u> defense system to fight
22

disease. Unfortunately, however, this approach did not always <u>work good</u>
23

enough to save the patient's life. Until the middle of the 1940s, every

hospital had a ward where patients with infections were kept for weeks

or even months until they either got better or died.

Then, on March 14, 1942, a woman named Ann Miller <u>lay</u> in a
24

Connecticut hospital, dying of a severe infection. The doctors had used

the only medicines they had, sulfa drugs and snake serum, but neither

<u>were helping</u>. Fortunately, her doctor had a friend <u>who knowed</u> about
25   26

an experimental drug that seemed to kill bacteria.

16. A. No change
    B. being
    C. has been
    D. were

17. F. No change
    G. a wound, or
    H. a wound or
    J. or wound

18. A. No change
    B. more seriouser
    C. more serious
    D. serious

19. F. No change
    G. were
    H. was being
    J. is

20. A. No change
    B. those modern
    C. they modern
    D. they're modern

21. F. No change
    G. bacteria because
    H. bacteria before
    J. bacteria, but also

22. A. No change
    B. body whose own
    C. body's own
    D. owners' body

23. F. No change
    G. worked good
    H. work well
    J. work better

24. A. No change
    B. lying
    C. laid
    D. lies

25. F. No change
    G. are helping
    H. was helping
    J. help

26. A. No change
    B. who'll know
    C. who know
    D. who knew

This drug, penicillin, had been discovered in 1928 by a British scientist,

Alexander Fleming, who noticed mold growing in a dish that contained

common <u>bacteria he</u> saw that the bacteria around the mold <u>have died</u>.
         27   28

It was not until the late 1930s, <u>however, that</u> scientists were able to
                                    29

separate the substance that <u>actual killed</u> the bacteria.
                             30

This experimental drug was rushed to the hospital and <u>was gave</u> to
                                               31

Ann Miller. Within hours she was <u>better within</u> days she was ready to go
                                    32

home. Ann Miller was the first person <u>what</u> penicillin cured. Now <u>they are</u>
                                    33   34

many drugs that fight bacteria, and such "miracle" cures happen

<u>thousands of times</u> each day.
          35

27. F. No change
    G. bacteria: He
    H. bacteria after he
    J. bacteria and

28. A. No change
    B. is dead
    C. having died
    D. had died

29. F. No change
    G. however, which
    H. however; since
    J. however they

30. A. No change
    B. actual kill
    C. actually killed
    D. actually kill

31. F. No change
    G. is giving
    H. gave
    J. was given

32. A. No change
    B. better; within
    C. better; since within
    D. better before

33. F. No change
    G. whom
    H. whose
    J. of which

34. A. No change
    B. they be
    C. there are
    D. there is

35. F. No change
    G. thousand of time
    H. thousand of times
    J. thousands of time

Reading Comprehension

Reading-comprehension questions test your ability to understand written material and to draw conclusions based on what you have read. The following approaches can help you answer reading-comprehension questions:

- Read the entire passage quickly.

- Read the questions that follow the passage.

- Read the passage again. As you read, think about the questions you will have to answer.

- Reread each question carefully. Choose the response that best answers the question. If necessary, go back and reread part or all of the passage.

You are going to read a passage about the growing problem of trash disposal from "America the Not-so-Beautiful" by Andrew A. Rooney. Answer the first two questions before you begin reading.

1. Which idea would you not expect to be discussed in this passage?
   (A) the types of trash people produce
   (B) the various manufacturers of garbage trucks
   (C) how trash is disposed of
   (D) the effects of trash disposal on the environment
   (E) what might happen if the trash problem is not dealt with

2. What do you suppose the author's purpose for writing this article might have been?
   (A) to talk about American beauty products
   (B) to trace the history of garbage through the ages
   (C) to advertise the services of a trash-disposal company
   (D) to get sympathy for garbage collectors
   (E) to inform people about the trash problem

Throwing things out is the American way. We don't know how to fix anything, and anyone who does know how is too busy to come, so we throw it away and buy a new one. Our economy depends on us doing that. The trouble with throwing things away is, there is no "away" left. . . .

5   We've been doing that for so many years that (1) we've run out of places to throw things because houses have been built where the dump was and (2) some of the things we're throwing away are poisoning the earth and will eventually poison all of us and all living things.

Ten years ago most people thought nothing of dumping an old bottle of
10   weed or insect killer in a pile of dirt in the back yard or down the drain in the street, just to get rid of it. The big companies in America had the same feeling, on a bigger scale. For years the chemical companies dumped their poisonous wastes in the rivers behind the mills, or they put it in fifty-gallon drums. . . . The drums rusted out in ten years and dumped their poison into the ground.

15   It rained, the poisons seeped into the underground streams and poisoned everything for miles around. . . .

      The people of the city of New York throw away nine times their weight in garbage and junk every year. Assuming other cities come close to that, how long will it be before we trash the whole earth?

20   Of all household waste, 30 percent of the weight and 50 percent of the volume is the packaging that stuff comes in.

      Not only that, but Americans spend more for the packaging of food than all our farmers together make in income growing it. That's some statistic. . . .

      If 5 billion people had been living on earth for the past thousand years as

25   they have been in the past year, the planet would be nothing but one giant landfill, and we'd have turned America the beautiful into one huge landfill.

      The best solution may be for all of us to pack up, board a spaceship, and move out. If Mars is habitable, everyone on Earth can abandon this planet we've trashed, move to Mars, and start trashing that. It'll buy us some time.

3. Which word best describes Rooney's feelings about the trash problem?
   (A) amusement
   (B) confusion
   (C) rejection
   (D) concern
   (E) indifference

4. What audience do you think Rooney was writing for?
   (A) mathematicians
   (B) the general public
   (C) garbage collectors
   (D) farmers
   (E) the food-packing industry

5. What does Rooney mean when he says "there is no 'away' left" (line 4)?
   (A) The world is getting smaller and smaller.
   (B) People are in poor physical condition and can't throw far any more.
   (C) Throwing things away is too much work for people.
   (D) There's no more room on the earth to dump trash.
   (E) Many people's houses look like garbage dumps.

6. What phrase has the same meaning as "thought nothing of" (line 9) as it is used in this passage?
   (A) ignored
   (B) did not agree with
   (C) were not concerned about
   (D) thought about nothing
   (E) forgot

7. What percentage of household waste is the packaging things come in?
   (A) 30 percent of the weight and 50 percent of the volume
   (B) 50 percent of the weight and 30 percent of the volume
   (C) 900 percent
   (D) 100 percent
   (E) 10 percent

8. What does the statement "That's some statistic" (line 23) suggest in this passage?
   (A) Farmers make too much money.
   (B) Farmers should package the food they grow.
   (C) It's amazing that what people pay for the packaging of food is more than the farmers who grow the food earn.
   (D) The packaging of food costs too much to even calculate.
   (E) The statement about the food packaging and farmers' incomes isn't true.

9. What is Rooney's attitude when he suggests that we should abandon Earth and settle on Mars?
   (A) uncertain
   (B) sarcastic
   (C) serious
   (D) aggressive
   (E) apologetic

10. What does Rooney really think people should do about the growing trash problem?
    (A) They should ignore it so that it will go away.
    (B) They should leave it behind and move to Mars.
    (C) They should build bigger garbage dumps.
    (D) They should all go on diets.
    (E) They should take it seriously and try to find practical solutions before it is too late.

Below are two passages about great African-American athletes and the courage they displayed on the baseball field. The first is "To Satch," a poem written by Samuel Allen in honor of a famous pitcher named Satchel Paige. The second is an excerpt from The Quality of Courage *by Mickey Mantle, an outfielder for the New York Yankees.*

Passage I—To Satch

Sometimes I feel like I will never stop
Just go on forever
Till one fine mornin'
I'm gonna reach up and grab me
5   a handfulla stars
Throw out my long lean leg
And whip three hot strikes burnin'
down the heavens
And look over at God and say
10   *How about that!*

Passage II—from *The Quality of Courage*

Sometimes courage is very quiet. People who saw Jackie Robinson play baseball remember him as a hard, aggressive, noisy ball player who was always in the middle of every argument—when he wasn't winning a game by stealing home or driving in the go-ahead run or making a game-saving play in the field. I
15   thought he was one of the best ball players I ever saw, and when he played against teams that I was on—in the World Series of 1952 and 1953 and 1955 and 1956—he always showed a lot of guts.

But he had even more courage his first year in the majors, 1947, when I was still a young high school kid in Oklahoma. That year Robinson hardly ever
20   opened his mouth, he never argued, he didn't get into any fights, he was the quietest, politest player anyone ever saw. When you think of Jackie's natural personality—he liked action, arguments, rough games, give and take, and he liked to be in the center of the stage, talking, yelling, taking charge—you wonder how he ever was able to control himself that first year. Especially in the face of the
25   riding he took, the things he was called. . . .

There's an odd thing about Jackie Robinson. I myself was never very friendly with him, and I have found that a lot of people who knew him in and out of baseball really dislike him. He's a hard man for some people to like because he isn't soft and smooth-talking and syrupy. He's tough and independent, and he
30   says what he thinks, and he rubs people the wrong way. But I have never heard of anyone who knew Jackie Robinson, whether they liked him of disliked him, who didn't respect him and admire him. That might be more important than being liked.

11. Which adjective best describes how the speaker feels at the end of the first passage?
    (A) angry
    (B) amused
    (C) humble
    (D) disgusted
    (E) excited

12. For Passage I, which sentence best states what the speaker thinks of Satchel Paige?
    (A) He was overly proud of himself.
    (B) He never played as well as he could have.
    (C) He was so good that he could have impressed God.
    (D) He never got the praise he deserved.
    (E) He was not good enough to play in the major leagues.

13. In Passage I, what is the speaker describing?
    (A) how Satchel Paige learned to pitch
    (B) what Satchel Paige will do when he dies
    (C) where Satchel Paige grew up
    (D) why Satchel Paige was a great pitcher
    (E) when Satchel Paige retired

14. What is Passage II mostly about?
    (A) Mickey Mantle's career
    (B) growing up in Oklahoma
    (C) how to win baseball games
    (D) Jackie Robinson's courage
    (E) playing in the World Series

15. According to Passage II, which word best describes Jackie Robinson's personality on the ball field?
    (A) aggressive
    (B) clever
    (C) rude
    (D) nasty
    (E) sneaky

16. In Passage II, what was it about Jackie Robinson in his first year in the majors that impressed the narrator most?
    (A) Robinson once scored by stealing home.
    (B) He somehow controlled himself and stayed quiet.
    (C) Robinson got into the middle of every argument.
    (D) He made a number of game-saving plays.
    (E) Robinson showed a lot of guts in the World Series.

17. Which sentence best describes the meaning of "he rubs people the wrong way" as it is used in Passage II (line 33)?
    (A) He bumps into other players.
    (B) He is not friendly to other people.
    (C) He likes to slide into other players.
    (D) He makes people angry.
    (E) He thinks he is better than other people.

18. Which adjective best describes the narrator's attitude toward Jackie Robinson at the end of passage II?
    (A) respectful
    (B) resentful
    (C) indifferent
    (D) frightened
    (E) confused

19. What do the narrators of both passages express about their subjects?
    (A) disappointment
    (B) confidence
    (C) admiration
    (D) dislike
    (E) envy

20. Which statement best expresses a theme that could apply to both passages?
    (A) Smooth-talking people cannot be trusted.
    (B) Winning is everything.
    (C) Great baseball players never die.
    (D) Great athletes deserve our respect.
    (E) Winners don't have to argue.

Strategies for Reading Placement

The Language of Literature is designed for heterogeneous classrooms; its literature and activities are meant to be accessible to students with a wide range of ability levels. In the course of the year, however, you may wish to evaluate a student's ability to perform successfully on grade level. The following informal strategies may help you determine the student's placement in the series.

Steps in Informal Placement

1. Choose a Selection

Choose a prose selection in *The Language of Literature* text that you feel the student will find interesting and about which he or she has some prior knowledge.

2. Evaluate Oral Reading

In order to assess the student's ability to recognize words on sight, have the student read aloud to you the first two or three paragraphs of the chosen selection, approximately 75 to 100 words. If the student can read at least 85 percent of the words correctly, he or she can probably read most of the words in the entire selection successfully.

To determine if there is 85 percent recognition, count the errors the student makes while reading. The following student behaviors count as errors *only* if the behavior changes meaning or prevents understanding.

- *Mispronunciations:* words that are mispronounced, with the exception of proper nouns and foreign words

- *Omissions:* words crucial to understanding a sentence or a concept that are left out

- *Additions:* words inserted in a sentence that change the meaning of the text

- *Substitutions:* words substituted for actual words in the text that change the meaning of a sentence. An acceptable substitution, which would not be counted as an error, might be the word *hard* for *difficult.*

Fifteen or more errors indicates that the selection may be too difficult for the student.

3. Evaluate Comprehension

Find the *Formal Assessment* resource book. Look up Selection Test and Additional Test Generator questions that accompany the selection you have chosen. From those tests, choose five questions that you believe are most representative of your own instruction. Choose some literal questions and some higher-level thinking-skill questions.

To make sure that students have a purpose for reading, read to them the questions you have selected. Then allow them to read the rest of the selection silently, encouraging them to keep these questions in mind.

When they finish reading, ask students to respond to the questions, either orally or in writing. If the student responds correctly or thoughtfully to four of the five questions, he or she will probably be successful in that text.

4. Determine Placement

If the student performs successfully both in oral reading and in comprehending what is read silently, the student should continue receiving instruction in that grade-level text. Those students who read somewhat above or below grade level will probably also be successful; both the Annotated Teacher's Edition and the Teacher's Resource File contain many suggestions and aids for helping those who have difficulty as well as challenging those who read well.

You may decide that the grade-level text is just too long or too easy for a student. In that case, you might place the student in a lower or higher grade-level *The Language of Literature* text.

Final decisions about placement may be based on other diagnostic information previously acquired about the student as well as further oral reading samples and comprehension tests. Finally, you as a teacher should take into consideration your own teaching style and expectations as you determine placement for each student.

Answer Key

Contents

The Language of Literature Test Answers

Unit One

Eleven

Selection Test, pp. 5–6

A. (15 points each) Notes will vary widely but could include the following traits and details:
1. Rachel's traits:
   a. emotional
   b. shy
   c. worried about how others judge her
   d. unassertive
   Details:
   a. She cries over a red sweater.
   b. She is unable to speak up for herself and tell Mrs. Price that the sweater is not hers.
   c. She thinks that Sylvia claims the sweater belongs to Rachel because Rachel is too skinny or because Sylvia just doesn't like her.
   d. She does what Mrs. Price tells her to do; she even puts on a sweater that does not belong to her.
2. Mrs. Price's traits:
   a. unkind
   b. sure of herself
   c. unwilling to listen
   d. insensitive
   Details:
   a. She forces Rachel to take the sweater and put it on.
   b. She thinks that she is right about the sweater and will not admit that she is wrong.
   c. She does not listen to Rachel or help her express herself.
   d. She does not seem to realize how much she has upset Rachel.

B. (5 points each)
1. a
2. c
3. b
4. d

C. (4 points each)
1. c
2. a
3. c
4. a

D. (20 points; students should answer one of the two)
1. Answers will vary. Most students will probably judge Mrs. Price's behavior unfavorably because she
   a. ignores Rachel's reactions.
   b. forces Rachel to wear the sweater.
   c. doesn't seem to notice or care that she is humiliating Rachel.
   d. fails to apologize for her mistake, even though it has driven Rachel to tears.

Some students may see Mrs. Price's behavior as forgivable, saying that
   a. teachers are too busy to worry about each individual student's needs.
   b. Rachel simply makes too big a deal out of the situation.
2. Answers will vary widely. Students who feel sorry for Rachel might note that, through no fault of her own,
   a. everyone has treated her poorly.
   b. her birthday has gone badly.
   c. she feels very unhappy.
   Students who feel irritated with Rachel might note that she
   a. should have stuck up for herself.
   b. is very moody and negative about everything.
   c. is too quick to feel sorry for herself.
   d. doesn't try to do anything to change her situation or her mood.
   Other answers should be supported with appropriate reasons or references to the story.

E. (14 points) Answers will vary widely, depending on students' personal experiences, situations, and viewpoints. Accept any answers that address the concern of the question and are elaborated by examples or details from the literature or from life.

President Cleveland, Where Are You?

Selection Test, pp. 7–8

A. (6 points each) Notes will vary but should suggest the following events:
1. Conflict: Jerry feels guilty because he contributes so little for his father's birthday gift.
2. Rising Action: Jerry collects president cards, and Armand falls in love with Sally.
3. Climax: Jerry gets a Grover Cleveland card.
4. Falling Action: Jerry tells Roger that he sold his Cleveland card to Rollie Tremaine. (He sold it so Armand could go to the dance with Sally.)
5. Resolution: Roger "forgives" Jerry for what he did.

B. (5 points each)
1. c
2. d
3. a

C. (4 points each)
1. b
2. a
3. c
4. a
5. b

D. (20 points; students should answer one of the two)
1. Answers will vary but should suggest these reasons:
   a. Jerry felt guilty for contributing so little for his father's birthday gift.

b. His brother Armand needed money to go to a dance with Sally Knowlton.

c. Jerry knew his father could not afford to help.

d. Jerry knew that going out with Sally was very important to his brother.

e. Jerry felt a need to do something for his family because they had always taken care of him.

2. Answers will vary. Students will most likely feel that Jerry did something "fine and noble" because he

a. gave up his own reward for his brother.

b. put his family's needs before his own.

c. risked his friendship with Roger and the others to help his brother.

Some students might think Jerry was a traitor because

a. he and his friend Roger were determined not to let Rollie get the glove.

b. Roger was miserable because Rollie got the glove and was being a showoff.

c. he put his family's needs before those of his friends.

E. (15 points) Answers will vary widely, depending on students' personal experiences, situations, and viewpoints. Accept any answers that address the concern of the question and are elaborated by examples or details from the literature or from life.

Scout's Honor

Selection Test, pp. 9–10

A. (6 points each) Notes will vary but should suggest the following:

1. The story takes place in 1946 on a weekend, probably during the summer.

2. The boys live in Brooklyn, a place "made of slate pavements, streets of asphalt (or cobblestone), and skies full of tall buildings."

3. The boys go to the Palisades in New Jersey, a "grove of trees" that was littered with "discarded cans, bottles, and newspapers—plus an old mattress spring."

4. The boys try to prove they are tough by camping in the "country," but they have trouble coping with an unfamiliar place. They are confused by the subway, frightened by having to cross the bridge, disoriented by fog, dampened by rain, and uncomfortable in their campsite.

B. (5 points each)

1. b
2. d
3. a
4. b

C. (4 points each)

1. b
2. c
3. a
4. b
5. c

D. (20 points; students should answer one of the two)

1. Answers will vary. Students may feel that the boys succeeded because they traveled to New Jersey on their own and were "tough" enough to admit that they were not enjoying themselves. Other students may feel that the boys failed because they gave up their plan to camp overnight and went home. Ways they tried to prove they were tough might include:

a. traveling on their own

b. crossing the George Washington Bridge

c. refusing to admit they were scared

d. camping out

e. coping with rain, smoke, and other discomforts

2. Answers will vary but should include some of the following:

Parts of the law the boys followed:

a. They were loyal and helpful to one another.

b. They were brave to cross the bridge and try to camp.

c. At the end, they were honest with one another.

Parts of the law the boys broke:

a. They lied to their parents when they claimed Mr. Brenkman was going on the trip.

b. They were not clean or reverent, since they got filthy, were looked on as "juvenile delinquents," and probably left all their trash at the campsite.

c. They were probably not obedient, since they took things from home without permission (the mattress, "my mother's favorite blanket").

E. (16 points) Answers will vary widely, depending on students' personal experiences, situations, and viewpoints. Accept any answers that address the concern of the question and are elaborated by examples or details from the literature or from life.

Nadia the Willful

Selection Test, pp. 11–12

A. (8 points each) Answers will vary. Possible answers include the following:

1. Theme: The best way to deal with painful events is to face them; or, ignoring painful events or pretending that they haven't occurred only prolongs suffering. Details: The sheik's command doesn't allow the people to deal with Hamed's death; their suffering doesn't end until they are allowed to talk about Hamed and share their feelings with others.

2. Theme: The wisdom of children should not be ignored. Details: Even a child (such as Nadia) has something to teach an adult (such as the sheik) about life (and death).

3. Theme: People need to speak out when the government acts in ways that are harmful to its citizens. Details: Nadia speaks out and defies the law when the sheik's command brings harm to her people.

B. (5 points each)
1. d
2. a
3. b
4. c

C. (4 points each)
1. b
2. c
3. b
4. a
5. a

D. (20 points; students should answer one of the two)
1. Answers will vary. Students might say the sheik believed his command would
   a. help people to miss Hamed less.
   b. make the pain of Hamed's death go away more quickly.
   c. allow their lives to get back to normal more quickly.
2. Answers will vary. Students might mention these points:
   a. The story takes place in the desert, and Hamed is lost in a sandstorm.
   b. In Bedouin culture, the sheik is a powerful leader. He is strict with his people because survival in the desert requires order and cooperation.
   c. People follow the sheik's orders because it is too dangerous to go it alone in the desert.
   d. Nadia is known for her willfulness because she is independent, which is unusual in Bedouin culture. However, Bedouins also value wisdom, so the sheik changes her title when she proves how wise she is.

E. (16 points) Answers will vary widely, depending on students' personal experiences, situations, and viewpoints. Accept any answers that address the concern of the question and are elaborated by examples or details from the literature or from life.

Unit One, Part One Test
pp. 13–14
A. (5 points each) Answers will vary but should suggest the following:
1. Nadia proved that she was wise by convincing the sheik that the best way to deal with his grief was to talk about Hamed and remember him.
2. Mrs. Price forced Rachel to take the red sweater, but it was not hers.
3. He wanted to collect a complete set of president cards so he could get a new baseball glove, and the President Cleveland card was the last one he needed.
4. They went camping to fulfill the Scout Craft requirement for Boy Scouts, or to prove that they were tough.

B. (20 points) Notes will vary. A model answer for Jerry in "President Cleveland, Where Are You?" follows.
1. Jerry struggles against his desire to get a new baseball glove and to make sure that Rollie Tremaine does not get the glove.
2. Yes, he wins the struggle.
3. Jerry feels guilty about giving so little money for his father's birthday present. He understands how important going to the dance is for his brother Armand. He knows that their father cannot help because he has no money and was recently laid off from work. He also understands that Armand and the rest of the family have made sacrifices, and he decides that he must make a sacrifice too, to help his brother.

C. (20 points each; students should answer two of the three)
1. Answers will vary. A model answer for Nadia in "Nadia the Willful" and Rachel in "Eleven" follows.
   Nadia took the greatest risk in that she
   a. defied her father's decree.
   b. risked banishment from the clan or other severe punishment.
   c. risked losing her home, friends, and family.
   Her actions were courageous because she understood the possible consequences but felt that she had to defy her father for the sake of her own peace, her father's peace, and the good of the community. Her actions were also reckless because her father was powerful, and she faced the possible dangers of trying to survive in the desert on her own.
   Rachel risks the least in that she
   a. only has to tell the teacher that the sweater is not hers.
   b. risks embarrassment in front of the other students but does not face any serious danger.
   Her actions are not courageous because she is too afraid even to tell Mrs. Price that the red sweater is not hers.
2. Answers will vary. A model answer for the narrator in "Scout's Honor" and Nadia in "Nadia the Willful" follows.
   The narrator in "Scout's Honor" would agree with this statement because
   a. he had to go on an overnight hike in order to advance to "Tenderfoot, Second Class."
   b. he had to lead the way across the bridge so he would not look like a coward.
   c. he had to go through with the camping trip so his friends would think he was tough.
   Nadia would agree with this statement because she had to
   a. remember Hamed to find her own peace.
   b. defy her father for the good of the clan.
   c. convince her father that his decree was a mistake.

3. Answers will vary. A model answer for "Nadia the Willful" and "Eleven" follows.

The setting of "Nadia the Willful" is important to the plot in that

a. Hamed is lost in a sandstorm.

b. the sheik is harsh and strict because the desert is dangerous, requiring cooperation and survival.

c. Nadia is known for her willfulness because she is an independent girl in a society that frowns on that.

d. people follow the sheik's orders because it is too dangerous to go it alone in the desert.

The setting of "Eleven" is not very important to the plot because similar events could occur

a. in practically any school or similar institution anywhere in the world.

b. at practically any time in modern history.

D. (20 points) Answers will vary. A model answer for the narrator in "Scout's Honor" follows.

The narrator faced the challenges of

a. going on an overnight hike.

b. leaving Brooklyn for the first time.

c. traveling without an adult.

d. crossing the George Washington Bridge.

e. trying to prove that he was tough.

The character stayed true to himself in that he

a. was determined to overcome the obstacles he faced, and he did overcome most of them.

b. knew that he was afraid and did not feel at all tough, and he admitted as much to his friends.

Matthew Henson at the Top of the World
Selection Test, pp. 15–16

A. (8 points each) Questions will vary but should be specific and appropriate to the source. They should also ask for important rather than trivial information. A model answer follows.

1. Captain Childs's diaries: What subjects did Matthew Henson like best as a student of Childs?

2. Robert Peary's autobiography: What strengths and abilities did Henson have that set him apart from the other members of the expedition?

3. Matthew Henson's friends: How did Henson feel about being overlooked for the honors that Peary received?

B. (5 points each)

1. a
2. d
3. c
4. b

C. (4 points each)

1. b
2. a
3. b
4. c
5. a

D. (20 points; students should answer one of the two)

1. Answers will vary but should include points similar to the following:

a. Henson learned to be a sailor, which was useful when he sailed to the Arctic with Peary.

b. Childs educated Henson in a variety of subjects, which enabled him to make valuable contributions to Peary's expeditions.

c. Under Childs's supervision, Henson worked hard, and in Peary's expeditions he had to be willing and able to work hard in the most difficult and dangerous conditions.

d. Henson probably learned to navigate and take readings, which helped him follow the route to the North Pole.

e. Henson experienced many different cultures, which may have helped him get along with the Eskimos.

2. Answers will vary but should include points similar to the following:

a. Since no one had ever been there before, finding the North Pole was difficult and planning for the expedition's needs was a challenge.

b. The extreme cold caused many of the men to quit the expedition due to frostbite and exhaustion. It also made repairing the sledges time-consuming and difficult.

c. Equipment failures and problems with handling the dogs slowed down the expedition and wore down the men's stamina.

d. Open channels of water slowed the men because they had to wait until ice closed over the water.

e. Thin ice led to one fatality among the men.

f. The inability to carry large amounts of food or to replenish supplies forced the men to travel at an exhausting pace.

E. (16 points) Answers will vary widely, depending on students' personal experiences, situations, and viewpoints. Accept any answers that address the concern of the question and are elaborated by examples or details from the literature or from life.

Summer of Fire
Selection Test, pp. 17–18

A. (6 points each) Answers will vary but should include some of the following points:

1. June: Lightning started two fires in Yellowstone, which were allowed to burn.

2. July: Fires spread rapidly. The North Fork fire started. Park officials decided to put the fires out. Fire fighters arrived.

3. August: More than 150,000 acres burned in one day. Fire fighters worked to protect park communities.
4. September: Fires threatened the Old Faithful area and park headquarters. Finally the rains came, and the fires were put out.

B. (5 points each)
1. d
2. a
3. c
4. a

C. (4 points each)
1. b
2. c
3. b
4. c
5. a

D. (20 points; students should answer one of the two)
1. Answers will vary but could include the following:
   a. The summer was expected to be a rainy one.
   b. Rain extinguished the first fires of the summer.
   c. Fires actually encourage forest growth by renewing soil nutrients and clearing out dead wood and branches.
   d. The first fires did not present a danger to animals or property.
2. Answers will vary but could include the following:
   a. The policy of allowing wildfires to burn should be reconsidered and modified.
   b. A combination of dangerous conditions, such as frequent lightning, dry conditions, and/or high winds, indicate that fire fighters should put out fires.
   c. Don't wait until park communities are in certain danger before sending in fire fighters.

E. (16 points) Answers will vary widely, depending on students' personal experiences, situations, and viewpoints. Accept any answers that address the concern of the question and are elaborated by examples or details from the literature or from life.

Ghost of the Lagoon
Selection Test, pp. 19–20
A. (12 points each) Answers will vary but should accurately describe one external and one internal conflict. Examples:
1. External conflict: Tupa is about to attack Afa, Mako's beloved dog. The conflict is resolved when Mako kills Tupa with his spear and rescues Afa.
2. Internal conflict: Mako struggles with his own fears. Mako wants to kill Tupa to avenge his father's death, but he is terrified of the shark. The conflict is resolved when Mako finds the courage to kill Tupa.

B. (5 points each)
1. c
2. b
3. a
4. b

C. (4 points each)
1. a
2. b
3. b
4. c
5. a

D. (20 points; students should answer one of the two)
1. Answers will vary but could include the following reasons:
   a. to save Afa
   b. to do the right thing
   c. to be a hero
   d. to make his mother and grandfather proud
   e. to collect the king's reward of 30 acres of land and a canoe
   f. to avenge his father's death
   g. to eliminate Tupa as a threat to his community
2. Answers will vary, but students could say that Tupa
   a. is an especially large and fierce shark.
   b. has killed many people, including three fishermen who were strong swimmers.
   c. has an especially frightening appearance because he is white and he glows.
   d. attacks at night.
   e. has been described as a ghost in terrifying tales.
   f. has always taken the animals left for him on the reef, but his appetite seems never to be satisfied.
   g. is associated with evil and bad luck.
   h. lives where people can't avoid going.

E. (16 points) Answers will vary widely, depending on students' personal experiences, situations, and viewpoints. Accept any answers that address the concern of the question and are elaborated by examples or details from the literature or from life.

from The Fun of It
Selection Test, pp. 21–22
A. (8 points each) Details may vary. Factual information should be listed for the newspaper account; information listed for the autobiography should be more personal and/or subjective. Examples:
1. a. During the flight, the manifold wing developed a crack.
   b. Seeing the flames at night through the crack made the problem seem worse.
2. a. For the transatlantic flight, the plane carried 350 gallons of fuel.
   b. Earhart consumed only a can of tomato juice.

3. a. In rainy weather, Earhart looked for a place to land.
   b. The last two hours of the flight were the most difficult.

B. (5 points each)
1. a
2. b
3. c
4. d

C. (4 points each)
1. b
2. a
3. c
4. c
5. a

D. (20 points; students should answer one of the two)
1. Answers will vary but should include details similar to the following:
   a. She was able to fly without her altimeter, which failed.
   b. She flew through a severe storm with lightning.
   c. She decreased her altitude when her plane picked up ice.
   d. She used instruments to fly through thick fog.
   e. She decided that the crack in the plane's manifold was not bad enough to force her to land.
   f. When the sun was too bright to fly at a high altitude, she flew under the clouds.
   g. With a badly vibrating manifold and a leaking reserve tank, she decided to land as soon as possible.
   h. To prepare for landing, she flew away from bad weather and into clear weather by turning her plane north over Ireland.
   i. When she couldn't find an airport, she landed safely in a meadow.
2. Answers will vary but could include the following:
   a. physical and mental strength; to stay alert during a long flight
   b. intelligence; to evaluate circumstances as they arise (e.g., ice forms at high altitudes because the air is cold; an airport is most likely located near a city)
   c. patience; for the monotony of, for example, a long flight over water
   d. level-headedness; to take effective action in emergencies and to distinguish emergencies from situations that are not emergencies
   e. determination to finish what one has started; necessary for long, difficult flights

E. (16 points) Answers will vary widely, depending on students' personal experiences, situations, and viewpoints. Accept any answers that address the concern of the question and are elaborated by examples or details from the literature or from life.

Older Run
Selection Test, pp. 23–24
A. (12 points each) Descriptions will vary but should include both a factual description and additional details that add humor. A model answer follows.
1. a. Paulsen puts on the brake to stop the sled. He stops so abruptly that he is thrown through the air and lands in a snow bank.
   b. Paulsen describes himself as cartwheeling through the air, ricocheting off the trestle, and landing head first in the snow, like a falling arrow.
2. a. Paulsen releases Cookie and she runs off.
   b. Paulsen explains how Cookie was special to him and how he was sure she would stay, but she took off in an instant. He was deserted by his favorite dog, so he called her a traitor.

B. (5 points each)
1. d
2. c
3. d
4. a

C. (4 points each)
1. b
2. c
3. c
4. a
5. b

D. (20 points; students should answer one of the two)
1. Answers will vary but should include points similar to any two of the following:
   a. Obedience: Cookie had hit the trestle and run out, thinking that was what Paulsen wanted.
   b. A mother's protective instincts: She stopped on the trestle when the pups fell.
   c. Dependence: She looked to Paulsen to solve the problem.
   d. Independence: She ran off with the rest of the pups instead of staying with Paulsen.
   e. Leadership: She (apparently) rounded up the other dogs.
   f. Loyalty: She returned, with the other dogs, to Paulsen.
2. Answers may take either point of view and should be supported with at least two reasons. A model answer follows.
   Paulsen's troubles were the result of bad luck rather than bad decisions. Although he said he had too many dogs, the run was going well until, through bad luck, they encountered a trestle from which the plywood had been removed. Paulsen didn't make things worse by trying to turn the sled around on the trestle, which would have been a bad decision. Releasing the dogs and pulling the sled home was the best decision in a bad situation.

E. (16 points) Answers will vary widely, depending on students' personal experiences, situations, and viewpoints. Accept any answers that address the concern of the question and are elaborated by examples or details from the literature or from life.

from **Woodsong**
Selection Test, pp. 25–26

A. (12 points each) Notes will vary but should be similar to the following:
1. a. Scarhead was tearing up the burn area in an effort to find food when Paulsen noticed him.
   b. Paulsen had been having a bad day. When he saw what Scarhead was doing, he got angry.
2. a. Paulsen threw a stick at Scarhead, and the angry bear reared up threateningly.
   b. Paulsen was frozen with fear and so close to Scarhead that he could see the red around the bear's eyes and smell its breath.

B. (5 points each)
1. a
2. d
3. c
4. a

C. (4 points each)
1. a
2. c
3. c
4. a
5. b

D. (20 points; students should answer one of the two)
1. Answers will vary. Students should note at least two of these attitudes expressed by Paulsen, in correct sequence:
   a. Having bears around was a novelty for Paulsen.
   b. Paulsen became familiar with the bears, naming them as if they were pets.
   c. Paulsen's encounter with Scarhead reminded him that bears could be dangerous.
   d. Paulsen came to see himself as no more and no less than bears or other animals in the woods.
2. Answers will vary. Students should note at least two of these emotions described or suggested by Paulsen.
   a. Anger: He picked up the stick and threw it at Scarhead.
   b. Apprehension: He froze as the bear turned toward him.
   c. Fear: As the bear hung over him, Paulsen could not think or move.
   d. Anger: After the bear lowered, Paulsen ran for his gun.
   e. Empathy: Deciding that he should spare Scarhead just as Scarhead spared him, Paulsen put down his gun.

E. (16 points) Answers will vary widely, depending on students' personal experiences, situations, and viewpoints. Accept any answers that address the concern of the question and are elaborated by examples or details from the literature or from life.

Unit One, Part Two Test
pp. 27–28

A. (5 points each)
1. b
2. d
3. a
4. b

B. (20 points) Answers will vary. A model answer for Matthew Henson and Amelia Earhart follows.
1. In "Matthew Henson at the Top of the World," Henson faces the problem of trying to reach the North Pole in harsh weather and brutal conditions.
2. In the excerpt from *The Fun of It,* Amelia Earhart faces the problem of trying to cross the Atlantic Ocean by herself at night, in stormy weather, and with malfunctioning equipment.
   How the situations are similar: Both Henson and Earhart set demanding goals for themselves by striving to be the first to achieve something. Both had to contend with difficulties outside themselves, such as extreme weather or climate and insufficient or malfunctioning equipment, which tested their abilities and determination. Both succeed in solving their problems and reaching their goals through determination, skill, and perseverance.

C. (20 points each; students should answer two of the three)
1. Answers will vary. A model answer for *Woodsong* follows.
   This selection suggests the lesson that it is foolish to forget that wild animals can be dangerous and that they should not be thought of as pets. This lesson is important because wild animals
   a. do not have the same characteristics that pets have.
   b. have no reason to be patient with humans.
   c. do not feel affection for humans.
   d. have no sense of loyalty to humans.
   e. are concerned only with their own safety and survival.
   f. do not necessarily understand that a human behaving in a certain way is not really a serious danger to them.
   g. can be much stronger than humans, and some can easily destroy humans.

2. Answers will vary. A model answer for "Ghost of the Lagoon" and *The Fun of It* follows.
   In "Ghost of the Lagoon":
   a. Mako risks his life and his dog to kill Tupa.
   b. His reward will be 30 acres of land and a canoe. In addition, he will avenge his father's death and become a hero to his people.
   In the excerpt from *The Fun of It*:
   a. Amelia Earhart risks her life to cross the Atlantic Ocean.
   b. Her reward will mainly be the satisfaction of proving that she could do it. In addition, she will become famous.
   Students might argue that either reward is greater. For example, students might argue that Mako's reward is greater because he becomes famous among his people but also has something tangible to show for his efforts (land and a canoe).
3. Answers will vary. Students should choose a person and give reasons for admiring him or her. Example: A student might admire Matthew Henson most because he
   a. worked hard all his life to earn everything he got.
   b. persevered in spite of the racial prejudice and discrimination he faced.
   c. achieved the remarkable feat of reaching the North Pole, even though he received no credit for his accomplishment, at least at first.
   d. achieved a feat that was much more difficult than the things the people in the other selections accomplished.
4. Answers will vary. A model answer for "Older Run" follows.
   In "Older Run," Gary Paulsen (the narrator) does something foolish when he takes his dogs on a long run, gets stuck on a trestle, and decides to let the dogs go. He then begins pulling the sled himself. Although Paulsen makes light of the situation, it is dangerous: it is late at night in winter, he is far from home, the temperature is 20 below zero, and he does not have a lot of provisions (other than dog food). To think that he could pull the sled home himself is quite foolish. More likely, he would exhaust himself and get into real trouble.

D. (20 points) Answers will vary. A model answer for "Ghost of the Lagoon" and *Woodsong* follows.
1. Mako in "Ghost of the Lagoon":
   a. Mako's most courageous act was deciding to kill the shark instead of trying to escape.
   b. Mako did this mainly because he had to save his dog, Afa; in addition, he wanted to avenge his father's death and win the reward offered by the chief.

2. Gary Paulsen in the excerpt from *Woodsong*:
   a. Paulsen's most courageous act was deciding not to shoot Scarhead.
   b. Paulsen put down his gun because he realized that he had foolishly provoked a large bear, that Scarhead had spared his life, and that he had no real reason to shoot the bear.

Unit Two

I'm Nobody! Who Are You?/It Seems I Test People/Growing Pains
Selection Test, pp. 29–30

A. (6 points each) Notes will vary but should suggest interpretations similar to the following:
1. How common, or bold, to talk about oneself all the time, even though it means nothing.
2. I have dark (or brown, or black) skin, but it is made of more than one color.
3. I am ready to be friendly.
4. She said my room was really messy.

B. (6 points each)
1. a
2. b
3. d
4. d
5. b

C. (26 points; students should answer one of the two)
1. Notes will vary but should suggest ideas similar to the following:
   The speaker in "I'm Nobody! Who Are You?" feels
   a. happy that she is not well known in the world.
   b. close to others who are also "nobodies."
   c. amused by, rather than envious of, those who are well known.
   d. eager to protect her privacy.
   e. no need to explain or apologize for the way she is.
   The speaker in "It Seems I Test People"
   a. offers an explanation for exactly how he is different.
   b. describes how his skin, voice, laughter, and walk make him stand out.
   c. seems to want to be friendly to other people.
   d. seems sad that others avoid him.
2. Notes will vary but should suggest that the poem is titled "Growing Pains" because it
   a. is about how hard it is to grow up.
   b. shows that adults as well as children experience pain in their lives.
   c. shows that part of growing up is learning to experience and understand the pain of others.

D. (20 points) Answers will vary widely, depending on students' personal experiences, situations, and viewpoints. Accept any answers that address the concern of the question and are elaborated by examples or details from the literature or from life.

Three Haiku
Selection Test, pp. 31–32

A. (10 points each) Notes will vary but might suggest the following:
1. The haiku by Bashō suggests a feeling of
   a. strangeness.
   b. unfamiliarity.
   c. confusion.
   It expresses ideas involving
   a. identity.
   b. questioning who one really is.
   c. the relationship between the way things appear and the way they are.
   d. the effect of a change in appearance on the way a person feels.
   e. a focus on the speaker/poet rather than on an external scene.
   f. the emotions of someone who is not used to getting new clothes.
2. The haiku by Issa suggests a feeling of
   a. wonder.
   b. appreciation of beauty.
   It expresses ideas involving
   a. a vision of the night sky.
   b. a way of looking at the Milky Way.
   c. a comparison of the night sky with light shining through holes in a paper.
   d. looking at nature with fresh eyes.
3. The haiku by Patterson suggests a feeling of
   a. warmth.
   b. love.
   c. kindness.
   It expresses ideas involving
   a. a grandmother sitting in the sun.
   b. an appreciation for the warmth of the sun.
   c. a sense that nature is helpful.
   d. an interesting way of looking at sunlight.
   e. a comparison of sunlight with a quilt.
   f. a vision of sunlight as a cover.
   g. an appreciation of the color in light.
   h. the love of the speaker for his/her grandmother.

B. (10 points each)
1. a
2. d
3. c

C. (20 points; students should answer one of the two)
1. Answers will vary. Students could say that these poems reveal that haiku
   a. comment on a simple scene or moment.
   b. are very short.
   c. use few words.
   d. use simple language.
   e. are quite precise (or specific).

f. communicate a feeling.

g. often paint a picture with words.

h. suggest a new or unusual way of looking at something.

2. Answers will vary. A model answer for Patterson's haiku follows.

a. There is an old woman sitting indoors near a window.

b. She has been feeling chilly.

c. The sun begins to shine on her lap.

d. Its warmth makes her feel more comfortable.

e. She is grateful for the warmth.

D. (20 points) Answers will vary widely, depending on students' personal experiences, situations, and viewpoints. Accept any answers that address the concern of the question and are elaborated by examples or details from the literature or from life.

All Summer in a Day
Selection Test, pp. 33–34

A. (12 points each)

1. Notes will vary but might include the following:

a. The people live on Venus.

b. They travel by spaceship.

c. They live indoors nearly all the time.

d. It rains all day, every day, for years at a time.

e. The sun comes out only once every seven years for one hour.

2. Notes will vary but might include the following:

a. The children go to school.

b. The children laugh and run and play in the sun.

c. Some of the children are mean to others.

d. One child is an outsider who feels lonely.

e. The children feel ashamed of what they have done to Margot.

B. (5 points each)

1. d

2. b

3. b

4. a

C. (4 points each)

1. c

2. a

3. a

4. c

5. b

D. (20 points; students should answer one of the two)

1. Answers will vary. Students might say that Margot's talking about the sun makes the other children feel

a. jealous of Margot because they've missed out on something wonderful that only she has experienced.

b. inferior to Margot because she knows more about the sun than they do.

c. distanced from Margot because they can't understand her feelings about the sun.

d. fearful of Margot because her memories of the sun seem to make her so different from them.

2. Answers will vary. Students who think that the children will be more accepting of Margot might say that this will occur because they

a. feel terrible for having been so cruel to her.

b. now know what it means to miss the sun.

Students who think that the children will be less accepting of Margot might say that this will occur because

a. the experience will probably cause her to be even quieter and sadder than before and, therefore, more different from them than ever.

b. they know that she may be going back to Earth, where she will see the sun every day.

c. their guilt about locking her in the closet will make them want to avoid her.

E. (16 points) Answers will vary widely, depending on students' personal experiences, situations, and viewpoints. Accept any answers that address the concern of the question and are elaborated by examples or details from the literature or from life.

Chinatown *from* The Lost Garden
Selection Test, pp. 35–36

A. (8 points each)

1–3. Students should provide three details and describe how they made Yep feel. Examples of details might include the

a. lack of greenery.

b. ivy-covered slope.

c. charming cottage.

d. surrounding wealthy white areas.

e. rough housing projects.

f. concrete school playground.

g. tunnel between Chinatown and the wealthy white neighborhood.

Examples of Yep's feelings might include

a. feeling like an outsider (or left out).

b. anger about the unfair treatment of Chinese people.

c. alienation.

d. confusion about his identity or place in the community.

e. a desire to fit in.

f. mixed feelings about wanting to be Chinese and wanting to be American.

B. (5 points each)

1. d

2. c

3. c

4. a

C. (4 points each)
1. b
2. a
3. a
4. c
5. b

D. (20 points)
1. Answers will vary. Students may say that the puzzle is Yep's
   a. identity.
   b. cultural background.
   c. understanding of who he is.
   d. sense of how he fits into the world.
   Students may say that he's having a hard time putting the pieces together because he
   a. goes to school in Chinatown but doesn't speak Chinese.
   b. is from an athletic family but isn't good at sports.
   c. knows little about his cultural background.
   d. doesn't feel completely at home in Chinatown or outside it.
   e. is expected to do and know things that he can't do or doesn't know.
2. Answers will vary. Students may say that Yep is separated from his classmates and friends by such things as
   a. his inability to speak Chinese.
   b. living outside Chinatown.
   c. being unskilled in sports and singing.
   Students may say that Yep is tied to his classmates and friends by such things as
   a. being a Chinese American.
   b. going to school in Chinatown.
   c. playing games and sports with them.
   d. spending time with them outside school.
   e. suffering from the same problems with white people's attitudes that they do.

E. (16 points) Answers will vary widely, depending on students' personal experiences, situations, and viewpoints. Accept any answers that address the concern of the question and are elaborated by examples or details from the literature or from life.

Unit Two, Part One Test
pp. 37–38
A. (5 points each)
1. b
2. a
3. d
4. a

B. (20 points) Answers will vary. A model answer for the haiku by Raymond Patterson follows.
In "Glory, Glory . . ."
   a. The image of the "kindly sun" that "Laid a yellow quilt"

   b. appeals to the sense of sight
   c. and is effective because it makes the sun seem like a kindly person, suggests a sense of warmth, and creates an image of a yellow quilt made of sunlight.

C. (20 points each; students should answer two of the four)
1. Answers will vary. A model answer follows.
   The speaker in "It Seems I Test People"
   a. has a problem relating to others because he is of mixed background ("skin sun-mixed"), has a loud voice, laughs too deeply, and comes on too strong.
   b. seems to feel sad about his problem because he wants to be friendly ("eyes packed with hellos"), but other people leave when he arrives ("my arrival bringing departures"). He seems to feel that he is worthy of others' attention and thus is somewhat confused or unclear as to why they don't respond more positively to him ("it seems I test people").
2. Answers will vary. A model answer for "Growing Pains" follows.
   a. In "Growing Pains," the mother became angry with her daughter/the speaker, criticized her at length ("said I was lazy and self-centered"), and hurt her deeply.
   b. The mother later apologized and explained that other things had gone wrong that day and that she felt terrible.
   c. The mother could have avoided hurting her daughter by explaining what was really bothering her in the first place.
3. Answers will vary. A model answer for "All Summer in a Day" follows.
   "All Summer in a Day" is enjoyable because it
   a. tells an interesting story.
   b. takes place in an unusual setting.
   c. makes the reader feel deep sympathy for Margot, who is the victim of such cruelty.
   d. makes the reader wonder what it would be like to live in a place with all rain and no sun.
   e. makes the reader feel sympathy for all the children on Venus who have not lived in a world with sunshine.
4. Answers will vary. A model answer for "Chinatown" follows.
   What makes Chinatown special is that
   a. it was like a small town although it was part of a big city.
   b. Chinese people had to live there because racism made it hard for them to rent or buy elsewhere.
   c. wealthier parts of the city were visible from Chinatown, which was relatively poor.
   d. the Chinatown projects, where many of Yep's classmates lived, were ugly, lacking in privacy, and dangerous.

e. Yep's father had grown up there and his many stories increased the strength of the son's ties to the place.

f. Yep had his own painful and pleasant experiences there.

D. (20 points) Answers will vary. Model answers for Margot in "All Summer in a Day" and Laurence Yep in "Chinatown" follow.

1. In "All Summer in a Day," Margot
   a. feels out of place because she lived on Earth until she was four and remembers what the sun was like, but the other children on Venus do not. The other children know she is different, and they ostracize her.
   b. could try to fit in better by sharing her memories of Earth or by talking with the children who, at the end, have now seen and felt the sun. A better solution for Margot might be to ask her parents to move the family back to Earth as soon as possible.

2. In "Chinatown," Laurence Yep
   a. feels out of place because he is Chinese but does not live in Chinatown and does not speak the language. He also has no athletic skills, even though everyone else in his family does.
   b. could feel better about the situation by learning to speak Chinese, by enjoying the good sides of both Chinatown and the "white world" outside, and by finding areas other than athletics in which he might succeed.

Aaron's Gift
Selection Test, pp. 39–40

A. (8 points each) Notes will vary but might include examples similar to the following:

1. Example: "Aaron felt under the shirt, gently, and gently took hold of the wounded pigeon."
2. Example: "Did you see this! Ten years old and it's better than Dr. Belasco could do. He's a genius!"
3. Example: "And Aaron was, it must be said, a Class A, triple-fantastic roller skater."

B. (5 points each)
1. a
2. c
3. d
4. d

C. (4 points each)
1. c
2. b
3. a
4. b
5. a

D. (20 points; students should answer one of the two)

1. Answers will vary but should suggest that Aaron's grandmother
   a. is kind-hearted, which is revealed by her feeding the birds and by Aaron's belief that she loves everything.
   b. loves animals, which is revealed by her feeding the birds and by her sadness as a child over her goat's death.
   c. has had a hard life, which is revealed by the story about the Cossacks.
   d. loves Aaron, which is revealed by her behavior toward him at the end of the story.
   e. respects bravery, which is revealed by her pride in Aaron at the end of the story.
   f. loves freedom, which is revealed by Aaron's belief that she would have let the pigeon go.

2. Answers will vary but should suggest ideas similar to the following:
   a. Aaron sees only a bruised face, but his grandmother sees the bravery that led to the bruises.
   b. Aaron's grandmother wants him to be proud of having fought so hard against cruelty.
   c. showing Aaron his face in a mirror is a way of telling him that he is more important to her than any gift he could give her.

E. (16 points) Answers will vary widely, depending on students' personal experiences, situations, and viewpoints. Accept any answers that address the concern of the question and are elaborated by examples or details from the literature or from life.

The Circuit
Selection Test, pp. 41–42

A. (8 points each) Notes will vary but might include examples like the following:

1. Sight: "She went through a white gate, past a row of rose bushes, up the stairs to the front door." This sentence describes the narrator's mother going to Mr. Sullivan's house.
2. Hearing: "A few minutes later, the yelling and screaming of my little brothers and sisters, for whom the move was a great adventure, broke the silence of dawn." This sentence describes the excitability and motion of Panchito's younger siblings.
3. Touch: "Papa sighed, wiped the sweat off his forehead with his sleeve, and said wearily: 'Es todo.'" This sentence describes Panchito's hard-working father.

B. (5 points each)
1. a
2. b
3. c
4. b

C. (4 points each)
1. a
2. b
3. c
4. b
5. c

D. (20 points; students should answer one of the two)
1. Answers will vary. Students might say that he probably feels
   a. deep disappointment.
   b. hopelessness.
   c. anger.
   d. sadness.
   e. frustration.
   In support, students might refer to
   a. the eagerness with which Panchito begins school.
   b. Panchito's relief at not working in the fields every day.
   c. the fact that moving will end his relationship with his teacher.
   d. the fact that his family moves often.
2. Answers will vary. Most students will probably say that Panchito will have a different life from his parents because
   a. he has learned to speak English fairly well, which will give him more opportunities than his father had.
   b. he is clearly eager to get an education and is managing to progress despite the many interruptions to his schooling.
   c. the fact that his teacher gives him extra attention suggests that teachers see that he has potential.
   d. he is eager to escape work in the fields.
   Students who think Panchito will continue his parents' way of life may say that
   a. although he wants to go to school, his education is constantly interrupted.
   b. his ability to speak and understand English is affected by the fact that for long periods of time he hears no English.
   c. his family needs him to work rather than go to school.

E. (16 points) Answers will vary widely, depending on students' personal experiences, situations, and viewpoints. Accept any answers that address the concern of the question and are elaborated by examples or details from the literature or from life.

Oh Broom, Get to Work
Selection Test, pp. 43–44
A. (8 points each) Notes will vary but should be similar to the following:
1. a. Yoshiko wants her mother to bury the dead bird.

   b. She is angry and resentful to find that her mother has a visitor.
   c. She likes to spend time with her mother and resents the family's visitors.
   d. She does not think much of most of the visitors and is sometimes rude to them.
2. a. Yoshiko and her sister are angry with the visitor who left his dirty bathwater in the tub.
   b. They are protective of their mother.
   c. They resent the work she has to do to take care of visitors.
3. a. Yoshiko and Keiko think Mr. Okada is funny because he is so awkward.
   b. They can't keep themselves from laughing when visitors do things they find amusing.
   c. They sometimes find it difficult to be polite.
   d. The girls have similar senses of humor and they share a bond of understanding.

B. (5 points each)
1. d
2. a
3. c
4. d

C. (4 points each)
1. a
2. a
3. b
4. c
5. c

D. (20 points; students should answer one of the two)
1. Answers will vary. Students must give at least three of the following reasons for Yoshiko not liking the visitors:
   a. They take her mother's time away from her.
   b. They are boring.
   c. They interfere with her family.
   d. They cause extra work for her and her sister.
   e. They cause extra work for her mother.
   f. They get in the way of her having fun.
2. Answers will vary. Students could describe such positive things as
   a. the laughter during dinners.
   b. the interesting visits from Reverend Kimura.
   c. learning kindness from her parents' example.
   d. having interesting stories to tell.
   e. learning about the customs of Japan.

E. (16 points) Answers will vary widely, depending on students' personal experiences, situations, and viewpoints. Accept any answers that address the concern of the question and are elaborated by examples or details from the literature or from life.

Western Wagons/Night Journey
Selection Test, pp. 45–46
A. (8 points each)

1. "They went with axe and rifle, when the trail was still to blaze, They went with wife and children, in the prairie-schooner days" (rhyme, repetition)

2. "We shall starve and freeze and suffer. We shall die, and tame the lands." (repetition)

3. "Now as the train bears west, / Its rhythm rocks the earth, / And from my Pullman berth" (rhyme)

4. "I watch a beacon swing / From dark to blazing bright, / We thunder through ravines / And gullies washed with light." (rhyme)

B. (6 points each)
1. b
2. d
3. c
4. b
5. a

C. (22 points; students should answer one of the two)
1. Answers will vary. Possible reasons why people moved west include
   a. they hoped to find gold.
   b. they were bored with living in a settled place.
   c. they wanted richer farmland.
   d. they were inspired by the sight of other travelers.
   e. they didn't want to be thought of as cowardly or weak.

   In response to the question of whether or not they understood their reasons for going, students may respond
   a. that they did not, since they say, "Lordy, never ask us why!"
   b. they did, since they give the above-listed reasons for going.
   c. they both did and did not, for the mix of reasons cited in a. and b. above.
2. Answers will vary but should suggest that Roethke conveyed a feeling of movement by the
   a. use of rhythm. Each line may be read in a rhythmic pattern with the stress on every second syllable, similar to the sound of a train (click-CLICK-click-CLICK).
   b. descriptions of what the speaker sees outside. The descriptions give a sense of the train's passage from one scene to another ("A suddenness of trees . . ."; "We thunder through ravines / And gullies washed with light").
   c. descriptions of what the speaker feels as a result of movement ("Full on my neck I feel / The straining at a curve"; "Wheels shake the roadbed stone").

D. (16 points) Answers will vary widely, depending on students' personal experiences, situations, and viewpoints. Accept any answers that address the concern of the question and are elaborated by examples or details from the literature or from life.

Unit Two, Part Two Test
pp. 47–48
A. (5 points each) Answers may vary but should be similar to the following:
1. It is told in the first person by Panchito.
2. a pigeon
3. "Western Wagons"
4. The title refers to a superstitious belief that covering a broom and standing it upside down will make an unwanted visitor leave.

B. (20 points) Answers will vary. Model answers for "Western Wagons" and "The Circuit" follow.
1. In "Western Wagons":
   a. Pioneers are traveling west.
   b. This journey is positive because people are moving west to seek their fortunes, find better places to live, or make better lives for themselves.
2. In "The Circuit":
   a. Panchito and his family move from place to place looking for work.
   b. The journey is negative because Panchito's family must constantly search for work, they must move their belongings, they never get to settle down and have a home, and the children do not have the opportunity for a good education.

C. (20 points; students should answer two of the four)
1. Answers will vary. A model answer for Aaron in "Aaron's Gift" follows.
   Aaron is tested by Carl and the gang of boys who
   a. pretend that they want him to be in their club.
   b. try to trick him into giving them his pigeon, which he had planned to give to his grandmother.
   c. try to roast the bird over a fire as a sacrifice.
   d. beat him up when he resists.
   Aaron passes the test because he fights back, saves the pigeon, and escapes from the boys.
2. Answers will vary. A model answer for "Oh Broom, Get to Work" follows.
   The narrator
   a. describes one of her mother's visitors as "a squat blob of a man—balding and gray—as silent as a mushroom." This description is effective because

comparing a man to a mushroom is surprising and funny. It is also accurate because the man is short and round, balding, gray, silent, and unmoving, just as a mushroom is.

    b. describes Reverend Kimura as "a red jelly bean in a jar full of black licorice." This description is effective because it emphasizes how different, exciting, and entertaining Reverend Kimura is compared to most of the uninteresting visitors they have.

3. Answers will vary. A model answer for "Western Wagons" follows.

The fact that the story of the westward movement is told mainly by the pioneers themselves as they set out has the following effects:

    a. It makes the pioneer days seem like they are happening in the moment rather than in the distant past.

    b. It creates an atmosphere of suspense, since you don't know whether these pioneers will succeed or fail.

    c. It creates a sense of confusion because you don't know exactly why the pioneers are leaving.

    d. It creates an atmosphere of excitement because the voices of the pioneers are excited.

4. Answers will vary. Model answers for "Aaron's Gift" and "Oh Broom, Get to Work" follow.

In "Aaron's Gift," the central symbol is the pigeon that Aaron finds and nurses back to health. The pigeon represents

    a. freedom because it escapes from the gang of boys trying to capture it.

    b. a link to his family and their past. The pigeon's escape reminds Aaron of his grandmother's goat, which was killed years ago by the Cossacks.

    c. Aaron's soul, or character. Aaron nursed the pigeon back to health, fought for what he believed in, and made sure that the pigeon went free, just as Aaron freed himself from the gang of boys.

In "Oh Broom, Get to Work," the central symbol is the broom that Yoshiko covers with a cloth and stands upside down in the doorway. The broom represents

    a. Yoshiko's resentment of all the visitors who invade the family's home.

    b. a link to the family's heritage. The use of the broom is based on an old Japanese superstition.

    c. Yoshiko's rebellion. She resents most of the visitors who come to the house, but she is generally polite to them. Leaving a towel on the upside-down broom expresses her dislike of the visitors and her desire to get rid of them.

D. (20 points) Answers will vary. Model answers for "The Circuit" and "Western Wagons" follow.

  1. In "The Circuit":

    a. The story suggests the idea that being an outsider makes life very hard.

    b. Panchito and his family must move constantly, so they do not have a real home. Their Mexican heritage makes it difficult for the family because they must learn to speak English to find employment and succeed in school, and they are treated poorly by some of the people they encounter (for example, by being forced to live in shacks and filthy huts for weeks at a time).

  2. In "Western Wagons":

    a. The poem suggests the idea that some people are willing to risk everything to become rich or to find better lives ("I'm off to California to get rich out there or die!").

    b. This poem relates to the heritage we, as Americans, all share. Many of our ancestors were pioneers, and our country was built on the ideals of freedom, individualism, and the spirit of the frontier.

Unit Three

Damon and Pythias
Selection Test, pp. 49–50

A. (10 points each) Notes will vary but should suggest ideas similar to the following.
1. a. This story will be about a prison.
   b. The play will be suspenseful.
2. Damon has already left the room; Pythias is so worried he is talking to himself.
3. a. Damon truly means that he would die for his friend.
   b. The people in the crowd are becoming upset and are building up enough courage, or sense of outrage, to rebel against the king; they want both Damon and Pythias to be set free.

B. (5 points each)
1. b
2. d
3. a
4. a
5. d
6. c

C. (20 points; students should answer one of the two)
1. Answers will vary. Students could say that Damon and Pythias represent
   a. honesty. Pythias disagrees with one of the king's laws and says so.
   b. friendship. Damon offers himself to the king in return for a favor to Pythias.
   c. loyalty. Pythias never considers fleeing from the king and not returning to save Damon.
   d. dependability, or keeping your word. Pythias leaves his own mother a day early to make sure he gets back on time.
   e. self-sacrifice. Damon willingly takes Pythias's place in prison.
   f. courage. Neither Pythias nor Damon backs down or changes his opinion when facing the threat of death.
2. Answers will vary but should suggest the following.
   a. At the beginning, the king is a cruel tyrant who values power and wealth. He does not tolerate criticism and does not care if people think he is cruel and unjust.
   b. The king is cynical about people. When Damon and Pythias switch places, the king does not believe that Pythias will return, and he mocks Damon for being such a fool. The king thinks that facing one's own death is enough to make any man become selfish.

c. at the end, the king releases both Damon and Pythias, and he admits to his people that he has at times been cruel and unjust.
   d. the king has changed his attitude about people because of the "strong and true friendship" between Damon and Pythias. He did not believe the two men would stay true to their word, but they did. The cruel tyrant who valued power and wealth above all else now declares that he would give it up to have a friend like Damon or Pythias.

D. (20 points) Answers will vary widely, depending on students' personal experiences, situations, and viewpoints. Accept any answers that address the concern of the question and are elaborated by examples or details from the literature or from life.

Cricket in the Road
Selection Test, pp. 51–52

A. (8 points each) Notes will vary but should suggest the following.
1. This line shows that Vern is someone who tries to solve problems and end disagreements fairly.
2. This line suggests that Amy has more of a temper than her brother, or that Amy expects others to solve her problems.
3. This line shows Vern's cheerful nature, his forgiving nature, and/or his fondness for his friend.

B. (5 points each)
1. d
2. c
3. a
4. b

C. (4 points each)
1. a
2. c
3. c
4. a
5. c

D. (20 points; students should answer one of the two)
1. Answers will vary. Students could say that Selo's main conflict is that he
   a. is angry with Vern and Amy but doesn't want to lose their friendship. He resolves this conflict by forgiving them, or he does not resolve it because he is not the one who clearly indicates that the fight is over.
   b. wants to be friends again with Vern and Amy but is afraid that they no longer want to be friends with him. He does not resolve this conflict himself, but it is resolved by Vern and Amy at the end of the story. (He participates in the solution by approaching them at the end.)

c. wants to be braver than he is. He does not resolve his fear of storms, and he seems not to have the courage to approach his former friends either. At the end, he may even be afraid of Vern and Amy for their willingness to forgive him.

2. Answers will vary. Students may predict that

a. the three kids will become friends again and go back to playing cricket in the road just as before. Evidence for this prediction: Vern is clearly willing to forgive Selo, and Selo is so happy to see his friends again. Students may also say that, based on their own experience, once former friends finally make contact after a fight, they usually get over their problem and become close again.

b. despite Vern's peace offering, it may be difficult for the three friends to go back to the way they were before the quarrel. Evidence for this prediction: it took the friends so long to make up, and even after Vern offers Selo first turn at bat, Selo is still upset and afraid of something.

c. the friends may be all right for now, but in the future, problems over who will bat first are bound to come up again. Since Selo still appears to be a very emotional and easily upset person, he may get angry or upset about cricket again.

D. (16 points) Answers will vary widely, depending on students' personal experiences, situations, and viewpoints. Accept any answers that address the concern of the question and are elaborated by examples or details from the literature or from life.

The Quarrel/Fable
Selection Test, pp. 53–54

A. (30 points) Notes will vary but should resemble the following.

Similarities between the plots of the two poems may include these:
a. Both involve a petty quarrel.
b. Both involve two characters.

Distinct features of the plot of "The Quarrel" may include these:
a. There is no reason given for the quarrel.
b. The length of the quarrel is clearly stated.
c. The quarrel is solved not by reasoning but by one person taking the blame and forgiving the other.
d. By the end of the poem, the quarrel is clearly over.
e. The speaker is one of the characters.

Distinct features of "Fable" may include these:
a. The reason for the quarrel has to do with the difference in size between the two characters.

b. The suggested solution to the conflict is based on one character's belief that the quarrel arose from a misunderstanding.
c. It is not clear whether or not the quarrel is actually ended.
d. The speaker is a narrator outside the story.

B. (5 points each)
1. d
2. b
3. b
4. a

C. (25 points; students should answer one of the two)

1. Answers will vary. Students may say that the brother and the squirrel are similar in that they
a. become involved in a quarrel.
b. want to end the quarrel.
c. say something to the other character with whom they are arguing that is designed to end the argument.

Students may say that the brother and the squirrel are different in that
a. one is a realistic character and one is a talking animal.
b. the brother is simply interested in ending the fight, but the squirrel is interested in making a point about differences.
c. the brother is willing to take all the blame, but the squirrel insists on standing up for its values and point of view.

2. Answers will vary. Students may point out the following similarities between the two poems' messages:
a. Both are about how quarrels can start without very clear or very important causes. In "The Quarrel," the narrator doesn't even know how the quarrel began. In "Fable," the cause is the mountain's silly belief that bigger is necessarily better.
b. Both show the importance of taking direct action to resolve a quarrel. In "The Quarrel," the brother makes the move and puts an end to a fight that is making both him and his sister miserable. In "Fable," the squirrel points out how silly the mountain's belief is and explains that both the mountain and the squirrel are equally valuable and important.

D. (25 points) Answers will vary widely, depending on students' personal experiences, situations, and viewpoints. Accept any answers that address the concern of the question and are elaborated by examples or details from the literature or from life.

Unit Three, Part One Test

pp. 55–56

A. (5 points each)
1. *Damon and Pythias*
2. a brother and sister (or two brothers)
3. He is upset because Amy will get to bat before him.
4. a mountain and a squirrel

B. (20 points) Answers will vary. Suggested answers for each listed character follow.
1. Damon cares about Pythias. He takes his friend's place in prison and risks his own life to help his friend settle his affairs.
2. Vern cares about Selo. He forgives Selo for throwing away the cricket bat and ball and reaches out by offering Selo first try with the new bat, even though Selo never apologized.
3. The brother cares about his sister. He takes all the blame for the quarrel on himself, even though he was probably not totally responsible.

C. (20 points each; students should answer two of the three)
1. Answers will vary. A model answer for the king in *Damon and Pythias* follows.
   In *Damon and Pythias*, the king
   a. changes from a cruel and merciless tyrant to a more compassionate ruler. He admits to his people that he has been cruel and unjust, and he releases both Damon and Pythias—men he had sentenced to death.
   b. changes from a cynical man to one who values friendship above all else. The king does not believe that Pythias will return, and he mocks Damon for being such a fool.
   These changes come about because Pythias returns on time to save his friend. The king is overwhelmed by the "strong and true friendship" between Damon and Pythias. He did not believe the two men would stay true to their word, but they did. When he sees the depth of their friendship, loyalty, and honesty, the king realizes that he has been wrong about Damon and Pythias. He reassesses his own values, and declares that he would give up his wealth and power for a single friend like Damon or Pythias.
2. Answers will vary. A model answer for "Fable" follows. I think that the lesson in the poem "Fable" is the one that I most need to apply in my own life because the squirrel teaches that
   a. it takes all kinds to make the world work.
   b. everybody and everything has value—not just big, powerful characters, but little, seemingly unimportant characters as well.
   c. quarrels are often not a simple matter of right and wrong but the result of different people seeing things from different points of view.

   d. it is important to be tolerant of others.
   e. it is important to have self-respect, no matter who you are.
3. Answers will vary. Model answers for "The Quarrel" and "Cricket in the Road" follow.
   The brother in "The Quarrel" is most successful because
   a. when he has a quarrel with his sister, he confronts her directly and takes all the blame for the sake of ending the quarrel.
   b. he does not quibble over who is at fault because he just wants to put the quarrel behind him.
   Selo in "Cricket in the Road" is least successful because
   a. he does not take any direct action to confront Vern and Amy or to solve the problem.
   b. he does not apologize for throwing the bat and ball into the bushes.
   c. he does not tell Vern and Amy that he wants to be friends again.
   d. he lets the quarrel go on for a long time for no apparent reason.

D. (20 points) Answers will vary. Model answers for Selo in "Cricket in the Road" and Pythias in *Damon and Pythias* follow.
1. Selo in "Cricket in the Road"
   a. starts an argument with his friends for no good reason, throws away Vern's bat and ball, and never apologizes.
   b. is clearly in the wrong, although he suffers for his bad behavior.
2. Pythias in *Damon and Pythias*
   a. disagreed with one of the king's laws, admitted as much to the king, and told the king that people were unhappy with the way he ruled.
   b. was clearly in the right when he stated his own opinion and accepted the consequences. However, he was probably wrong to allow Damon to take his place in prison. Pythias did everything he could to fulfill his part of the bargain, but Damon risked his life and came very close to losing it.

Abd al-Rahman Ibrahima

Selection Test, pp. 57–58

A. (4 points each)
1. secondary
2. secondary
3. primary (or secondary)
4. primary
5. secondary
6. primary (or secondary)

B. (5 points each)
1. b
2. a

3. c
4. a

C. (4 points each)
1. b
2. b
3. a
4. b
5. c

D. (20 points; students should answer one of the two)
1. Answers will vary. Students may point out that Ibrahima
   a. saw from the beginning that his captors were ruthless and that anyone who was weak or who resisted would be killed.
   b. must have suffered terribly during the ship voyage, which must have weakened Ibrahima's body and mind.
   c. went from being a prince to being a slave with no power, not even the power to communicate at first. This must have made him feel alone and helpless.
   d. refused to work and was whipped. The pain forced him to give in, which must have been humiliating.
   e. ran away but soon realized he could neither survive in the woods nor find a safe place anywhere to live. He was forced to return to Foster in order to survive.
   f. gave up on ever returning home and married a woman in America.
   g. nonetheless remained determined to be the same person he had always been and maintained his beliefs in Islam, keeping its rituals as well as he could.
2. Answers will vary. Students might point out that Foster (and other slave owners)
   a. believed that Africans were savages and had no feelings.
   b. ignored or denied the idea that Africans had any kind of honorable or respectable heritage.
   c. probably believed that all Africans were uneducated.
   Foster (and others) would probably have been surprised to learn that
   a. Ibrahima's people had a complex system of government.
   b. Ibrahima was an educated man who could read and write.
   c. Ibrahima was of royal blood.
   d. the Fula knew healing techniques that could cure a badly infected leg.

E. (16 points) Answers will vary widely, depending on students' personal experiences, situations, and viewpoints. Accept any answers that address the concern of the question and are elaborated by examples or details from the literature or from life.

from The Story of My Life
Selection Test, pp. 59–60

A. (4 points each) Notes will vary but should include
1. touch
2. sight, touch
3. touch
4. smell
5. touch

B. (5 points each)
1. d
2. b
3. d
4. c

C. (4 points each)
1. c
2. c
3. a
4. c
5. a

D. (20 points; students should answer one of the two)
1. Answers will vary. Students may point out that before learning language, Helen
   a. alternated between rage and a lack of interest in life.
   b. sensed things but could not create coherent thoughts.
   c. had violent emotions but could not feel tenderness or sorrow.
   d. felt lost and confused.
   e. felt a need for love.
   Students may point out that after Helen began to learn language, she felt or experienced
   a. the "thrill of returning thought."
   b. a comprehension of what language was.
   c. an eager desire to learn.
   d. remorse for her temper.
   e. excitement about the future.
   Students should also discuss what Helen's experience suggests about the importance of language to human beings. For example, students might note the following.
   a. Without language, there can be no coherent thought.
   b. Emotions cannot be understood without words to describe them.
   c. Language enables us to communicate with others, from whom we can receive affection and love.
   d. Language enables us to learn and develop.
   e. The ability to communicate can make people feel hopeful and emotionally gratified, whereas the inability to communicate can make people feel depressed, pessimistic, or lost and confused.

2. Answers will vary. Students may point out that Anne Sullivan

  a. must have worked with the blind before because she knew finger spelling and had brought Helen a doll made by blind children.

  b. was warm and affectionate because she hugged Helen as soon as she met her.

  c. was strong-willed because she got into a struggle with Helen over the difference between "mug" and "water."

  d. was patient because she kept trying with Helen.

  e. was calm because she didn't punish Helen for breaking the doll.

  f. was imaginative because she tried different ways to convey language to Helen.

E. (20 points) Answers will vary widely, depending on students' personal experiences, situations, and viewpoints. Accept any answers that address the concern of the question and are elaborated by examples or details from the literature or from life.

Street Corner Flight/Words Like Freedom
Selection Test, pp. 61–62

A. (8 points each) Answers will vary but should suggest ideas similar to the following.

1. In "Street Corner Flight," you can infer that the speaker

  a. has firsthand knowledge or experience of the kind of "concrete barrio" described in the poem.

  b. may live there now ("From this side").

  c. is probably older than the two boys in the poem.

  d. views the neighborhood in a negative way, perhaps as plain and lifeless ("concrete barrio").

2. You can infer that the speaker

  a. cares deeply about freedom.

  b. probably feels isolated or trapped in the barrio, as the boys are.

  c. feels sad that the pigeons can fly away but the boys cannot.

  d. has seen both "worlds," the barrio and the "other side."

3. In "Words Like Freedom," you can infer that the speaker

  a. cares deeply about freedom and thinks about it all the time.

  b. is probably an adult.

  c. may have won or been granted freedom recently or has recently learned its meaning for him or her.

  d. appreciates freedom in a way that others cannot.

4. You can infer that the speaker

  a. has suffered in the past.

  b. was not always free.

  c. has recently learned information that deepens his or her appreciation of freedom.

  d. assumes that the reader has not had the same experiences he or she has had.

  e. feels that many people cannot understand why the word *liberty* would make him or her cry.

B. (5 points each)

1. a
2. c
3. d
4. d
5. b
6. b

C. (20 points, students should answer one of the two)

1. Answers will vary. Students may point out that the image of

  a. a "concrete barrio" suggests an environment where there is little beauty or life.

  b. the "small boys" suggests helplessness.

  c. the release of the birds "into the air" suggests sudden freedom and change, and it contrasts with the image of the barrio.

  d. gliding above traffic suggests peace and quiet in contrast to noise and congestion.

  e "labyrinths of food stamps" suggests that poor people are trapped in a maze.

  f. "the other side . . . / a world away" suggests that there is another part of the city where people have freedom and opportunity, but the boys in the barrio cannot get there.

2. Answers will vary. Students may point out that

  a. the speaker says that words like *freedom* are "Sweet and wonderful to say." He implies that freedom is a concept that is important to talk about and believe in, but he may also be suggesting that it is easier to talk about freedom than to experience it or understand it.

  b. the speaker says that freedom plays on his heartstrings every day, suggesting that he is constantly yearning for freedom. This image suggests that freedom is more than just an idea; it is a strong emotional need.

  c. by saying that the word *liberty* almost makes him cry, the speaker suggests a lot of pain attached to the word. This suggests that although he finds the idea of liberty beautiful and cares about it, there is also something negative in the way he perceives the idea. He may feel that being at liberty is good, but he does not have total freedom.

  d. the simple final words "If you had known what I know / You would know why" suggest that the idea of liberty is painful and very hard to talk about because of experiences or reasons the speaker cannot really share with the reader.

D. (18 points) Answers will vary widely, depending on students' personal experiences, situations, and viewpoints. Accept any answers that address the concern of the question and are elaborated by examples or details from the literature or from life.

The School Play
Selection Test, pp. 63–64
A. (5 points each) Notes will vary but should suggest that the tone is
   1. humorous and fearful.
   2. sad and sympathetic, or humorous (if they assume Ruben is being a wise guy).
   3. thoughtful, sad, or serious.
   4. humorous, silly, or ironic.
B. (8 points each)
   1. d
   2. c
   3. a
C. (4 points each)
   1. a
   2. c
   3. b
   4. c
   5. a
D. (20 points; students should answer one of the two)
   1. Answers will vary. Students may note that Robert is
      a. a good speller because that is how he got a part in the play.
      b. responsible because he practices his lines over and over.
      c. not terribly tough because he is afraid of Belinda Lopez.
      d. thoughtful and curious, because he would like to have a job recalling facts.
      e. kind-hearted because he pities the people in the Donner party.
      f. observant because he notices many details around him.
      g. basically optimistic because he enjoys being in the play even though he made a mistake in his one line.
   2. Answers will vary but should suggest that
      a. Soto may be trying to say that life is pretty difficult, but to enjoy it you do not need to achieve great things. You just need to try hard, be grateful for all you have, and enjoy your achievements.
      b. Soto writes about students from a modest economic environment performing a play about pioneers who starved to death.
      c. the props and costumes are modest and the play itself is very simple.
      d. nobody does a great job, yet the teacher and the students are pleased.

   e. Soto is also saying "you gotta suck it up in bad times." In other words, you have to be tough and do what is difficult when things get bad, whether you are starving in a blizzard or trying to remember your lines in a school play.
E. (16 points) Answers will vary widely, depending on students' personal experiences, situations, and viewpoints. Accept any answers that address the concern of the question and are elaborated by examples or details from the literature or from life.

Ode to My Library
Selection Test, pp. 65–66
A. (15 points each) Answers will vary.
   1. Images of power and beauty might include the
      a. Incas in the mountains "Who lived two steps / From heaven."
      b. speaker's vision of himself as an airplane pilot.
      c. "Aztec warrior."
      d. Aztec's "band of feathers / On his noble head."
      e. Aztec's "cuts of muscle," "a boulder of strength in each arm."
      f. Aztec's machete, able to "slice open a mountain."
      g. Aztec's ability to "send our enemies tumbling" with a wave of his arm.
   2. Images of the small and ordinary might include the
      a. small size of the library (just two rooms).
      b. globe that the speaker dropped.
      c. fish tank with one blue fish.
      d. crayon stuck in the pencil sharpener.
      e. water fountain.
      f. librarian and her glasses.
      g. broken phonograph.
      h. *abuelitos* and the dusty ranch.
      i. read-a-thon.
B. (6 points each)
   1. c
   2. c
   3. a
   4. b
   5. a
C. (20 points; students should answer one of the two)
   1. Answers will vary. Students should explain that an ode is a serious lyric poem, often written in praise or honor of something. "Ode to My Library" is an appropriate title because it reflects how strongly the speaker feels about his small local library. The speaker feels this way because
      a. the library is a place where the speaker can learn about the glory of the Incas and the Aztecs, use his imagination (to become an airline pilot or a warrior), enter activities such as the summer read-a-thon, and participate in decorating the walls with murals.

b. the library symbolizes the speaker's ethnic background. It has maps of the United States and Mexico, and it has information and pictures of the Incas and the Aztecs. The speaker refers to it as "*my* library" and refers to "*our* enemies and "*our* family of people."

c. the library represents the speaker's pride in his background and in himself, which he would like to show off to his grandparents.

2. Answers will vary but might suggest that the speaker of the poem is

a. proud of the library and what it represents.

b. proud of his accomplishments (painting the Aztec warrior on the mural and reading 30 books in the read-a-thon).

c. humble and modest. He knows that the library is small and has a number of things in it that don't work, such as the phonograph.

d. interested in his heritage. He studies the Incas and the Aztecs.

e. observant. He knows there is a crayon in the pencil sharpener, for example, and he says the fish in the fish tank is always pouting.

f. imaginative. He fantasizes about being an airplane pilot and about being like the Aztec warrior.

g. amused by the quirky details of the library, such as the librarian who reads with her glasses hanging around her neck.

h. somewhat sad and lonely. He keeps wishing he could bring his grandparents to the library, but they live far away.

D. (20 points) Answers will vary widely, depending on students' personal experiences, situations, and viewpoints. Accept any answers that address the concern of the question and are elaborated by examples or details from the literature or from life.

The Jacket

Selection Test, pp. 67–68

A. (6 points each) Answers will vary but should suggest ideas similar to the following.

1. Describing the jacket as "the color of day-old guacamole" indicates that the narrator does not like the jacket, hates the color, and is disappointed that his mother got him something different from what he wanted.

2. Comparing girls to "loose flowers" blowing away suggests a feeling of loss and a sense of beauty disappearing. The narrator feels sad and lonely at having been abandoned and envious of the boys who attract the girls.

3. Comparing his forearms to the "necks of turtles" reveals how awkward, unattractive, and shy the narrator felt when he wore the jacket.

4. The narrator feels longing for the girls walking by, strong envy for the couples, and a sense of exclusion from the togetherness of couples who feel so close to each other that "their heads [are] like bookends."

5. The narrator resents the jacket, which he feels he has to take with him and cannot get rid of. Like an ugly brother, the jacket reflects on its wearer and makes the narrator look and feel bad about himself.

B. (5 points each)

1. c
2. b
3. a

C. (4 points each)

1. a
2. b
3. b
4. c
5. a

D. (20 points; students should answer one of the two)

1. Answers will vary. Students may point out that Soto was unhappy because

a. he did not have a girlfriend.

b. his mother gave him an ugly jacket that he would have to wear for a long time.

c. his dog ripped his jacket.

d. he thought everyone was talking about how ugly his jacket was.

e. he was doing poorly in school.

f. his family was poor (they did not have enough money to buy him another jacket, and the children had to drink powdered milk).

g. he was bullied by other students in the schoolyard.

h. his jacket started falling apart and became too small for him, but he still had to wear it.

i. he felt self-conscious and unattractive.

2. Answers will vary. A model answer follows for the scene described in the last paragraph of the selection, in which the writing appeals to the senses of

a. sound: "called to dinner," "said grace," "I gagged too," "a grunt"

b. sight: "steam silvered my mother's glasses," "made ugly faces at their glasses of powdered milk," "The faces of clouds were piled up, hurting," "that green ugly brother"

c. taste ("big rips of buttered tortilla that held scooped-up beans")

d. touch: "my jacket across my arm," "a cold sky," "slipped into my jacket," "breathed over my shoulder"

E. (15 points) Answers will vary widely, depending on students' personal experiences, situations, and viewpoints. Accept any answers that address the concern of the question and are elaborated by examples or details from the literature or from life.

Unit Three, Part Two Test
pp. 69–70

A. (5 points each)
1. d
2. b
3. b
4. c

B. (20 points) Answers will vary. A model answer follows.
Positive experience:
a. Character: Helen Keller in *The Story of My Life*
b. She suddenly understood that the letters "w-a-t-e-r" stood for *water*.
c. It was a positive experience because it opened Helen's mind to an understanding of language, which helped her form thoughts and understand her emotions.
Negative experience:
a. Character: Abd al-Rahman Ibrahima
b. He was taken to a country where he could not communicate with the people who were controlling his life.
c. It was a negative experience because he could not convince his owner that he was of royal blood and could not pursue his release from slavery.

C. (20 points each; students should answer two of the four)
1. Answers will vary. A model answer for "Abd al-Rahman Ibrahima" follows.
Dr. Cox did the most to help another human being because
a. the person he helped, Ibrahima, was in the worst possible state. He had been deprived of his freedom and his rights as a human being.
b. Cox lived in a society that believed that slavery was justified.
c. Cox first tried to help Ibrahima by speaking directly with his owner.
d. when his first attempt failed, Cox pledged to spend the rest of his life working for Ibrahima's freedom.
e. although he died before Ibrahima was set free, Cox told Ibrahima's story to many people, one of whom actually helped Ibrahima escape slavery.
2. Answers will vary. A model answer for "Words Like Freedom" and "The School Play" follows.
a. "Words Like Freedom" has a very serious, almost sorrowful tone, whereas "The School Play" has a lighthearted, humorous, at times even silly tone.

b. This is appropriate because "Words Like Freedom" has a very serious subject and deals with the big, serious concepts of liberty and freedom. The poem has a sad tone because the speaker refers to bad things he has seen that seem to relate to a lack of freedom.
c. "The School Play" has a lighter tone because it deals with the fairly unimportant subject of some kids putting on a class play. It has a humorous tone because the characters have a lot of silly problems, such as not being able to remember a single line in a play.
3. Answers will vary. A model answer for "The Jacket" follows.
In "The Jacket":
a. The statement means that you have to be tough and do difficult things when times are bad.
b. For the narrator of "The Jacket," times are bad in that he and his family are poor, and his mother has gotten him an ugly jacket.
c. The narrator realizes that he has to "suck it up" in spite of how much he hates the jacket. He knows that his mother has no money to buy another jacket, and he will be stuck wearing this one for at least a few years.
d. He puts up with scorn, isolation, and loneliness that comes with the jacket (in his view), but he does not throw the jacket away and he apparently never tells his mother exactly how he feels about it.
4. Answers will vary. A model answer for Ibrahima ("Abd al-Rahman Ibrahima") and Anne Sullivan (*The Story of My Life*) follows.
Ibrahima was the victim of the greatest misfortune in that he
a. lost his freedom, family, people, and land.
b. lost the power and status of his position in a royal family.
c. was beaten, humiliated, underfed, and overworked.
d. died on his way back to his homeland.
Anne Sullivan won the greatest victory in that she
a. overcame Helen Keller's deafness, blindness, and stubborn willfulness to teach her how to communicate.
b. made Helen Keller understand the basic concepts of language.
c. opened up whole new worlds to Helen Keller.
d. helped Keller become an excellent writer; a loving, sensitive human being; and a role model to countless others.

D. (20 points) Notes will vary. Model answers for "Abd al-Rahman Ibrahima" and "Ode to My Library" follow.

1. In "Abd al-Rahman Ibrahima":
   a. Ibrahima faces the barriers of slavery, inability to communicate with the slave owners, and racial prejudice.
   b. These barriers stand in the way of his goals of returning to his home and family and regaining his freedom and social stature.

2. In "Ode to My Library":
   a. The speaker faces the barriers of being young, having little control over what he can do, and being unable to fly a plane. His family doesn't seem to have money for plane tickets, and "his" library doesn't have good technical resources.
   b. These barriers stand in the way of his goals of bringing his grandparents to the library and, in a sense, developing a greater appreciation for his own heritage. The lack of resources in the library doesn't bother him because the books and the environment stimulate his imagination.

Mid-Year Test
pp. 71–78

A. 1. c
  2. b
  3. a
  4. c
  5. a
  6. d

B. 7. a
  8. d
  9. b
  10. c

C. Answers may vary but should include points similar to the following.

11. Janet wants to play on the Mapes Street baseball team, but Richard will not let her.
12. Janet is confident or sure of herself and her abilities. She is stubborn, as you can tell from her refusal to accept anything less than what she asked for. She has been generous and affectionate toward Richard in the past, but she refuses to be friends with someone who treats her unfairly. She also has been hurt by Richard (she is "kicking back") but uses humor to cover up her pain.
13. Much of the humor comes from exaggeration ("I hope when you go to the dentist he finds twenty cavities"), from sarcasm ("Why don't you and your team forget about baseball and learn something nice like knitting, maybe?"), and from ironic comments ("Nobody ever said that I was unreasonable").

D. 14. d
  15. a
  16. b
  17. c

E. Answers may vary but should include points similar to the following.

18. Both Janet and Richard are stubborn, both insist they are right, and both cover up their real feelings with humor and sarcasm. Richard is able to compromise and give in, but Janet is not. Richard tries to maintain traditions, but Janet wants to break them.
19. His team has lost every game; some of his players are injured; his all-boys team couldn't do much worse; his friend Janet is a good player and really wants to play; he can patch up his friendship with Janet.
20. She threatens to take back everything she has ever given him and end their friendship; she points out how poorly his team is doing; she mentions her own talents in baseball; she makes fun of him and his team; she refuses to give up or give in; she suggests that he and the other boys should take up knitting, traditionally a girl's skill.

Writing Exercise Scoring Guide

4 An **exceptional** paper
- has a clear and consistent focus.
- has a logical organization.
- uses transitions effectively to connect ideas.
- supports ideas with details, quotations, examples, and/or other evidence.
- exhibits well-formed sentences varying in structure.
- exhibits a rich vocabulary, including precise language that is appropriate for the purpose and audience of the paper.
- contains almost no errors in usage, mechanics, and spelling.

3 A **proficient** paper
- has a relatively clear and consistent focus.
- has a logical organization, although it may be unnecessarily mechanical.
- uses some transition words and phrases to connect ideas, but they do not always clarify connections effectively.
- supports ideas with details, quotations, examples, and/or other evidence.
- exhibits some variety in sentence structure.
- uses vocabulary that is appropriate for the purpose and audience.
- contains a few errors in usage, mechanics, and spelling.

2 A **basic** paper
- has a fairly clear focus that may occasionally become obscured.
- shows an organizational pattern, but relationships between ideas may sometimes be difficult to understand.
- contains supporting evidence that may lack effect and so only superficially develops ideas.
- has complete and varied sentences most of the time.
- contains several errors in usage, mechanics, and spelling that cause distraction and some confusion about meaning.

1 A **limited** paper
- has a topic but does not include any elaboration, or it only minimally addresses the topic and lacks discernible ideas.
- has only a few, simple sentences.
- contains little or no plausible support for ideas.
- shows limited word choice.
- contains numerous and serious errors in usage, mechanics, and spelling that cause confusion about meaning.

A paper is unable to be scored if it is
- illegible.
- unrelated to the topic.
- only a rewording of the prompt.
- written in a foreign language.
- not written at all.

Revising/Editing
1. b
2. a
3. c
4. d
5. b
6. c

Unit Four

Lob's Girl
Selection Test, pp. 79–80

A. (8 points each)
1. Lob and Sandy become inseparable, and/or Lob comes to live with the Pengellys.
2. While riding a bicycle on this road, Sandy is struck by a speeding truck.
3. Lob gains entry into the hospital and goes to see Sandy.

B. (5 points each)
1. a
2. c
3. b
4. c

C. (4 points each)
1. c
2. c
3. a
4. b
5. c

D. (20 points; students should answer one of the two)
1. Answers will vary. Students might describe events such as the following.
   a. Sandy and Lob experienced "love at first sight" when they met on the beach.
   b. Twice, Lob traveled more than 400 miles on his own to return to Sandy.
   c. Sandy was overjoyed when Lob traveled all the way from Liverpool to be with her.
   d. Both Lob and Sandy were terribly sad when Mr. Dodsworth reclaimed Lob.
   e. When Lob came to live with the Pengelly family, there was no question he was Sandy's dog: he followed her everywhere and slept by her bed.
   f. Sandy stirred from her coma when she heard the dog's voice.
   g. The surprise ending suggests that Sandy and Lob were so close that Lob came back from death to save her.
2. Answers will vary. Students could say that others recognize and respect the bond between Sandy and Lob, giving examples such as the following.
   a. Mr. Dodsworth acknowledges the bond and gives Lob to the Pengelly family.
   b. Although Mr. Pengelly is reluctant to take on the added expense of feeding Lob, he knows Sandy will be unhappy without the dog.
   c. Although the other Pengelly children also love Lob, they recognize that Lob and Sandy's bond is special.
   d. Sandy's doctors agree to violate hospital rules to allow Lob to be at Sandy's bedside.

E. (16 points) Answers will vary widely, depending on students' personal experiences, situations, and viewpoints. Accept any answers that address the concern of the question and are elaborated by examples or details from the literature or from life.

My First Dive with the Dolphins
Selection Test, pp. 81–82

A. (12 points each) Notes will vary. Model answers follow.
1. a. Dolphins have individual "personalities."
   b. He is treated differently by each dolphin.
2. a. Dolphins are beautiful creatures.
   b. He examines the details of one of the dolphins close-up.

B. (5 points each)
1. c
2. a
3. d
4. b

C. (4 points each)
1. a
2. b
3. a
4. b
5. c

D. (20 points; students should answer one of the two)
1. Answers will vary but should reflect students' understanding that the diver used the term *magic* to refer to the experiences that the writer would have interacting with the dolphins. In addition, students might say that the diver would describe these experiences as magic because they are truly delightful, awe-inspiring, and mysterious and because he couldn't explain those experiences.
2. Answers will vary. Possible answers include the following.
   a. One of the author's purposes is to entertain, as shown by his choosing to write about his first dive, which was probably one of the most interesting of all his dives because the experience was completely new. He also concentrates on the amusing and suspenseful things that happened to him (such as his encounters with the dolphins).
   b. One of the author's purposes is to inform. He not only describes what happened to him on his first dive but also includes many facts that help to explain the reasons that the dolphins behave and appear as they do.
   Other answers should be supported with appropriate reasons and reference to the selection.

E. (16 points) Answers will vary widely, depending on students' personal experiences, situations, and viewpoints. Accept any answers that address the concern of the question and are elaborated by examples or details from the literature or from life.

Something Told the Wild Geese/ Questioning Faces
Selection Test, pp. 83–84

A. (14 points each) Answers will vary in "If you answered yes" sections. A model answer follows.
1. "Something Told the Wild Geese"
   a. Yes. Example of rhyme: *glossed* and *frost*
   b. Yes. Example of repetition: "Something told the wild geese"
2. "Questioning Faces"
   a. Yes. Example of rhyme: *aspread* and *red*
   b. Yes. Example of repetition: *window* (glass and sill); *glass* and *glassed*

B. (8 points each)
1. a
2. c
3. b
4. a

C. (20 points; students should answer one of the two)
1. Answers will vary. A model answer follows. Students may predict a verse added to "Something Told the Wild Geese" that describes
   a. the flight of the geese when the weather grows colder.
   b. the setting of the fields and orchards once the geese depart.
   c. the geese in their new setting.
   Students may predict a verse added to "Questioning Faces" that describes
   a. the children's reaction to what they have seen.
   b. the owl's actions after banking away from the window.
2. Answers will vary. Accept answers that accurately describe the rhythm and that interpret its meaning or overall feeling. A model answer follows.
   a. "Something Told the Wild Geese" has a back-and-forth rhythm created by alternating long and short lines. This rhythm suggests a sort of push and pull between the geese's comfort in the summer setting and their awareness that the dangers of winter are approaching, and so adds to the tension of the poem.
   b. "Questioning Faces" has a strong, steady rhythm because the poem's lines are of equal length (i.e., ten syllables each). The strong and steady rhythm complements the visual images of the owl's speed and strength as well as the forceful impact on the window glass that it narrowly avoids.

D. (20 points) Answers will vary widely, depending on students' personal experiences, situations, and viewpoints. Accept any answers that address the concerns of the questions and are elaborated by examples or details from the literature or from life.

Zlateh the Goat
Selection Test, pp. 85–86

A. (5 points each) Notes will vary.
1. Conflict: Aaron has been told to sell Zlateh the goat, but he does not want to; or Aaron is unable to get to the butcher's shop in town because he and Zlateh get caught in a blizzard.
2. Key events in the rising action might include
   a. Aaron starting his journey with Zlateh.
   b. Aaron and Zlateh becoming lost in a blizzard.
   c. Aaron and Zlateh taking shelter in a haystack.
   d. Aaron drinking Zlateh's milk while waiting out the blizzard.
3. The climax might be described as
   a. Aaron recognizing that he and Zlateh need each other.
   b. Aaron deciding never to part with Zlateh.
   c. Aaron turning toward home after the storm instead of toward the town.
4. Events in the resolution might include
   a. Aaron returning home with Zlateh.
   b. Aaron's sisters hugging Zlateh and giving her special treats.
   c. Reuven's business improving.
   d. the family celebrating Hanukkah.
   e. Zlateh's being allowed inside the house to visit the family.

B. (5 points each)
1. b
2. d
3. a
4. c
5. d

C. (4 points each)
1. a
2. b
3. c
4. a
5. b

D. (20 points; students should answer one of the two)
1. Answers will vary but should reflect students' understanding that Zlateh depends on Aaron to find safe shelter from the blizzard, to provide her with companionship during the storm, and/or to make sure that she is not sold to the butcher. Students' answers should reflect that Aaron depends on Zlateh for warmth, food, and companionship during the blizzard.

2. Answers will vary. A model answer follows.
At the beginning of the story, the family loves Zlateh, but because Reuven's business has been bad and there is little money for the Hanukkah celebration, they feel the necessity to sell her to the butcher. At the end of the story, the family is grateful to Zlateh for keeping Aaron alive during the blizzard. They love her even more, could never again think of selling her, and treat her almost as a member of the family.

E. (15 points) Answers will vary widely, depending on students' personal experiences, situations, and viewpoints. Accept any answers that address the concern of the question and are elaborated by examples or details from the literature or from life.

Unit Four, Part One Test
pp. 87–88
A. (5 points each)
1. b
2. a
3. c
4. b

B. (20 points) Notes will vary. Model answers for the writer in "My First Dive with the Dolphins" and Aaron in "Zlateh the Goat" follow.
1. a. the writer in "My First Dive with the Dolphins"
   b. the dolphin called Lucky
   c. respect
   d. When the diver is in Lucky's territory, Lucky warns him with a klonking sound; however, Lucky does not charge or hurt the diver.
2. a. Aaron in "Zlateh the Goat"
   b. Zlateh
   c. love and gratitude
   d. When they are stranded together in a blizzard, Zlateh's presence comforts and reassures Aaron. She seems almost like a sister to him. Also, the warmth of Zlateh's body and her milk, which Aaron drinks, enable him to survive.

C. (20 points each; students should answer two of the four)
1. Answers will vary. A model answer follows for "Something Told the Wild Geese" and "Zlateh the Goat."
   a. "Something Told the Wild Geese" is set at the end of summer and is filled with details of abundance or ripeness that describe the transition from summer to fall. But the poem also warns of the approaching winter, and images of snow, ice, and frost alternate with the summer images.
   b. The plot of "Zlateh the Goat" hinges on a sudden change in the weather. Aaron has been sent to sell Zlateh to the butcher when the two of them are caught in a blizzard. Because Zlateh helps Aaron

survive the blizzard, he repays her by resolving never to part with her.
2. Answers will vary. A model answer using the owl in "Questioning Faces" and Lob in "Lob's Girl" follows.
   a. The owl in "Questioning Faces" is an example of a wild animal because it has no real relationship with or dependence on humans. The children in the poem observe the owl, but they do not interact with it. Moreover, humans may actually pose a threat to wild animals. In the poem, for example, the glass windows of the children's home confuse the owl, and it only narrowly avoids flying into the glass.
   b. A tame animal, by contrast, depends on humans, and humans may also depend on the animal. "Lob's Girl" illustrates the deep, mutual love between a girl and her dog. At the beginning of the story, Lob seems unable to live without Sandy. At the end of the story, Sandy's connection to Lob is apparently the only thing that can pull her out of her coma.
3. Answers will vary. A model answer for Lob in "Lob's Girl" follows.
   a. Lob in "Lob's Girl" has the most human qualities because Lob seems to claim Sandy for himself.
   b. He is determined to stay with her.
   c. He keeps trying to get into the hospital.
   d. He knows that Grandma can help him.
   e. Usually it is humans who choose their pets, but in this story it is the other way around.
4. Answers will vary. A model answer follows for "My First Dive with the Dolphins."
I would like to relive the experience of the writer in "My First Dive with the Dolphins" because he was able to encounter and appreciate so many different animal "personalities." His experience also seems appealing because people rarely get the chance to interact with marine creatures, such as dolphins.

D. (20 points) Answers will vary. A model answer follows for "Lob's Girl" and "My First Dive with the Dolphins."
1. Lob in "Lob's Girl"
   a. Lob travels across England twice, from Mr. Dodsworth's home in Liverpool, to be with Sandy.
   b. Mr. Dodsworth observes the behavior, and so does Sandy.
   c. Mr. Dodsworth is frustrated by the trouble and expense Lob has cost him, and he accepts Lob's choice to be with Sandy. Sandy is overjoyed every time Lob arrives and is especially glad when he is allowed to stay permanently.
2. Ernestine in "My First Dive with the Dolphins"
   a. Ernestine playfully approaches the writer and encourages him to hang on as she pulls him along through the tank.

b. The writer experiences Ernestine's playfulness.

c. The writer is astounded and delighted by his interaction with Ernestine. He willingly plays along.

The Phantom Tollbooth
Selection Test, pp. 89–90

A. (8 points each) Answers will vary but should reflect students' understanding of fantastic elements of the play. Examples follow.

1. Settings
   a. Dictionopolis, where features such as street signs, lampposts, windows, and doors are in the shapes of letters
   b. Digitopolis, a dark place full of glittering rocks and shining numbers
2. Characters
   a. Tock, a talking dog with the body of a clock
   b. Dodecahedron, a 12-sided figure with a different human face on each side
3. Events
   a. When Dischord pours liquid from a bottle, there is a loud explosion and Dynne appears.
   b. The Senses Taker puts Milo, Tock, and Humbug into a trance. When Milo drops his Package of Laughter, laughing is heard and the spell is broken.

B. (5 points each)
1. b
2. d
3. a
4. c

C. (4 points each)
1. b
2. c
3. a
4. c
5. a

D. (20 points; students should answer one of the two)
1. Answers will vary but should reflect students' understanding that by keeping the peace between Azaz and Mathemagician, Rhyme and Reason ensure that words and numbers are used in balance and that the value of each is understood and appreciated. In addition, students might say that the role of Rhyme and Reason suggests there is no single correct type of wisdom or learning, and that all types can be valued and used.
2. Answers will vary but should reflect students' understanding that Milo is at first a person who thinks time moves slowly. By the end of the play, Milo thinks time moves quickly and is full of things to do. Students should also note that Milo changes because his experiences in the Land of Wisdom and the Land of Ignorance help him recognize how much there is to learn and what wonderful adventures he can

have by putting his imagination and his precious time to use.

E. (16 points) Answers will vary widely, depending on students' personal experiences, situations, and viewpoints. Accept any answers that address the concern of the question and are elaborated by examples or details from the literature or from life.

The Walrus and the Carpenter/Fairy Lullaby
Selection Test, pp. 91–92

A. (10 points each) Notes will vary. Examples follow.

1. Setting
   a. Realistic detail: a seashore with sand and water
   b. Fantastic detail: the sun shining in the middle of the night
2. Character
   a. Realistic detail: a carpenter who talks and weeps
   b. Fantastic detail: a walrus who talks and weeps
3. Plot
   a. Realistic detail: The carpenter eats oysters.
   b. Fantastic detail: Oysters take a walk.

B. (6 points each)
1. d
2. b
3. a
4. c
5. a

C. (20 points; students should answer one of the two)
1. Answers will vary. Students who think that most readers do not feel upset by what happens to the Oysters could point out that
   a. the whole poem is nonsense.
   b. the Oysters are not at all real or believable.
   c. the poem is funny, not serious.
   Students who think that most readers feel upset by what happens to the Oysters could point out that
   a. the Walrus and the Carpenter lied to the Oysters.
   b. the Oysters eagerly followed the Walrus and the Carpenter.
   c. the eldest Oyster did not warn the others they would be eaten.
   d. the Oysters turned blue with fear when they realized their fate.
2. Answers will vary but should reflect students' understanding of the poem's details. A model answer follows.
   "Fairy Lullaby" has the soothing and peaceful qualities of a lullaby because the fairies ward off all types of creatures, such as spiders, newts, and worms, that might disturb the queen's sleep. In addition, the chorus sings a soothing repetitive line containing sounds from the word "lull," a verse that is meant to lull the queen to sleep.

D. (20 points) Answers will vary widely, depending on students' personal experiences, situations, and viewpoints. Accept any answers that address the concern of the question and are elaborated by examples or details from the literature or from life.

Three Limericks

Selection Test, pp. 93–94

A. (10 points each) Notes will vary. Examples of humor in each limerick follow.

1. Prelutsky: the idea that someone could swallow a watch and then spit out the time
2. Nash: the rhyming of the character's name with *bugle*, the idea that he could sneeze in different keys, the idea that he did so rather than pay for a bugle
3. Lear: the idea that birds could nest in a beard and the man with the beard would not notice

B. (8 points each)

1. a
2. b
3. d
4. c

C. (20 points; students should answer one of the two)

1. Answers will vary but should suggest ideas similar to the following.
   The characters are alike in that
   a. they are all ridiculous.
   b. each one does something that could not really happen.
   The characters are different in that they make different impressions.
   a. Ben seems foolish for swallowing his watch.
   b. Dougal MacDougal seems clever for learning to make musical sneezes.
   c. The old man seems unlucky to have birds nesting in his beard.
2. Answers will vary but should reflect students' understanding of the limerick. For example:
   a. Writing an effective limerick about something sad or serious would be difficult because the limerick's rhythm and rhyme pattern create a bouncy, singsong effect.
   b. The form of a limerick seems best suited to topics that are cheerful or nonsensical.
   c. The limerick is too short and quick to describe something serious or sad in enough detail.

D. (18 points) Answers will vary widely, depending on students' personal experiences, situations, and viewpoints. Accept any answers that address the concern of the question and are elaborated by examples or details from the literature or from life.

The Fun They Had

Selection Test, pp. 95–96

A. (12 points each) Notes will vary but should resemble the following.

1. Setting
   a. When: in the future; specifically, 2157
   b. Where: Margie's home, or the family's home
2. Comparison
   a. Difference: Children do not go to a school; they learn at home.
   b. Similarity: Children still have to do homework; or parents still pressure children to get their work done.

B. (5 points each)

1. a
2. c
3. a
4. d

C. (4 points each)

1. a
2. c
3. b
4. a
5. c

D. (20 points; students should answer one of the two)

1. Answers will vary. Most students will suggest that Margie would probably like school better if she had a person for a teacher because
   a. Margie was having trouble in school because her mechanical teacher was giving her tests that were too difficult.
   b. the problem went on and on until the county inspector fixed the mechanical teacher.
   c. a real teacher could have figured out the problem immediately, or Margie could have asked a real teacher for help as soon as she had trouble.
   d. Margie seems to envy students of the past because they got to interact with real people, whereas she interacts only with the mechanical teacher.
2. Answers will vary.
   Advantages of Margie's type of school might include
   a. not having to waste time getting to or from school.
   b. being able to study and learn in a private, quiet setting.
   c. not having to worry about peer pressure and making friends.
   Disadvantages of Margie's type of school might include
   a. never getting away from school, since it is at home.
   b. not having opportunities to make and socialize with friends.
   c. not having opportunities to learn in groups or hear other students' ideas and opinions.
   d. not having other children to do homework with.

E. (16 points) Answers will vary widely, depending on students' personal experiences, situations, and viewpoints. Accept any answers that address the concern of the question and are elaborated by examples or details from the literature or from life.

The Sand Castle
Selection Test, pp. 97–98

A. (24 points) Notes will vary.

Details about Mrs. Pavloff's world when she was a child might include three of the following.
a. The seashore was a place to enjoy.
b. People wore bathing suits and swam in the ocean.
c. Seagulls, eagles, and other birds could be seen.
d. Seashells could be found along the shore.
e. The sun was a source of warmth.
f. People enjoyed going outside.

Details about her grandchildren's world might include three of the following.
a. The weather is constantly warming.
b. The sun's rays are dangerous.
c. People must wear protective clothing when they go outside.
d. The earth has been scorched by the sun.
e. Seagulls, eagles, and other birds have vanished.
f. There are no more seashells.

B. (5 points each)
1. c
2. b
3. a
4. d

C. (4 points each)
1. c
2. a
3. b
4. a
5. c

D. (20 points; students should answer one of the two)
1. Answers will vary but should suggest ideas similar to the following.
   Mrs. Pavloff thinks her grandchildren's world is dreadful.
   a. She feels sorry because they haven't experienced simple pleasures such as feeling the warm sun on their bodies, swimming in the ocean, playing in the sand, and having picnics.
   b. The children have never been able to enjoy nature by, for example, watching wild birds or collecting seashells.
   c. The children cannot go outside without protective clothing, goggles, and gloves.
   d. They cannot enjoy the experiences she had with her parents and her grandfather because the world has changed.

2. Answers will vary but should suggest that
   a. Mrs. Pavloff's memories make her happy because she relives the joy and excitement she experienced as a young girl spending the day at the beach with her family and seeing an eagle with her grandfather.
   b. the memories make her sad because she knows that her grandchildren will never have the same experiences; the sun problem makes it impossible for them to swim and play in the ocean.

E. (16 points) Answers will vary widely, depending on students' personal experiences, situations, and viewpoints. Accept any answers that address the concern of the question and are elaborated by examples or details from the literature or from life.

Unit Four, Part Two Test
pp. 99–100

A. (5 points each)
1. They are needed to settle the quarrel between Azaz and Mathemagician, to restore harmony in the land of Wisdom.
2. to entertain or to make readers laugh
3. "The Fun They Had"
4. the sun (or any place exposed to the sun's rays)

B. (20 points) Answers will vary. Model answers for Milo in *The Phantom Tollbooth* and Mrs. Pavloff in "The Sand Castle" follow.
1. In *The Phantom Tollbooth:*
   a. Milo
   b. Milo learns that he can solve many problems by thinking.
   c. Instead of feeling bored by everything, Milo is eager to learn all he can.
2. In "The Sand Castle":
   a. Mrs. Pavloff
   b. Mrs. Pavloff takes her grandchildren to the beach and makes sand castles with them.
   c. She finds some happiness and hope in sharing something she loves with her grandchildren, despite her despair over the environmental damage.

C. (20 points each; students should answer two of the four)
1. Answers will vary. A model answer for "The Sand Castle" follows.
   "The Sand Castle" offers the vision that is most likely realistic because
   a. it predicts how people might actually live in the future if Earth's ozone layer is destroyed.
   b. scientists have already discovered that the ozone layer has been damaged by pollution.
   c. without the ozone layer, the environment would change in drastic ways, and many plants and animals would die out.

d. people have already begun to adapt their way of life to protect themselves from the sun.

e. older people remember what life was like before the ozone was damaged, but children don't always understand what life was like before.

2. Answers will vary but should reflect students' understanding of characters' situations or problems. A model answer for the character in Ogden Nash's limerick follows.

   This advice is for Dougal MacDougal, the bugler. Instead of making musical sneezes, he should buy himself a bugle. If he relies on sneezing, he can only make music when he has a cold. But if he buys a bugle, he can make music whenever he wants.

3. Answers will vary. A model answer for "Fairy Lullaby" follows.

   In "Fairy Lullaby," the queen is surrounded by good and evil.

   a. The evil things are creatures, such as snakes, spiders, and hedgehogs, that might harm the queen while she sleeps.

   b. The fairies, who are good, sing a warning song to the creatures to keep them away.

4. Answers will vary but should accurately incorporate details of the setting the student chooses. A model answer for the seashore from "The Walrus and the Carpenter" follows.

   The seashore from "The Walrus and the Carpenter" would be an interesting place to visit. I would especially like to swim at night in the ocean while both the sun and the moon shine on the water. I would also like to walk along the sandy beach with the little Oysters.

D. (20 points) Answers will vary. A model answer follows. The most appealing world is Dictionopolis, as described in *The Phantom Tollbooth.*

   a. Main features include edible words and letters, a talking dog, kindhearted characters, and clever word play.

   b. It is appealing because the characters are funny, the whole world is imaginary, and it makes one think about the meanings of words and expressions.

   The least appealing world is the one described in "The Fun They Had."

   a. Main features include going to school at home and having a machine for a teacher.

   b. It is not appealing because one would not get to meet other children, learning from a machine would be boring, and the whole world would seem impersonal.

Unit Five

Words on a Page
Selection Test, pp. 101–102

A. (8 points each) Notes will vary but could include ideas similar to the following.

1. Character

   a. Lenore displays her writing talent in a story about a girl much like herself, one who treasures the peace and harmony she feels in her own home but also dreams of exploring the world.

   b. Lenore's story reflects her own feelings and struggles with herself and her father.

   c. Lenore is a person of Native American heritage who is greatly influenced by the outside culture and the ambitions that her teacher has for her but who still feels a deep connection to her father and his more traditional values.

   d. Pete, her father, represents home and the Ojibway way of life.

2. Setting

   a. The area around the Shadow River, where Lenore spends time with her father, shows the importance of home and Lenore's Ojibway heritage.

   b. Lenore's school presents outside influences that may lure her away from home.

3. Plot

   a. Lenore conflicts with her father when her interest and talent raise the possibility that she should leave home to attend university and pursue a career as a writer.

   b. The conflict is resolved when Lenore assures her father that she will return home and that what she wants to write about is her home and her people.

B. (5 points each)
1. d
2. c
3. a
4. c

C. (4 points each)
1. b
2. a
3. c
4. a
5. b

D. (20 points; students should answer one of the two)
1. Answers will vary. Students could say that Pete does not value Lenore's talent, feels threatened by it, or disapproves of her interest in developing it, and could give reasons such as the following:

   a. The Ojibway have an oral story tradition, and Pete thinks that Native American ways are best.

b. Pete is afraid that if Lenore goes to university to develop her talent, she will never return home.

c. Lenore's talents attract attention from outsiders Pete does not know or trust, such as her teacher and principal.

d. Pete never learned to read and write himself, and he has been too ashamed to admit that to Lenore.

2. Answers will vary but should include points similar to the following.

Connie

a. advises Lenore not to push her father too much, to let him come around to accepting her ambition to write.

b. reacts the way she does because she understands Pete's feelings about Lenore, thinks he will come around in time, and knows that he will react badly if he is provoked.

Miss Walker

a. is frustrated by Pete's lack of interest in Lenore's writing.

b. confronts him angrily and suggests he doesn't care about Lenore.

c. reacts as she does because she does not know or understand Pete, feels strongly about Lenore's gifts as a writer, places a very high value on education, and knows that Lenore may not pursue a writing career without her father's approval.

E. (16 points) Answers will vary widely, depending on students' personal experiences, situations, and viewpoints. Accept any answers that address the concerns of the questions and are elaborated by examples or details from the literature or from life.

from **All I Really Need to Know I Learned in Kindergarten**

Selection Test, pp. 103–104

A. (8 points each)

1. Notes will vary. Students could note that the selection

a. relates the author's own experiences, ideas, and opinions.

b. includes some autobiographical information, such as his description of his annual effort to write a personal credo.

c. is based on real events rather than a made-up story.

2. Notes will vary but may mention

a. the author's earlier attempts to write a personal credo that left no loose ends.

b. how the inspiration to write a short, simple credo came to the author at a gasoline station.

c. that the author's old car ran badly when filled with deluxe gasoline.

3. Notes will vary but may include opinions such as

a. the author's lengthy credo sounded like a Supreme Court brief.

b. to write a personal credo only one page in length implies naive idealism.

c. everything the author needs to know he learned in kindergarten.

d. any of the kindergarten rules, extrapolated into adult terms, holds true and firm.

e. the world would be a better place if we all had cookies and milk every afternoon and then took a nap.

f. when you go out in the world, it is best to hold hands and stick together.

B. (5 points each)

1. a
2. c
3. b
4. a

C. (4 points each)

1. b
2. c
3. a
4. c
5. b

D. (20 points; students should answer one of the two)

1. Answers will vary but might suggest that our world is like a kindergarten class in that

a. it works best when all of us recognize and abide by accepted rules that are intended to keep everyone safe. For example, a kindergarten rule such as "Don't hit people," when extrapolated to adult terms, means that nations should not engage in wars and that peace should be a goal embraced by all nations.

b. there is wonder all around us that we should appreciate.

c. we should treat one another as we would like to be treated ourselves.

d. we must attend to basic cleanliness and clean up our own living space.

e. the best way to live is to keep everything in balance, especially work and play.

f. fairness and sharing are still essential.

2. Answers will vary but should indicate that

a. we must all watch out for dangers.

b. helping one another is better than trying to do everything alone.

c. each of us has some responsibility for the welfare of others, including family members, friends, and even strangers.

d. when we take an action or make a choice for our own benefit, we should question whether it may be harmful to others, and if so, we must make a different choice. For example, recycling waste materials requires much more time and effort than simply throwing the materials in the trash. We may eliminate an annoying weekly chore by not recycling, but we also add unnecessarily to the amount of environmental pollution that affects all of us as well as future generations. If every family does its part to recycle waste materials, the whole world will benefit.

E. (16 points) Answers will vary widely, depending on students' personal experiences, situations, and viewpoints. Accept any answers that address the concern of the question and are elaborated by examples or details from the literature or from life.

You Sing (Sonnet 52)/How to Paint the Portrait of a Bird
Selection Test, pp. 105–106

A. (14 points each) Notes will vary but should include two sensory details, such as the following, for each poem.
1. In "You Sing (Sonnet 52)"
   a. "peels the husk of the day's grain" appeals to the senses of sound, sight, and possibly touch.
   b. "pine trees speak with their green tongue" appeals to the senses of sight and sound.
   c. "birds of the winter whistle" appeals to the sense of sound.
   d. the entire second stanza appeals primarily to the sense of sound.
   e. "your voice soars with the zing and precision of an arrow" appeals to the senses of sound and sight.
   f. "your voice scatters the highest swords" appeals to the senses of sight and sound.
   g. "cargo of violets" appeals to the sense of sight and possibly the sense of smell.
2. In "How to Paint the Portrait of a Bird"
   a. "a cage with an open door" appeals to the sense of sight.
   b. "observe the deepest silence" appeals to the sense of sound.
   c. "gently close the door with the paint-brush" appeals to the senses of sight and touch.
   d. "the green leaves" appeals to the sense of sight.
   e. "the freshness of the wind" appeals to the senses of touch and sound.
   f. "dust in the sun" appeals to the sense of sight.
   g. "the sound of the insects in the summer grass" appeals to the sense of sound.
   h. "pluck very gently one of the quills" appeals to the sense of touch.

B. (9 points each)
1. c
2. a
3. b
4. d

C. (20 points; students should answer one of the two)
1. Answers will vary but should suggest ideas similar to the following.
   In "You Sing (Sonnet 52)"
   a. the song the speaker hears is the voice of inspiration, and it is a sound which the speaker hears better than any other sound.
   b. when the speaker hears the voice, he/she feels open to the beauty of the world, capable, and energized.
   In "How to Paint the Portrait of a Bird"
   a. the cage represents the desire to create art, and the bird's arrival represents the initial inspiration or idea.
   b. the painter is told how to tend to the bird/inspiration, all the while waiting patiently for it to sing.
   c. the bird's song represents the fully developed work of art that results from the initial inspiration if it is properly and patiently tended.
2. Answers will vary but should suggest that the speakers in the two poems view inspiration in very different ways.
   a. In "You Sing (Sonnet 52)," inspiration is presented as a powerful force that is essentially irresistible to the speaker.
   b. In "How to Paint the Portrait of a Bird," inspiration seems much more fragile. It is portrayed as something that must be tended with the utmost care and patience. Even then, the poem suggests, the inspiration may fail to develop, despite the best efforts of the artist who tries to nurture it.

D. (16 points) Answers will vary widely, depending on students' personal experiences, situations, and viewpoints. Accept any answers that address the concern of the question and are elaborated by examples or details from the literature or from life.

The Scribe
Selection Test, pp. 107–108

A. (8 points each)
1. Notes will vary, but students might say that James
   a. wants to help others.
   b. has confidence in his writing abilities.
   c. is not interested in making money.
   d. does not think Mr. Silver and Mr. Dollar treat their customers well.
2. Notes will vary, but students might say that James
   a. does not want to break the law.
   b. is intimidated by the cop.
   c. is too respectful to argue with the cop.
   d. does not want to get into trouble.

3. Notes will vary, but students might say that James
   a. inspires the loyalty of others.
   b. seems, to an older person, to need defending.
   c. has won the support of people he helped.
4. Notes will vary, but students might say that James
   a. is too young or naive to understand how banks make his neighbors feel.
   b. is practical and frugal, and he wants to save money when possible.

B. (6 points each)
1. c
2. b
3. c
4. a
5. b

C. (20 points; students should answer one of the two)
1. Answers will vary. Students could say that James
   a. wants to help people.
   b. doesn't want the neediest people in the neighborhood to be taken advantage of by the Silver Dollar.
   c. doesn't want to see his neighbors embarrassed by their lack of education.
   d. has nothing he'd rather do with his time.
2. Answers will vary. Students might identify the theme as one of the following.
   a. One person can make a difference in other people's lives by being willing to make an effort. James makes a difference when he sets up his table.
   b. People suffer in many ways from the inability to read and write. The people in James's neighborhood who can't read and write are taken advantage of by the Silver Dollar.
   c. Overcoming one's fears is necessary to success or improvement in life. When Mrs. Franklin overcomes her fear of the bank, she is able to open an account that makes her feel proud and prevents her from having to pay to cash checks at the Silver Dollar. Other themes should be supported with appropriate references to the story.

D. (18 points) Answers will vary widely, depending on students' personal experiences, situations, and viewpoints. Accept any answers that address the concerns of the questions and are elaborated by examples or details from the literature or from life.

Crow Call
Selection Test, pp. 109–110

A. (6 points each) Answers will vary but should suggest ideas similar to the following.
1. a. The hunting shirt represents her father's concern for his daughter or her link to him.
   b. It suggests that the daughter wants to become closer to her father and that the father understands what his daughter wants and needs.
2. a. The father's gun represents war or death, the ability to hurt others, or the father's absence in the last few years when he was away at war.
   b. The narrator is afraid of the father's gun and the pain or hurt it could cause and does not want him to use it.
3. a. Cherry pie represents the narrator or the family that the father has not been a part of for some time.
   b. If the father had been around, he would have known the narrator's favorite food was cherry pie; his willingness to buy it for her suggests that he wants to get to know her again.
4. a. The crow call represents an appeal for communication as well as a way for the daughter to gain a place in her father's life.
   b. The crow call is the narrator's role in the hunt; she uses the crow call to bring the crows out of hiding, but she is also making an appeal to her father to communicate with her.

B. (5 points each)
1. d
2. b
3. a
4. d

C. (4 points each)
1. c
2. a
3. b
4. b
5. c

D. (20 points; students should answer one of the two)
1. Answers will vary but should indicate at least three of the following concerns.
   a. The narrator is worried that she will not know what to do during the hunt or that she will do something wrong.
   b. She is afraid of her father's gun or of being shot.
   c. She is worried that if they kill crows, the crows' babies will have no one to take care of them.
   d. She is afraid that her father has been gone too long and that she might not be able to get to know him again.
   e. She is worried that she will disappoint her father.
2. Answers will vary but should suggest ideas similar to the following.
   a. The father says of the crows, "It's a strange thing, but by now they don't even know who their babies are." Similarly, the father doesn't really know his baby/daughter or who she really is because he has been away in the war.
   b. The father says that crows don't know any better than to eat crops and that "Even people do bad things without meaning to." In a way, the father is explaining the war and why he has been away; he may also be explaining his own actions in the war if he had been forced to hurt or kill others.

c. The crows are hiding and unseen until the narrator calls to them; similarly, the narrator and her father are "hidden" until they make an effort to get to know each other.

d. The narrator says of the crows that answer her call, "They think I'm their friend! Maybe their baby, all grown up!" The narrator implies that she has called out to the crows and they trust her; it would be an act of betrayal to shoot them. In a way, the narrator may be implying a similar message to her father; she wants to get to know him, and she would consider it an act of betrayal if he hurt her or left her again.

E. (16 points) Answers will vary widely, depending on students' personal experiences, situations, and viewpoints. Accept any answers that address the concern of the question and are elaborated by examples or details from the literature or from life.

from Looking Back

Selection Test, pp. 111–112

A. (6 points each) Answers will vary but should suggest ideas similar to the following.

1. a. When she was little, Lowry thought the girl's name was Modest Storewrecker; the name seemed normal at the time.
   b. As an adult, Lowry wonders if the girl has lived up to her name—until she finds out that the girl's name was Mardis Storacker.

2. a. As a child, Lowry liked to bully her little brother. She got very upset with him for breaking the head of one of her dolls, thought he was a pest at times, and thought they were very different from each other.
   b. As an adult, Lowry has forgiven her brother, and she sees how alike they really are.

3. a. As a child, Lowry admired the character Jody, thought he looked "sad and beautiful," and sometimes imitated the scene; but she did not know what a vigil was.
   b. As an adult, she looks back at the experience with a bemused attitude at how romantic and silly she was and at how her sister mocked her for imitating Jody's vigil ("that weird thing by her bed").

4. a. As a child, Lowry loved the football uniform and "wanted to wear it forever."
   b. As an adult, she realizes that the reason she enjoyed wearing the uniform so much is that it made her "feel powerful and brave," traits that she had never had in real life.

B. (5 points each)
1. d
2. a
3. b
4. c

C. (4 points each)
1. a
2. b
3. a
4. a
5. c

D. (20 points; students should answer one of the two)
1. Answers will vary. Positive memories might include
   a. having a friend named Modest Storewrecker.
   b. bullying her little brother.
   c. reading *The Yearling* and pretending to be Jody.
   d. wearing the football uniform and acting like a boy playing football.
   Negative memories might include
   a. having to wear an ugly bathing suit.
   b. times when her brother was a pest.
   c. the time her brother broke the head of her antique doll.
   d. wearing lederhosen from Switzerland.

2. Answers may vary but should suggest ideas similar to the following.
   a. She was probably affectionate and easy to get along with. (She says she got along well with her little brother most of the time.)
   b. She probably felt that she was weak and that she lacked courage. (She liked to bully her little brother, who was too small to fight back; she says she was never powerful or bold.)
   c. She was romantic and liked to dream or fantasize. (After reading *The Yearling,* she wanted to be a boy who lived in the swamp with wild animals for friends.)
   d. She probably felt somewhat intimidated by her older sister, who seemed to make fun of her, criticize her, or ignore her most of the time.
   e. She felt humiliated when she had to wear the clothes her mother had bought for her in Europe, such as the lederhosen.

E. (16 points) Answers will vary widely, depending on students' personal experiences, situations, and viewpoints. Accept any answers that address the concern of the question and are elaborated by examples or details from the literature or from life.

Unit Five, Part One Test

pp. 113–114

A. (5 points each)

1. *All I Really Need to Know I Learned in Kindergarten*
2. The bird sings.
3. Lenore's father disapproves of her dream of becoming a writer.
4. the excerpt from *Looking Back*

B. (20 points) Answers will vary. A model answer follows for Lenore in *Words on a Page* and Robert Fulghum, author of *All I Really Need to Know I Learned in Kindergarten*.

In *Words on a Page:*

a. Lenore's goal is to become a writer someday and/or to write about her home and her people.

b. Her goal is linked to her education in that it is Lenore's teacher who recognizes her writing talent and works to support her efforts.

c. Her goal is also influenced by lack of education: Lenore's father is illiterate, and he at first opposes her goal; he has mixed feelings about Lenore becoming educated.

In *All I Really Need to Know I Learned in Kindergarten:*

a. Robert Fulghum's goal is to write an effective and useful credo to guide the way he lives his life.

b. Fulghum's goal is linked to his education because he distills his credo to the basics of what he learned years before when he was in kindergarten. He realizes that he does not gain more wisdom each year with additional education; the most important things in life are based on what he learned in the beginning.

C. (20 points each; students should answer two of the four)

1. Answers will vary. A model answer for James in "The Scribe" follows; students should mention at least three points similar to the following. James is admirable because he

a. sees his neighbors being taken advantage of by a check-cashing business and is offended.

b. decides to use his own writing skills to help his neighbors.

c. offers free scribe services to his neighbors.

d. brushes off a setback when the cop shuts his business down.

e. leads his neighbors to the bank.

f. thinks about applying for a license to be a scribe after watching a neighbor overcome her fear of the bank.

2. Answers will vary. A model answer for "You Sing (Sonnet 52)" follows.

The inspiration described in this poem comes from within. Evidence for this view might include the following.

a. The speaker addresses "You," a voice that does not have a body or a name.

b. Despite all the natural sounds that surround the speaker (e.g., birds whistling, tools jangling, wheels creaking), the speaker hears only "your voice."

c. The voice has tremendous power and beauty (e.g., it "scatters the highest swords" and "returns with its cargo of violets").

3. Answers will vary. A model answer for "How to Paint the Portrait of a Bird" follows.

The message of the selection may be something similar to "The creation of something beautiful or worthwhile requires the greatest care and patience." Reasons the theme is important may include that it helps readers

a. recognize that discouragement and failure are parts of the creative process.

b. appreciate that true inspiration is rare, beautiful, and must be nurtured.

c. understand that creation is a process, not an object or a product.

4. Answers will vary. Model answers for *Words on a Page* and "Crow Call" follow.

In *Words on a Page,* adults and children learn from each other.

a. The story illustrates how adults can pass along important values and traditions to their children. Pete is proud of his Ojibway heritage, and he passes the values and traditions of the Ojibway on to Lenore.

b. Lenore learns and shares her father's love of their home and hopes to write about her people someday.

c. Pete also learns from his child. He realizes that Lenore has talent as a writer, and he realizes that becoming educated will not necessarily drive her away from her home and family. She wants to write about the same values and traditions he is trying to preserve.

In "Crow Call," an adult learns from a child.

a. The father realizes that he does not know his daughter well (for example, that her favorite food is cherry pie).

b. He realizes that she needs him.

c. He learns that building a trusting relationship with his daughter is more important than killing crows.

d. He learns that his daughter has grown up and changed while he was gone and that he must make an effort to get to know her.

D. (20 points) Answers will vary. A model answer for James in "The Scribe" follows.

Notes about the process James goes through to find his own voice may mention points similar to the following.

a. James opens his scribe service with good will and enthusiasm.

b. When a cop shuts down James's service because he does not have a license, James feels angry and defeated.

c. Instead of giving up, James helps his neighbors again by encouraging them to set up bank accounts.

d. Watching Mrs. Franklin overcome her fear of the bank, James gains the confidence to consider applying for a license to be a scribe.

From this process, James gains new knowledge and learns that

a. people respect and listen to him.

b. he has good ideas.

c. giving up accomplishes nothing.

d. fear gets in the way of success.

e. if an obstacle stops him, he should look for a way around it.

The Dog of Pompeii

Selection Test, pp. 115–116

A. (12 points each)

1. Historical facts or events will vary but might include three of the following.

a. An earthquake had destroyed much of Pompeii 12 years before this story starts.

b. Pompeii was rebuilt after this earthquake.

c. Mt. Vesuvius emitted smoke before the eruption.

d. The people of Pompeii gathered each day in the forum.

e. The people of Pompeii participated in a celebration once each year when the Roman emperor visited the city.

f. The eruption of Mt. Vesuvius buried Pompeii.

g. Some residents of Pompeii fled to the ocean and escaped in boats.

h. Archaeologists excavated and studied the remains of Pompeii 1800 years after Mt. Vesuvius erupted.

i. Mount Etna erupted and destroyed two towns in Sicily.

2. Details imagined by the writer will vary but could include any three details related to the actions, experiences, and/or feelings of the story's fictional characters. Examples:

a. Bimbo goes out three times a day to get food.

b. The wife of Marcus Lucretius cleans her house in preparation for a visitor.

c. Men in the forum discuss the significance of the column of smoke over Vesuvius.

B. (5 points each)

1. b

2. a

3. b

4. c

C. (4 points each)

1. b

2. c

3. a

4. b

5. a

D. (20 points; students should answer one of the two)

1. Answers will vary. Students may say that Bimbo goes back to the city to

a. get food for Tito.

b. get Tito one of the raisin cakes that are his favorites.

Students may say that this shows that Bimbo is

a. more concerned about Tito than himself.

b. more concerned about fulfilling his duty than about his own safety.

c. loyal.

d. brave.

e. caring.

2. Answers will vary. Most students will say that Bimbo is a hero because he

a. saves Tito's life.

b. risks his own life to save Tito's.

c. sacrifices his own life in the process of trying to provide food for Tito.

d. takes care of Tito on a daily basis.

e. provides for Tito without any reward other than friendship.

Students who say that Bimbo is not a hero should support that answer.

E. (16 points) Answers will vary widely, depending on students' personal experiences, situations, and viewpoints. Accept any answers that address the concern of the question and are elaborated by examples or details from the literature or from life.

Tutankhamen

Selection Test, pp. 117–118

A. (6 points each)

1. Notes will vary, but students might indicate that Howard Carter

a. was British.

b. was working with Lord Carnarvon to locate Tutankhamen's tomb.

c. searched for five years before discovering the tomb.

d. waited for Carnarvon's arrival before exploring the tomb.

2. Notes will vary, but students might indicate that Lord Carnarvon
   a. was British.
   b. provided the financing for Carter's search for the tomb.
   c. returned to England while Carter continued the excavation.
   d. was summoned to the tomb by Carter and explored it with him.
3. Notes will vary, but students might indicate that the Valley
   a. is an area where the burial tombs of many pharaohs are located.
   b. is the location of Rameses VI's tomb.
   c. is the location of Tutankhamen's tomb.
   d. was, at the time of Carter and Carnarvon's work, littered with the refuse of previous excavations.
   e. was a tourist attraction.
4. Notes will vary, but students might indicate that
   a. it was approached by a staircase.
   b. its first door carried seals of Tutankhamen and the cemetery.
   c. a passage filled with stones lay beyond the first door.
   d. its second door showed signs of being opened and reclosed.
   e. the second door led into a room filled with objects, such as carved gilt couches, two statues of a king, caskets, vases, shrines, beds, chairs, a throne, food offerings, and chariots—but no coffin.
   f. its third door also showed signs of being opened and reclosed.
   g. beyond a hole behind a couch, more objects were strewn about all over the floor.

B. (5 points each)
1. d
2. c
3. b
4. d

C. (4 points each)
1. a
2. b
3. a
4. c
5. b

D. (20 points; students should answer one of the two)
1. Answers will vary widely but could include
   a. evidence found in the valley that provided a clue to the tomb's location.
   b. Carter and Carnarvon's determination to find the tomb even after many years of failed efforts.
   c. Carter and Carnarvon's refusal to believe the "experts" who thought that the tomb had already been discovered.

d. Carter's thoroughness in searching every last part of the area.
   e. Carnarvon's ability to finance their dream.
2. Answers will vary widely, but students might mention
   a. the inspiration to learn more about archaeology and ancient Egypt because the selection leaves many questions unanswered.
   b. the inspiration to become an archaeologist because the selection makes the profession sound so interesting and exciting.
   c. the thrill of "being there" when a fascinating archaeological find is discovered.
   d. the idea that anyone, after five years of struggle, could be so patient and disciplined as to cover up the entrance and wait two weeks to open it—mainly out of gratitude for financial support and faith.

E. (16 points) Answers will vary widely, depending on students' personal experiences, situations, and viewpoints. Accept any answers that address the concerns of the questions and are elaborated by examples or details from the literature or from life.

The First Emperor

Selection Test, pp. 119–120

A. (8 points each) Notes will vary. The author's main ideas might be described as
1. greatest archeological find; overshadow the discovery of King Tut's tomb or something similar.
2. forever searched for the secret of immortality; victim of liars and tricksters or something similar.
3. the tomb was well protected; loaded crossbows booby-trapped to shoot intruders or something similar.

B. (5 points each)
1. a
2. c
3. b
4. d

C. (4 points each)
1. a
2. b
3. c
4. b
5. a

D. (20 points; students should answer one of the two)
1. Answers will vary but could include points similar to the following.
   a. Shih Huang Ti was a cruel tyrant who did very little for the ordinary people of China.
   b. Today, Shih Huang Ti is seen as a historical figure who united China and became the first emperor in a line of succession that lasted 2000 years.
   c. He ordered the Great Wall built and ordered a tomb built for himself—both of which bring tourists, wealth, and prestige to China.

d. Today, Shih Huang Ti is a historical figure who has no power over people (and can thus be appreciated more easily).

2. Answers will vary. Most students will say that the author's main purpose is to inform and will support that view with some of the following points.

a. The selection includes a good deal of information about Shih Huang Ti, his tomb, and Chinese history and culture.

b. It is entertaining only in that the information is fascinating; it does not present an entertaining drama or story with fictional characters.

c. The author expresses few strong opinions.

d. The author doesn't use much persuasive language.

e. The author doesn't seem to make any great effort to change the reader's point of view on the subject.

Other answers should be supported with appropriate reasons and reference to the selection.

E. (16 points) Answers will vary widely, depending on students' personal experiences, situations, and viewpoints. Accept any answers that address the concern of the question and are elaborated by examples or details from the literature or from life.

Barbara Frietchie

Selection Test, pp. 121–122

A. (15 points each)

1. Notes will vary but could suggest that Barbara Frietchie raises the flag because

a. her town has just fallen to Confederate forces.

b. the flag is a symbol of loyalty to the Union.

c. the flag stands for freedom.

d. it is important to her to express her defiance and rejection of the forces that have just taken over her town.

e. doing so might raise the spirits of her townspeople and encourage them not to cooperate with the enemy.

2. Notes will vary but could suggest that Stonewall Jackson allows the flag to fly because he

a. is ashamed of his earlier impulse to shoot it down.

b. recognizes the rights of others to display their loyalty.

c. realizes its importance to Barbara Frietchie and others.

d. doesn't want to seem ungentlemanly by picking on an old woman.

e. realizes that one old woman's protest is not, after all, much of a threat to his army.

B. (6 points each)

1. b
2. c
3. a
4. b
5. a
6. c

C. (20 points; students should answer one of the two)

1. Answers will vary; students should provide at least two reasons to back up their opinions. Students who think that Barbara Frietchie's action is worth the risk might say that

a. people should stand up for their beliefs, even if it means risking their lives.

b. loyalty and freedom are important to human dignity, and without them life has little meaning.

c. as a woman and an older person, Frietchie is not perceived as much of a threat (and therefore is likely to get away with her action).

Students who don't think her action is worth the risk might say that

a. although the flag is an important symbol, it is only a symbol and not worth losing one's life.

b. it is more important to survive and fight for loyalty and freedom than to die for a symbol of those ideas.

2. Answers will vary. Students might say that the main message concerns the idea that

a. standing up for one's beliefs can influence others in positive ways.

b. symbols have an important place in our lives.

c. freedom and loyalty are worth risking one's life for.

d. the freedom we enjoy today has been won for us and handed down by people like Barbara Frietchie.

D. (14 points) Answers will vary widely, depending on students' personal experiences, situations, and viewpoints. Accept any answers that address the concern of the question and are elaborated by examples or details from the literature or from life.

Unit Five, Part Two Test

pp. 123–124

A. (5 points each)

1. a
2. b
3. d
4. a

B. (20 points) Answers will vary. A model answer for "The First Emperor" follows.

1. a. practicality, common sense, patience, self-discipline, or something similar

b. With only a limited number of archaeologists available to excavate Shih Huang Ti's tomb, they accepted that the project would proceed slowly.

2. a. enthusiasm, hopefulness, or something similar

b. Based on what had been uncovered so far, the archaeologists were hopeful that more priceless treasures would be uncovered and would be in good condition.

C. (20 points each; students should answer two of the four)

1. Answers will vary. A model answer for Howard Carter in "Tutankhamen" follows.

   Carter rose above his own interest and did the right thing because he
   a. summoned his partner, Lord Carnarvon, and awaited his arrival before entering the tomb through the door that had been excavated.
   b. could have easily indulged his tremendous desire to explore the tomb immediately.
   c. could have claimed sole credit for discovering the tomb.
   d. could even have stolen some of its contents for himself.

   By waiting for Carnarvon, Carter demonstrated enormous self-restraint, an admirable sense of fair play, and loyalty to the partner whose financing had made the excavation possible. As a result of Carter's action, he and Carnarvon were able to share the credit for discovering the tomb, the thrill of exploring it together, and the satisfaction of seeing their determination and hard work pay off.

2. Answers will vary. A model answer follows for Pompeii, the setting of "The Dog of Pompeii."

   Reasons for visiting Pompeii might include wanting to
   a. stand among the ruins of an ancient city that no longer exists and imagine how it once looked.
   b. see and understand the damage that can result from a volcanic eruption.
   c. observe Mt. Vesuvius from a distance and imagine what it might have looked like on the day it erupted.
   d. see how the area of the buried city has been excavated by archaeologists.
   e. look for the ruins of specific places described in the selection, such as the wall and the forum.
   f. retrace the journey that real people would have made from the city to the sea to escape the falling ash.

3. Answers will vary. A model answer for "The First Emperor" and "Barbara Frietchie" follows.

   In "The First Emperor," Shih Huang Ti's attitude toward death may be described as
   a. irrational, since death is inevitable.
   b. fearful.
   c. all-consuming, since he went to great lengths to avoid or postpone it.
   d. pathetic or sad.

   In "Barbara Frietchie," the title character's attitude toward death may be described as
   a. fearless, since she knowingly takes an action that risks her life.

   b. reckless or foolish, for the same reason.
   c. noble, since she is willing to die for her convictions.

4. Answers will vary. A model answer for Tito in "The Dog of Pompeii" follows.

   Reasons to feel sympathy for Tito include the following.
   a. He is blind.
   b. He is an orphan.
   c. His only companion is a dog who serves as friend, pet, parent, and protector all in one.
   d. He is poor and homeless.
   e. For food he relies almost completely on what Bimbo brings him.
   f. He loses Bimbo when the volcano destroys Pompeii.

D. (20 points) Answers will vary. Model answers for "Barbara Frietchie" and "The Dog of Pompeii" follow.

   In "Barbara Frietchie," Barbara Frietchie's need or problem was
   a. living in the midst of a war and witnessing the enemy's movements.
   b. expressing political views.
   c. being unable to stop the enemy or prevent them from moving through town.

   Her need/problem might be compared to
   a. people today who live in countries torn apart by war or political strife.
   b. people living in countries occupied by foreign powers.
   c. people who feel compelled to express their political views and who put themselves at risk by doing so.

   In "The Dog of Pompeii," Tito's need or problem was
   a. his blindness.
   b. being an orphan.
   c. his homelessness and poverty.
   d. the loss and upheaval he experienced as the result of the volcano.

   His need/problem is similar to that of people today who
   a. are disabled.
   b. are orphans.
   c. are homeless.
   d. experience losses that result from natural disasters, such as floods, earthquakes, and hurricanes.

Unit Six

Links to Unit One
Selection Test, pp. 125–126

A. (8 points each)

1. Notes will vary, depending on the challenge that students choose to discuss. Most students will address Daedalus' escape from the tower and include notes suggesting the following ideas.
   a. Challenge: Escaping from the tower with his son
   b. Response: He builds wings so that he can fly away from the tower.
   c. Consequences: They escape, but his son falls to his death.
2. Notes will vary but should suggest the following ideas.
   a. Challenge: Defeating Athena in a weaving contest
   b. Response: She weaves a beautiful tapestry that depicts injustices committed by gods.
   c. Consequences: Athena turns her into a spider.
3. Notes will vary but should suggest the following ideas.
   a. Challenge: Getting her daughter back from the underworld
   b. Response: She threatens to make the earth barren forever if she does not get Proserpina back.
   c. Consequences: Jupiter orders Pluto to return Proserpina.

B. (5 points each)
1. a
2. d
3. a
4. c

C. (4 points each)
1. c
2. a
3. b
4. a
5. c

D. (20 points; students should answer one of the two)
1. Answers will vary widely. Students who think that the message involves the dangers of conceit or too much pride might say that
   a. it is foolish and dangerous to think of oneself as equal to or better than a god.
   b. the message is still important because conceit and too much pride are qualities that people today possess.
   c. the message is (or is not) important because respecting a divinity is (or is not) as important today as it was for the ancient Greeks.
   d. the message is not important because very few people today believe in the types of gods the ancient Greeks believed in.

Other students may feel that the message
   a. is that when a person believes that he or she is much better than others or doesn't have to behave as regular people do, that person is in for a big surprise.
   b. is still important because many people today see themselves as being more important than others.
Still other students may say that the message
   a. is that people can try their hardest and be exceptionally good at something only to find themselves punished for challenging someone with greater power.
   b. is important because many people feel threatened by people with skills equal to or superior to their own.
   c. is not important today because it discourages excellence and ambition.
2. Answers will vary but could include points similar to the following:
   In "The Boy Who Flew":
   a. Daedalus deserves to lose his son because he defies the gods by learning to fly.
   b. Or, he does not deserve his punishment because he has destroyed the Minotaur and saved the young Athenians who would be sacrificed each year; he is trying to escape from an unjust punishment; his son is too young to die for his own foolishness.
   In "Arachne":
   a. Arachne deserves to be turned into a spider because she insults the old woman, is too proud of her abilities, and never credits her father's contribution to her weaving.
   b. Or, Arachne does not deserve her punishment because she is an inexperienced young woman and Athena seems equally prideful, vengeful, and jealous of others, despite her reputation for wisdom.
   In "The Story of Ceres and Proserpina":
   a. Ceres does not deserve to lose her daughter because neither she nor Proserpina has done anything to provoke Pluto, who kidnapped Proserpina.
   b. Or, she does deserve to lose Proserpina for part of the year because she threatens to destroy the earth for selfish reasons; the goddess should have some sense of responsibility for all the innocent people who had nothing to do with the kidnapping.

E. (16 points) Answers will vary widely, depending on students' personal experiences, situations, and viewpoints. Accept any answers that address the concern of the question and are elaborated by examples or details from the literature or from life.

Links to Unit Two
Selection Test, pp. 127–128
A. (12 points each)
1. Notes will vary but could suggest ideas similar to the following.
   a. The boy is disobedient and rebellious.
   b. He moves in with the old man, causes enormous problems by disobeying the old man's directions, but is forgiven in the end.
   c. The boy becomes obedient and helpful after that because he is grateful for the old man's kindness.
2. Notes will vary but could suggest ideas similar to the following.
   a. The narrator feels lonely, alone, incomplete, or out of place because, unlike her parents and her cousins, she has no siblings or because, unlike her parents and Tantie, she has nothing to count people on.
   b. This situation is changed when Tantie shares the story of the necklace with the narrator and gives her the necklace.
   c. This makes the narrator feel less out of place because it gives her something to count her cousins on and makes her feel special.

B. (5 points each)
1. b
2. d
3. b
4. d

C. (5 points each)
1. b
2. a
3. a
4. c

D. (20 points; students should answer one of the two)
1. Answers will vary. Many students will say that the folktale teaches that kind behavior is rewarded and rude or mean behavior is punished and that this is a good lesson to learn. Others may note the same or a similar lesson but feel that this is not a good lesson to learn because
   a. it is not true. Kind behavior is often not rewarded at all except by any good feeling it brings to the person who behaves that way, and so the lesson causes false expectations.
   b. it encourages people to behave kindly in the hope of receiving a reward rather than simply because it is the right thing to do.
   Other students may point to another lesson, such as the idea that
   a. one should not judge people based on their appearance.

   b. one never knows when a seemingly ordinary person may actually be quite powerful.
   c. it is impossible to know what the effects of a kind or mean action may be.
   Students who point to one of these lessons are likely to feel that it is a good lesson to learn because it will make people both kinder and more cautious.
2. Answers will vary. Some students might say that the boy is behaving wrongly because
   a. he disobeys clear orders that are given to him by the owner of the house he is occupying.
   b. the man who tells him what to do is being kind and helpful to him.
   Other students might say that the boy isn't behaving wrongly because his
   a. first act of disobedience is based on his judgment. He thinks that the old man has made a mistake in telling him how many beans to cook.
   b. second act of disobedience is motivated by the most natural and reasonable kind of curiosity. The old man doesn't tell him why he shouldn't open the door, so he doesn't expect that opening it will endanger his life.

E. (16 points) Answers will vary widely, depending on students' personal experiences, situations, and viewpoints. Accept any answers that address the concern of the question and are elaborated by examples or details from the literature or from life.

Links to Unit Three
Selection Test, pp. 129–130
A. (12 points each)
1. Notes will vary but should suggest ideas similar to the following.
   a. Cám is cruel to her elder sister when she tricks T'âm to become Number One Daughter and later when she eats T'âm's fish.
   b. T'âm is kind to her father, her sister, and the fish.
   c. In the end, T'âm is chosen by the prince and Cám is rejected.
2. Notes will vary but should suggest ideas similar to the following.
   a. The princess makes fools of her suitors, and King Thrushbeard, one of those suitors, makes a fool out of her by tricking her.
   b. The princess, who wastes all her advantages, loses those advantages and becomes a pauper.
   c. The princess becomes a queen only after she has learned, as a beggar's wife, to be humble.

B. (5 points each)
1. b
2. d
3. c
4. a

C. (4 points each)
  1. b
  2. b
  3. c
  4. a
  5. c

D. (20 points; students should answer one of the two)
  1. Answers will vary, but students could say that the proverb relates to T'âm in the following ways.
     a. She is beautiful on the outside (as is "a jewel box of gold and jade").
     b. She is beautiful on the inside (as are the "jewels of great price" inside the jewel box).
     c. It communicates the idea that she has many good qualities and virtues.
     d. It communicates the idea that her inner qualities are what make her appear physically beautiful or that, because she is physically beautiful, she must also be virtuous.
     e. It communicates the idea that she is a person of rare beauty and value.
  2. Answers will vary. Some students will feel that she deserves the treatment she gets because
     a. her pride is so strong and her mockery is so cruel that she must suffer severely in order to change.
     b. without severe punishment, her behavior would only grow worse.
     c. since she has completely wasted the privilege, wealth, power, and opportunities available to her as a princess, there is no good reason that she should continue to have access to these things.
     Other students might say that she doesn't deserve the treatment she receives because
     a. no woman should be forced to accept a suitor who does not please her, no matter how proud or mocking her personality may be.
     b. although her behavior is obnoxious, she doesn't actually hurt anyone. No one suffers, other than from wounded pride, from the way she behaves. She, however, suffers both emotionally and physically.
     c. she was raised by her father, the same man who punishes her for behavior that he either encouraged her in, or at least didn't discourage her from, long ago.

E. (16 points) Answers will vary widely, depending on students' personal experiences, situations, and viewpoints. Accept any answers that address the concern of the question and are elaborated by examples or details from the literature or from life.

Links to Unit Four
Selection Test, pp. 131–132
A. (8 points each) Answers will vary widely but might include the following traits.
  1. In "Why Monkeys Live in Trees":
     a. Vanity is portrayed as a weakness when Leopard spends hours staring at his own reflection.
     b. Cleverness is portrayed as a strength when it enables the monkeys to win the contest.
  2. In "The Legend of the Hummingbird":
     a. Prejudice is portrayed as a weakness when the king tries to prevent his daughter from seeing the young man from the Carib tribe.
     b. Devotion, love, or faithfulness is portrayed as a strength when Alida and Taroo both ask for help and are granted their wishes.
  3. In "The Living Kuan-yin":
     a. Greed is portrayed as a weakness when the "kind host" learns that his trees will bear fruit only when he gives away half his treasure.
     b. Charity, compassion, or kindness to others is portrayed as a strength when Po-wan is rewarded in the end.

B. (5 points each)
  1. b
  2. d
  3. a
  4. d

C. (4 points each)
  1. a
  2. c
  3. a
  4. b
  5. c

D. (20 points; students should answer one of the two)
  1. Answers will vary. Students who feel that King Gorilla should be angry may say that
     a. the rules for the contest don't allow for the way the monkeys win, so Monkey cheats King Gorilla out of his gold.
     b. Monkey doesn't have to enter the contest, but since he has, he should compete fairly.
     c. Monkey clearly knows that he is cheating. Otherwise, he would reveal what he is doing to win the contest.
     Students who don't feel that King Gorilla should be angry might say that
     a. what the monkeys do is clever and a reasonable response to a contest in which failure is more or less guaranteed.
     b. King Gorilla tricks the animals by not telling them what the black dust is, knowing that they will not be able to eat it.

c. King Gorilla seems to have set up a contest that he knows no one can win, so he has no right to be angry when the monkeys trick him in response.

d. Monkey does not break King Gorilla's rules if the rules do not specify that one individual (and not a group) must eat the whole pile.

2. Answers will vary but should reflect students' understanding that

a. in this folktale, the "wishes" are fulfilled through answers to questions.

b. in most "three wishes" stories, the people behave foolishly and end up worse off or with nothing.

c. in this folktale, the person behaves generously and all the wishes are granted.

d. in this folktale, four wishes are granted.

E. (16 points) Answers will vary widely, depending on students' personal experiences, situations, and viewpoints. Accept any answers that address the concerns of the questions and are elaborated by examples or details from the literature or from life.

Links to Unit Five

Selection Test, pp. 133–134

A. (12 points each)

1. Answers will vary but should suggest ideas similar to the following.

a. Frog's goal is to be a singer.

b. No one wants Frog to sing, or only birds are allowed to sing.

c. Frog talks his way into the Friday night concert. He forces his way back onstage after being ridiculed, impresses the audience, and creates a new form of music—rhythm and blues.

2. Answers will vary but should suggest ideas similar to the following.

a. Her goal is to represent her people, or accompany her husband, in an honorable way.

b. Her people are fighting a larger force of soldiers in battle, and her brother is surrounded by Crow warriors.

c. Buffalo Calf Road Woman impresses everyone on both sides of the battle by riding in and saving her brother.

B. (5 points each)

1. d
2. b
3. a
4. c

C. (4 points each)

1. a
2. b
3. c
4. c
5. b

D. (20 points; students should answer one of the two)

1. Answers will vary but might include the following. "The Frog Who Wanted to Be a Singer" suggests that

a. people do not respond well to things that are out of the ordinary, such as a frog that wants to sing.

b. it can be difficult to get people to give newcomers a chance.

c. many people are closed-minded about music, art, and their own likes and dislikes.

d. a person who feels strongly enough about a goal will find a way to succeed.

e. people must believe in themselves.

"Where the Girl Rescued Her Brother" suggests that

a. people must maintain their pride and dignity.

b. everyone admires or respects great acts of courage, as when warriors on both sides stopped fighting to watch the girl's feat.

c. a person's true character emerges in times of crisis, as Buffalo Calf Road Woman's did when facing the grizzly and when watching the battle.

2. Answers will vary.

For "The Frog Who Wanted to Be a Singer," cultural values and customs might include the following.

a. In this particular forest, frogs don't sing, only birds do.

b. Parents encourage their offspring to pursue their desires, as Frog's parents did.

c. People with similar interests form groups, and others are considered outsiders.

d. Old traditions are hard to change.

For "Where the Girl Rescued Her Brother," cultural values and customs might include the following.

a. Men defend their people in battle, but their women often accompany them.

b. Being honorable and moral is expected and rewarded.

c. Women share the responsibilities of their husbands.

d. People believe that they should die with honor and dignity.

e. Courage is greatly admired.

E. (16 points) Answers will vary widely, depending on students' personal experiences, situations, and viewpoints. Accept any answers that address the concern of the question and are elaborated by examples or details from the literature or from life.

Unit Six Test

pp. 135–136

A. (5 points each) Some answers will vary but should suggest the following.

1. "The Living Kuan-yin"
2. "The Legend of the Hummingbird"
3. He pretends to be a beggar and marries the princess.
4. He is a rain god or the thunder god.

B. (20 points) Notes will vary. A model answer for the boy in "The Disobedient Child" follows.

The boy learns that
a. disobedience can have disastrous effects.
b. it is dangerous to do things without having any idea what the consequences might be.

C. (20 points each; students should answer two of the four)

1. Answers will vary. A model answer for "Why Monkeys Live in Trees" follows.

The myth explains why monkeys live in trees. The explanation is a good one because
a. it is funny and entertaining.
b. in real life, monkeys are known for being relatively intelligent and mischievous, and that is what gets Monkey and his friends in trouble in this myth.
c. in real life, many animals live in trees to avoid becoming prey, and this is what happens in the myth.

2. Answers will vary. A model answer for Chin Po-wan in "The Living Kuan-yin" and the princess in "King Thrushbeard" follows.

Chin Po-wan is treated fairly because
a. what happens to him is controlled by his own behavior.
b. the same thing that causes him problems (his generosity) also saves him in the end.
c. he makes decisions about what to do and those decisions affect his fate.
d. nobody changes any rules on him or lies to him or forces him to do things that he doesn't want to do and shouldn't have to do.

The princess is treated unfairly.
a. Although she is rude and thinks she is better than everyone else, the punishment she receives is more than she deserves.
b. Her treatment would be fair if, as a result of her behavior, no one liked her much or no one wanted to marry her.
c. Being forced to marry someone she doesn't even know, much less love, is completely unfair.
d. Being lied to and treated badly by the man she marries makes the unfairness even worse.

3. Answers will vary. A model answer for "Arachne" might include the following points.
a. "Arachne" shows that the ancient Greeks valued skills such as weaving and qualities such as humility, respect and fear for the gods, and gratitude to the gods.
b. These values are obvious from the story because Arachne's skill as a weaver is highly respected, but her conceit, her lack of respect for the gods, and her ingratitude to the gods and to her father are criticized and punished.

c. The society's values are also obvious from the story because what happens to Arachne is treated as a reasonable consequence of her actions.

4. Answers will vary. A model answer for Tantie in "The Bamboo Beads" follows.
a. This character's kindness causes her to give bread to a strange and somewhat frightening person who is hungry.
b. As a result, Tantie is rewarded with the bamboo beads and becomes responsible for "keeping count" of 33 children.

D. (20 points) Notes will vary. A model answer for the frog in "The Frog Who Wanted to Be a Singer" follows.

In "The Frog Who Wanted to Be a Singer," the frog struggles against other members of his community and the traditional belief that frogs cannot be singers. He wins this struggle because
a. he refuses to give up.
b. he practices very hard.
c. he forces the other animals to listen to his song, and they are impressed.

End-of-Year Test
pp. 137–146

A. 1. c
   2. a
   3. d
   4. b
   5. b
   6. c

B. 7. d
   8. b
   9. a
  10. d

C. Answers may vary but should include points similar to the following.

11. The author's main purpose is to describe how he and his family raised a lion cub in Africa. Other purposes might be to give information about raising lion cubs, to explain how to raise a lion, or to entertain readers with an interesting account.

12. Kipling uses chronological order, or time sequence, to organize this essay. The organization could also be considered steps in a process.

13. For most of the essay, Kipling describes the events in a matter-of-fact way, as if nothing unusual was happening, and that's how the reader feels about it at first. However, he also includes wry comments ("And she said, 'I thought so,' and went into the house to give orders.") and describes moments of curiosity ("That was curious."). These observations make the reader see the humor in the situation and feel a sense of wonder about the instinctive behavior of animals.

D. 14. a
  15. c
  16. b
  17. d

E. Answers may vary but should include points similar to the following.

18. Sullivan was different from a kitten in that he did not chase his tail or do foolish tricks, was never silly or amusing, and never showed off.

19. Students might feel that bringing up a lion was easy because the narrator and his family got helpful advice, never had any real difficulties, and raised a healthy cub in spite of the general agreement that the cub would die. Other students might feel that raising a lion was not easy because so many things could go wrong but that Kipling made it seem easy by the way he described the experience.

20. The narrator probably realized that the lion belonged to nature and was part of a larger, much older world that did not need any human involvement; that humans were insignificant in the larger realm of the African wild; or that Sullivan was growing up, and instinctive behavior governed his actions.

Writing Exercise Scoring Guide

4 An **exceptional** paper
- has a clear and consistent focus.
- has a logical organization.
- uses transitions effectively to connect ideas.
- supports ideas with details, quotations, examples, and/or other evidence.
- exhibits well-formed sentences varying in structure.
- exhibits a rich vocabulary, including precise language that is appropriate for the purpose and audience of the paper.
- contains almost no errors in usage, mechanics, and spelling.

3 A **proficient** paper
- has a relatively clear and consistent focus.
- has a logical organization, although it may be unnecessarily mechanical.
- uses some transition words and phrases to connect ideas, but they do not always clarify connections effectively.
- supports ideas with details, quotations, examples, and/or other evidence.
- exhibits some variety in sentence structure.
- uses vocabulary that is appropriate for the purpose and audience.
- contains a few errors in usage, mechanics, and spelling.

2 A **basic** paper
- has a fairly clear focus that may occasionally become obscured.
- shows an organizational pattern, but relationships between ideas may sometimes be difficult to understand.
- contains supporting evidence that may lack effect and so only superficially develops ideas.
- has complete and varied sentences most of the time.
- contains several errors in usage, mechanics, and spelling that cause distraction and some confusion about meaning.

1 A **limited** paper
- has a topic but does not include any elaboration, or it only minimally addresses the topic and lacks discernible ideas.
- has only a few, simple sentences.
- contains little or no plausible support for ideas.
- shows limited word choice.
- contains numerous and serious errors in usage, mechanics, and spelling that cause confusion about meaning.

A paper is unable to be scored if it is
- illegible.
- unrelated to the topic.
- only a rewording of the prompt.
- written in a foreign language.
- not written at all.

Revising/Editing

1. b
2. a
3. d
4. c
5. c
6. a

Standardized Test Practice
Answer Key

Spelling
Part A
1. B
2. A
3. C
4. D
5. E
6. C
7. A
8. D
9. B
10. E
11. D
12. C
13. A
14. E
15. B
16. C
17. C
18. E
19. D
20. A

Part B
21. C
22. B
23. B
24. A
25. D
26. C
27. C
28. A
29. D
30. B
31. B
32. A
33. B
34. C
35. D
36. C
37. B
38. A
39. D
40. D

Vocabulary
1. C
2. A
3. D
4. B
5. C
6. D
7. B
8. A
9. B
10. B

Sentence Completion
1. D
2. B
3. E
4. A
5. B
6. C
7. C
8. E
9. D
10. A
11. B
12. B
13. D
14. C
15. A
16. E
17. E
18. B
19. C
20. B

Capitalization and Punctuation
Part A
1. C
2. B
3. A
4. D
5. B
6. C
7. B
8. B
9. A
10. D
11. C
12. A
13. C
14. D
15. B

Part B
16. B
17. B
18. A
19. D
20. B
21. A
22. C
23. B
24. C
25. A
26. C
27. D
28. C
29. D
30. B

Analogies
1. D
2. A
3. B
4. C
5. E
6. B
7. C
8. C
9. A
10. D
11. D
12. B
13. E
14. A
15. C
16. C
17. D
18. B
19. A
20. C
21. E
22. B
23. E
24. D
25. B

Error Identification
1. C
2. B
3. D
4. A
5. E
6. C
7. C
8. C
9. B
10. A
11. B
12. E
13. B
14. D
15. C
16. D
17. A
18. A
19. C
20. C

Error Correction
Part A
1. B
2. C
3. D
4. A
5. C
6. C
7. B
8. D
9. A
10. C
11. B
12. B
13. D
14. A
15. C

Part B
16. D
17. G
18. C
19. J
20. B
21. F
22. C
23. H
24. A
25. H
26. D
27. J
28. D
29. F
30. C
31. J
32. B
33. G
34. C
35. F

Reading Comprehension
1. B
2. E
3. D
4. B
5. D
6. C
7. A
8. C
9. B
10. E
11. E
12. C
13. B
14. D
15. A
16. B
17. D
18. A
19. C
20. D

Teacher Notes

Teacher Notes

Teacher Notes

Teacher Notes

Teacher Notes

Teacher Notes

Teacher Notes

Teacher Notes

Teacher Notes

Teacher Notes